£5.00

THE BRITISH BOMBER SINCE 1914

The Avro Vulcan B. Mk. 2 displays its striking delta form at high altitude. (*Avro Photo.*)

THE
BRITISH BOMBER
SINCE 1914

Sixty Years of Design
and Development

PETER LEWIS

PUTNAM
LONDON

By the same author

THE BRITISH FIGHTER SINCE 1912

BRITISH AIRCRAFT
1809–1914

SQUADRON HISTORIES

BRITISH RACING AND
RECORD-BREAKING AIRCRAFT

ISBN 0 370 10040 9

Printed and bound in Great Britain for
Putnam & Company Limited
9 Bow Street, London WC2E 7AL
by Fletcher & Son Ltd, Norwich
Set in Monotype Plantin
First published 1967
Second Edition 1974

To

GEORGE RUDOLPH VOLKERT

In appreciation of his significant
contribution to the evolution of the
British bomber

CONTENTS

PREFACE

In the swiftly-receding past of just over half a century ago, four naval aeroplanes climbed away from Antwerp to carry out the first organized British air raid in an era in which—by long-standing tradition—Great Britain's offensive power was still vested on land in the Army and at sea in the Royal Navy. None among those witnessing the quartet of puny, swaying biplanes dwindling into the distance could have foreseen that from this insignificant start there was thenceforward to evolve—at a phenomenal pace—a specialized weapon of unprecedented power which was ultimately to oust all previous manned weapons to constitute the primary means of attack of nations at war.

Military and naval interest in the aeroplane in the United Kingdom manifested itself initially in its services as a scout—soon armed and developed as a fighter—so that its use as a launcher of bombs and torpedoes was at first slower in being effectively pursued. Once established, however, development was rapid and *The British Bomber since 1914* outlines the increasingly complex pattern of evolution of a class of aircraft in the creation of which British designers and engineers soon became pre-eminent.

In both World Wars—and particularly during that of 1939–45—the emphasis was, perforce, on quantity production of a few proven types, but, paradoxically, the 1920s and the 1930s were responsible for the design and construction in peacetime of an impressive array of bombers and torpedo-bombers, both in response to official requirements and as Private Ventures. A proportion of the aircraft of the later years of this period were subsequently to attain renown during the heroic and strenuous days of battle which lay ahead.

The conception of bombing and torpedo-carrying aircraft in Great Britain over five decades is a subject of such prodigious complexity and so interdependent a nature that any attempt to compile the history in its entirety is of necessity inhibited by commercial and security considerations. A procedure similar to that employed for *The British Fighter since 1912* has therefore been adopted in *The British Bomber since 1914* to record chronologically a total of over five hundred and sixty diverse aircraft types, including those constructed, their variants and many relinquished projects.

The compilation of *The British Bomber since 1914* has been assisted immeasurably by the ready contribution made by the following organizations: Wm. Beardmore and Co. Ltd.; Boulton Paul Aircraft Ltd.; Bristol Siddeley Engines Ltd.; British Aircraft Corporation (Operating) Ltd.; Filton Division of British Aircraft Corporation (Operating) Ltd.; Flight Refuelling Ltd.; Handley Page Ltd.; Avro Whitworth, de Havilland and Hawker Blackburn

Divisions of Hawker Siddeley Aviation Ltd.; Rootes Motors Ltd.; Short Brothers and Harland Ltd.; Vickers Ltd.; Westland Aircraft Ltd.; Air Attachés and Headquarters—Argentine Air Force; Argentine Naval Aviation; Belgian Air Force; Indian Air Force; Irish Air Corps; Israel Defence Force/ Air Force; Royal Australian Air Force; Royal Canadian Air Force; Royal Netherlands Naval Air Service; Royal New Zealand Air Force; South African Air Force.

Valuable assistance has been rendered by the staff of several Departments of the Ministry of Aviation and by the Conservateur en Chef du Musée Royal de l'Armée et d'Histoire Militaire of Belgium. In addition I am greatly indebted to Mr. David Dorrell, Editor of *Air Pictorial*, and to Mr. J. M. Ramsden, Editor of *Flight International*, for the facilities which they so kindly granted to me, also to Miss Ann C. Tilbury, Photographic Librarian of *Flight International*, for her usual resourcefulness.

My gratitude must be expressed as well for the kindness of Maj. J. L. B. H. Cordes, the late Dr. G. V. Lachmann, Air Chief Marshal Sir Arthur M. Longmore, Wg. Cdr. Norman Macmillan, Mr. John D. North, Mr. Harald J. Penrose and Mr. George R. Volkert in providing useful information to enhance the narrative.

Lastly, a well-deserved word of appreciation is due to my wife for her willing help in numerous instances, all of which lightened the task.

Views expressed are my own and do not necessarily represent those of the Ministry of Aviation.

P. M. H. L.

Benfleet,
Essex.
February, 1967

PREFACE TO SECOND EDITION

During the seven years which have passed since the first edition of *The British Bomber since 1914* was published, there has been, as was to be expected since the deplorable cancellation of TSR-2, little to encourage the designers and constructors responsible until 1967 for the traditional British bomber concept.

In this revised edition, therefore, the opportunity has been taken to provide up-to-date information and illustrations for the Hawker Siddeley Nimrod. Included also are details of the Panavia 200 MRCA collaborative venture, to which the British contribution is the British Aircraft Corporation's responsibility for the nose section and cockpits, rear fuselage and tail units.

P. M. H. L.

Benfleet,
Essex.
February, 1974.

Sopwith Torpedo Seaplane Type C of 1914, one of the earliest of its class. (*Hawker Photo.*)

CHAPTER ONE

THE SEED IS SOWN

The first half of the twentieth century cannot but assume its place in history as the era in which—amid a plethora of outstanding scientific achievements—annihilation of an enemy by onslaught from the skies was decisively established remarkably swiftly in an effectual, and an ultimately prodigiously powerful, form.

Yet, despite the realization of the devastating new weapon by scientists and its adoption and widespread employment by air arms during the past five decades, the basic idea of aerial bombardment is far from being the prerogative of those responsible for its eventual inception.

Long before the advent of the means to fly, and in an epoch eminently conducive to constructive reflection, predictions of destruction raining down from the heavens on the surprised and terrified heads of both good and bad below issued forth from a number of far-sighted sages and philosophers. Surviving writings of the wise men living and meditating hundreds of years ago, demonstrate time and time again that their thoughts turned constantly to the unsolved and baffling problem of harnessing the air for the purpose of travelling with a facility equalling that enjoyed for aeons on both land and water. Indeed, the relative absence of obstacles in the atmosphere encouraged the hope and the belief that the unimpeded passage thus offered would endow humans fortunate enough to be able to fly with advantages vastly superior to those enjoyed by their earthbound brethren.

Although countless hours were devoted to examining ways and means of ascending into the air, no practical progress was achieved in spite of the fact that the materials necessary for the fabrication of a simple glider had for long been available. When the numerous impressive architectural and ingenious scientific accomplishments of the ancients are appraised it becomes increasingly strange that there is no definitive record of—as far as

11

is known—even a crude glider being fashioned after the birds wheeling so tantalizingly overhead.

And so time passed and the sky remained unconquered—except in the fertile imagination of the thoughtful. Among the earliest recognized suggestions that assault might be expected from the empyrean is that made in the tale recounted by Sinbad the Sailor in *The Arabian Nights*. This still failed to forecast mechanical means of missile delivery but described the raid on his vessel at sea by two great rocs bearing boulders in their claws. The first bird aimed wide of the boat and did not damage it, but the second roc's stone plunged straight into the centre of the craft, splitting it into myriad fragments. Their purpose achieved, the rocs lingered not but made good their escape.

A more objective prognostication of aerial warfare came in the seventeenth century from Father Francesco de Lana, a Jesuit priest of Rome with an intense and lifelong interest in science. In his *Prodromo*, a work published at Brescia in 1670, his enthusiasm and thorough scientific research led him to foretell with comparative accuracy the terrible consequences of the ability to bring war to an enemy from the welkin. De Lana devoted a great deal of thought to the design of his aerial ship, to be supported by four copper globes from which the air had been evacuated. The supposition was that, exhausted of their atmosphere, the globes would rise, thereby transporting the underslung vessel and its passengers aloft. Taking this proposal a stage farther, de Lana could foresee his airborne ship being adapted for warlike purposes in which it could be propelled and guided over the territory of a foe, bearing with it a cargo of explosive bombs and incendiaries. The seer imagined the crew unloading their weapons not only on to targets on land but also on ships sailing through the waters. Nearly two hundred and fifty years were to pass before de Lana's vision of aerial attack came true and then in a form which eventually surpassed by far his ideas of the magnitude of destruction possible by the new means to which his accomplished brain had given birth. Although, generally, they had little enough monetary resources available, the majority of early scientific experiments enjoyed complete freedom of access to the paths along which they felt the urge to tread. De Lana's vocation, however, with its attendant vows of poverty denied him the ability to do anything more than commit his thoughts to manuscript.

The mortal danger which might well beset those on the ground, should men of ill-will attain the power to fly and to transport the means of war to those whom they should choose to attack, not surprisingly engaged the attention of that most illustrious of thinkers, Dr. Samuel Johnson. Writing in 1759, the great Englishman foresaw the utter lack of defence against any determined foe armed with the capability of assault on those on earth or at sea.

In a number of recorded instances, therefore, the eventual possibility of blows from the as-yet-unconquered firmament had been appreciated. Lacking, however, was simply the machinery for transforming fantasy into fact. Gradually, the passage of time—which invariably brings the solution to so many age-old problems—had its effect. In an era which witnessed an ever-increasing proportion of effort devoted to scientific experiment, the challenge of human flight drew to itself ever more attention. This enthusiasm was especially marked on the Continent of Europe, with France standing in the forefront during the eighteenth century. Although Great Britain was in the vanguard of contemporary technological discovery, the country's inventors were—in the main—devoting their talents to objectives other than aerial travel.

Until France found itself embroiled in 1789 in the all-embracing Revolution, excellent progress had been made in the previous few years in the direction of the goal of flight. The patient, steady research carried out by the brothers Etienne and Joseph Montgolfier culminated on 4th June, 1783, in the unmanned ascent at Annonay, Vivarais, of their hot-air balloon, followed five and a half months later—on 21st November—by the historic first human flight by François Pilâtre de Rozier and the Marquis d'Arlandes, carried by a Montgolfier balloon sustained for 25 minutes by heated air. Only ten days later, on 1st December, 1783, Charles and Robert rose from the Tuileries to accomplish the first human ascent in a balloon filled with hydrogen.

In Britain extreme caution was displayed in indulging in the new pursuit, and it fell to the Italian Vincent Lunardi, secretary at the Neapolitan Embassy in London, to perform the first ascent, which took place on 15th September, 1784, from the Artillery ground at Moorfields in London. Enthusiasm swiftly replaced scepticism, and it was not long before, on 7th January, 1785, the Frenchman Jean-Pierre Blanchard and the American Dr. John Jeffries together made the first aerial crossing of the English Channel, from Dover to Calais.

Within the next five years, the energetic French contribution to the advance of the science of flight came to an abrupt halt, and the initiative in systematic research passed across the water to England to find a sympathetic home in what may be thought to have been a singularly unlikely place, the country seat of an astute Yorkshire baronet—Sir George Cayley of Brompton Hall, near Scarborough. This brilliant and versatile inventor concentrated his attention on the heavier-than-air aspect of flying to great effect, although a hundred years were to pass after his death in 1857 before he eventually received the full recognition which was his due. Although Cayley was firmly convinced of the ultimate navigation of the skies and does not appear to have considered that such a new-found art might be adapted for war, a few years prior to his death a balloon was employed on a bombing raid during 1849 by the Austrian forces who were attacking Venice.

Despite this instance of the adaptation of the balloon as a weapon of war, little further serious military use was made of it in the immediate future. The year 1870, however, did see it brought to the aid of the citizens of Paris, besieged by the Prussians. The French balloons were not used in an offensive rôle but proved a boon in flying out with letters and dispatches and, on occasion, with passengers.

Within the next twenty years many more experimenters were to apply themselves to the task of achieving flight with wings until, finally, the deed became an accomplished fact. Concurrently, in several countries, the problem

13

was being tackled with varying degrees of success, first with motorless flight and, subsequently, with the assistance of early petrol engines. The timely arrival of a reasonably adaptable prime mover went a long way towards providing fairly quickly the means of success in the lengthy struggle to take-off, soar through the once-forbidden air and to return safely again to the welcome ground. It fell to the Wright brothers to succeed in flying successfully and consistently ahead of all others, but, once they had demonstrated the new art in public, their achievement was soon emulated by many newcomers.

Throughout the earliest years of the innovation of the aeroplane there was relatively little thought in the minds of the pioneer constructors and pilots that their creations should be developed specifically as offensive weapons to form part of their respective countries' armed forces. As far as the early aeronauts were concerned, the first decade of the twentieth century saw them absorbed with the effort to evolve their primitive vehicles into viable machines possessing a reasonable degree of safety, reliability and a worthwhile performance.

The intriguing idea of unmanned delivery of bombs to an enemy had been postulated by The Aerial Torpedo Syndicate Ltd. of London, which offered during the 1890s to supply aerial torpedoes capable of dropping a ton of explosive each upon arrival over a target to which they had been guided automatically. Such a system had much in its favour if it could be brought to a state of reliability to make its adoption worthwhile. The carrier aircraft were intended to be launched in large numbers towards the objective several hundreds of miles away and were to be expendable after having released their bombs. The most important advantage claimed for the aerial torpedo was the elimination of the exposure of aircrew to retaliatory attack by enemy defences. The concept of unmanned delivery was itself excellent and undoubtedly worthy of all-out intensive development to bring it to fruition. Nevertheless, sufficient support was not forthcoming, and no progress was made towards its consummation in the near future. Such an attractive proposition still continued to occupy a few inventive minds, and spasmodic attention was given to it for the next fifty years, culminating eventually in a weapon embodying the main principles of unmanned delivery but in a modified form so that, when the pilotless flying bomb ultimately emerged as a practical device, the entire weapon—airframe and explosive—hurtled down on to the helpless target.

The turn of the century brought with it the Edwardian era, a decade which was destined to prove of the utmost importance in aeronautics and to witness the arrival at the gates of the realm of controlled flight.

In Great Britain the immense problem of constructing a heavier-than-air machine which would bear a man aloft in safety and respond to his will had drawn many to devote their time and money to strive for the answer. In each of the countries of Northern Europe and in the United States of America scientific progress in numerous spheres had proceeded on more or less parallel lines. Although many differences in detail were obvious, the general result was the same, and particular advantages were quickly shared, adopted and adapted. The pursuit of aeronautics was no exception to the rule, with an

14

ever-expanding band of experimenters delving more and more deeply into the complexities of the subject, primarily in Australia, Britain, France, Germany, Italy, Russia, Spain and the United States. Four main paths were explored by means of models and full-size machines: these were the ornithopter, helicopter, glider and propeller-driven aircraft. Both the ornithopter and the helicopter had attracted devotees for a long time past. The rotating-wing concept was to go through a very long and arduous period of development before its subsequent triumph of acceptance, but the idea of flapping wings was finally abandoned as a serious system of achieving flight. The main weight of effort was concentrated consequently on the system of wings for the provision of lift, horizontal and vertical auxiliary surfaces carried fore and aft of the mainplanes to provide control, and a body to accommodate the aeronaut.

England was particularly fortunate in possessing such an outstandingly talented figure in Sir George Cayley, who, as early as the outset of the nineteenth century, had arrived at the aeroplane's ultimate basic layout. Despite Cayley's unselfish attitude in publicizing his conclusions and the details of his experiments, up to the time of his death he was unable to break down the barriers of scepticism and lack of interest which, in general, greeted the results of his endeavours.

Notwithstanding, the second half of the nineteenth century brought with it a quickening of pace and a positive intensification of aeronautical research in every direction. Early enthusiasts who had made comparatively little practical progress disappeared one by one from the scene and a fresh group of experimenters arose whose contributions to the new science ultimately ensured their names permanent and prominent places in the growing and fascinating history of aeronautics. This progression was encouraged undeniably by the vitality and activity evident in all other fields of scientific achievement.

Of the greatest value and consequence to the cause of aeronautics was the advent of the internal-combustion engine, upon which the aeroplane was to rely so heavily for the first few decades of its life. In its early years the petrol engine retained an inherent disadvantage of high weight at a time when it was essential that this should be kept to the barest possible minimum in order that experience in powered flight might be attained.

Although throughout the 1880s there was still relatively little outward indication of the imminent viability of the practical flying machine, widespread momentum was gathering inexorably until, of a sudden, flying had become a reality. Great Britain's contribution during the last important stages until the turn of the century came from such men as the Anglicized American Hiram S. Maxim, Horatio F. Phillips and Percy S. Pilcher, among others of lesser distinction.

Maxim made a valiant attempt to use steam as the power to lift his enormous machine from its rails in his endeavour to construct a winged apparatus which would at least rise from the earth. This feat it proved that it could achieve in 1894, but his contrivance constituted nothing else of practical benefit towards successful flight.

15

Phillips was a capable and serious experimenter on logical, scientific lines and produced particularly valuable results from his admirable investigations into the properties of aerofoils.

Of the three, Pilcher made the greatest progress in the direction of powered flight, first with sustained trials with his hang gliders—the Bat, Beetle, Gull and Hawk—and with his intended application of power in 1899 to a later machine. Pilcher's invaluable work was brought to a tragic and abrupt termination with the collapse of the bamboo tailboom of his Hawk while under towed take-off and his subsequent death from injuries sustained in the accident.

With the death of Pilcher and also the loss earlier of his inspiration and mentor Lilienthal, there came a comparative lull in full-scale experimental heavier-than-air construction in Europe. Such progress in practical airborne experiment as was being made in the late 1890s was dominated by the free balloon and the dirigible. Nevertheless, beneath the surface the seeds sown by the few resolute empiricists of earlier years were germinating steadily, encouraged and assisted by the general surging forwards of the tide of technological advance in the civilized countries of the world.

The last few years of the nineteenth century had seen a sober, practical progression towards the ultimate goal, the result of patient application of brains and hands on the parts of many—including Pilcher in Britain, Lilienthal in Germany, and Chanute and Langley in America.

Evolution of the all-important four-stroke petrol engine, first run successfully in 1876 by the German engineer Dr. Otto, proceeded concurrently until, in 1899, the brothers Orville and Wilbur Wright of Dayton, Ohio, felt themselves attracted sufficiently to the subject to join in the small group of widely scattered devotees. The temperament of the pair of cycle-manufacturers was instrumental in providing the necessary patient, steady and logical approach to the problem which led eventually, on 17th December, 1903, to their achieving the first four successful flights. Their well-earned initial triumph spurred the brothers on to continued concentrated effort, so that, by 1905, their No. 3 Flyer had been evolved into a consistent, practical flying machine. During that year the news that heavier-than-air flight had become a reality started to spread. The brothers were ready to negotiate with the military authorities for the exploitation of their invention, but failed initially with both the American and British officials, owing to the demonstrably unbusinesslike attitude of the respective governments, a factor to be encountered as a foregone conclusion by anyone dealing with officialdom at any period.

After a lapse of some two and a half years, the Wright brothers in May, 1908, resumed their flying and then came fully into the open to give public demonstrations and to receive their due acclaim. In the meantime, the experimenters in Europe had been struggling on with varying degrees of success in their earnest endeavours to fly their aeroplanes regularly and successfully, but had been completely unable to reach anything approaching the standard accomplished by the American pair. The impact which the Wright brothers made meant that there was not now to be any looking back. The point of no return had been reached, and the flying machine had survived its lengthy, uncertain and halting genesis.

As far as Great Britain was concerned, even in 1908 and early 1909 the group of pioneer constructors and pilots were still faced with an uphill labour. Official assistance and encouragement for the aeroplane were virtually non-existent. A small amount of lighter-than-air activity was in being, with expansion and positive progress hampered by the usual obstacle bedevilling the British Services—that of lack of adequate funds. The aeroplane was still looked upon askance by those appointed and paid to minister to the defence needs of the British nation.

A novel invention of inestimable and far-reaching significance had made its appearance, and swift, correct assessment of its unlimited ultimate potential and value as a part of the British armed forces could rapidly have bestowed on the country an unassailable lead in the exciting and stimulating new field. Such progress as was being made in 1908 and 1909 was left mainly to impecunious private constructors, with Cody and Dunne constituting the exceptions until the sponsorship which they received at Farnborough ceased during April, 1909.

The lukewarm attitude of the military services still persisted with little advance discernible in any aspect of aeronautics in which the Army and the Navy condescended to take part. Since 1878 experiments had been conducted with balloons, backed by a balloon store established in the same year under Capt. R. P. Lee, R.E., at Woolwich Arsenal. The store was moved in 1882 to the School of Military Engineering at Chatham and supplemented in 1886 by the setting up of the Balloon School at Lidsing, Kent. The very successful participation in June, 1889, of a detachment of balloons in the summer manoeuvres at Aldershot led to the Balloon establishment being transferred to Aldershot. Increasing enthusiasm was responsible for the formation of the Balloon Section, Royal Engineers, during 1890, together with the voting of an Air Estimate for £4,300. Two years later, in 1892, the Factory and School were set up in Balloon Square in the Stanhope Line of the Royal Engineers in Aldershot South Camp. June, 1894, saw an added interest in the possibilities of airborne aids when a man-lifting kite section was added as well, and the same year witnessed the full establishment of the Balloon Factory at Aldershot. The Boer War brought a call in 1899 for balloon detachments to be sent to South Africa to aid observation, resulting in a natural increase in production at the Factory, the superintendent of which, Col. J. L. B. Templer, visited Alberto Santos-Dumont in Paris during January, 1902, to appraise the inventor's non-rigid airships. Templer's recommendation that the Factory should proceed with airship development was not assisted by a 50% reduction in allocation of funds from £12,000 to £6,000, but he was successful in obtaining permission to start airship design and construction.

During 1904 development of aero engines was another important step towards practical flying, and the year was also that in which Col. J. E. Capper crossed the Atlantic to visit the Wright brothers with a proposal that they should come to England to continue their heavier-than-air experiments.

The scheme failed with the refusal of the Treasury to provide the money required.

Despite the lack of an energetic lead from the Government, within the Factory activity increased steadily and a broadening of the scope of experiment was manifest in the course of 1904 and 1905. This expansion brought about in 1905 the removal of the Balloon Factory and the Balloon Section of the Royal Engineers to a new site at South Farnborough and the eventual alteration of name in 1908 to His Majesty's Balloon Factory.

In April, 1909, came the cessation of official aeroplane experiments at the Factory when the War Office decided that the total expenditure of £2,500 made to date was too great, considered in conjunction with the comparative lack of success so far by both Cody and Dunne in evolving sound, usable aircraft for the Army. Research with airships was still to be carried on at the Factory, and while the *Baby*, designed by Col. Capper, was being completed, during April, 1909, the Hon. C. S. Rolls again approached the Factory with his offer to bring an aeroplane to Farnborough—this time a Wright biplane. Acceptance of his earlier proposal, made in October, 1908, and offering a Farman–Delagrange biplane, had been deferred owing to current opinion that the flying space available was too small for manoeuvring. This time Rolls's offer was accepted, and a few Army officers were trained on the Wright until its owner's death at Bournemouth on 12th July, 1910.

1909 was a year of note in the history of the Factory, as it was that in which it was reorganized from 5th May until, in December, the Balloon Factory and the Balloon School were separated. At the beginning of 1910 the appointment of Mervyn J. P. O'Gorman as superintendent of the Factory, which took effect at the end of 1909, began to show results when a policy of scientific research and development was instituted to inaugurate the part which the centre was to play for the future in the evolution of the aeroplane.

On 17th October, 1910, came the War Office's announcement of an increase in the scope of the Balloon Factory's work, and further evidence of the leisurely awakening to the potentialities of the aeroplane came on 28th February, 1911, when the news was released of the proposed formation of the Air Battalion of the Royal Engineers. This was to be charged with the task of 'creating a body of expert airmen, organized in such a way as to facilitate the formation of units ready to take the field with troops. . . . In addition, the training and instruction of men in handling kites, balloons and aeroplanes, and other forms of aircraft, will also devolve upon this battalion.' The following month the Secretary of State for War's White Paper included £85,000 for new dirigibles and aeroplanes, and 1st April, 1911, saw the official replacement of the Balloon Section, R.E., by the Air Battalion. Just over three weeks later, on 26th April, the Balloon Factory became the Army Aircraft Factory with Mervyn O'Gorman still acting as its superintendent.

So, two years after the decision to cease work on aeroplanes for the War Office, the Government was obliged by the advance of aviation to think again and to adopt an entirely new and opposite policy of belatedly encouraging and establishing aeronautics as a part of the British armed services. The decision came not a minute too soon, and the reluctance, parsimony and procrastination displayed during the Edwardian period towards the inevitable acceptance of flying was shortly to prove costly to the country in the extreme in lives and materials.

Meanwhile, abroad, the aeroplane had finally made its operational début in war. During the conflict which broke out in Libya in October, 1911, between Italy and Turkey, the Italian Army assembled a small force of six aircraft which proved very successful and completely surprised the unsuspecting Turks near Azizia when the first machine—a Blériot flown by Capt. Piazza—purred overhead while on an hour's reconnaissance flight from Tripoli on 23rd October. Two days later, on 25th October, Capt. Moizo took-off on another scouting mission. It was but a short step to adapt the machines for an offensive rôle, so that Lt. Cavotti was able to fly over the Turkish troops on 1st November, 1911, and drop four bombs on them in the first bombing raid to be made by an aeroplane. This was soon followed by more bombs flown over to crash down on the heads of the irate Turks, the Italians feeling well pleased with their initiative and the results achieved with primitive machines at so early a stage in their development. The aeroplane had thus established itself as a weapon of war and occupied a position thenceforth from which it has yet to be dislodged.

A certain amount of interest in the dropping of bombs from aeroplanes had been shown in America when, in January, 1911, a Wright biplane was employed at San Francisco by the U.S. Army to carry out the first test with a live bomb. Lt. Riley E. Scott, late of the U.S. Army, was soon afterwards in 1911 responsible for the logical step of producing the first bomb-sight to be made in the U.S.A., but his invention was turned down by the War Department. In July, 1911, Glenn Curtiss made bombing tests when he flew over the outline of a battleship which had been set out with flags on Lake Keuka and dropped dummy bombs on it from his machine.

The general picture during the few years before the advent of the 1914–18 War was, therefore, one of very slow progress by the armed services of interested countries in adopting and exploiting the aeroplane, despite its appreciation by enthusiastic and conscientious individuals.

The British Army and Navy administration displayed the same sense of easy-going apathy and dearth of dynamic spirit and energy in promoting an effective air arm as was evident also in other countries, despite the unsettled international atmosphere and the obvious portents of the increasingly rapid drift to the point of eruption into a calamitous war.

The change of name for the Army Aircraft Factory to that of the Royal Aircraft Factory came with the issue on 11th April, 1912, of the White Paper entitled *Memorandum on Naval and Military Aviation* and providing for the establishment to undertake under the aegis of the War Office: 'The higher training of mechanics for the Royal Flying Corps; tests with British and Foreign engines and aeroplanes; experimental work; the existing work in the manufacture of hydrogen and generally meeting the requirements of the

Airship and Kite Squadrons; and general maintenance of the Factory and its policy.'

The Royal Flying Corps mentioned was constituted by a Royal Warrant on 13th April, 1912, and came into being a month afterwards on 13th May. The most pressing problem facing the newest addition to Britain's fighting services lay in the provision of suitable flying equipment. By mid-1912 several firms of constructors were proceeding in a determined manner to produce progressively improved aeroplanes, but with the emphasis mainly on civil training types, owing to the absence of a well-defined programme originating in the War Office and the Admiralty which would order types required to perform specific operational duties. The 1912 Military Trials were staged on Salisbury Plain, ostensibly to remedy the situation, but failed miserably in their objective.

The overall impression which held sway, not only in the United Kingdom, was that the aeroplane might conceivably be useful as an instrument of scouting in time of war, but offered little prospect of proving of further service. This opinion appeared to be shared by those responsible for the general policy of both the Army and the Navy.

Nevertheless, the idea of adapting the aeroplane to play its part in taking the offensive to the enemy by transporting a load of bombs with the purpose of dropping them visually with accuracy was one which had caught the imagination of several designers. While the Military and Naval Wings of the Royal Flying Corps were busily engaged in organizing their men and machines into some semblance of useful forces, several ideas were being investigated among the small group of aircraft constructors to test theories and schemes for bomb-dropping. The machines so far developed were able to carry only marginal loads, and yet the bombs themselves were still comparatively small.

1913 was a year in which the attempt was made to produce bomb-carrying aeroplanes by equipping existing designs with sights and racks. The British and Colonial Aeroplane Company were early in the field when they converted the Coanda Improved Military Monoplane works number 151 into a T.B.8 biplane on its return to Filton from Halberstadt, Germany, in August, 1913, and sent it out to Rumania in the following October fitted with a bomb-rack.

Number 198, built from the beginning as a T.B.8, was more ambitious in its equipment and was finished specially for the firm's stand at the Paris Salon de l'Aéronautique in November, 1913. The work of improvement was carried out under the direction of Mons. Henri Coanda and gave the machine controls in the rear cockpit only, leaving the front cockpit free to accommodate the bomb-release mechanism and a prismatic type of bomb-sight. The offensive load consisted of twelve 10 lb. bombs housed in a revolving container beneath the fuselage. As the lowermost bomb left its mounting, the rack turned to place the next bomb in position and automatically set the fuse. In addition to being released individually, the bombs could also be dropped in one batch.

Although a conversion from the Coanda Military Monoplane design, the T.B.8 turned out to be a great improvement over its predecessor and a very

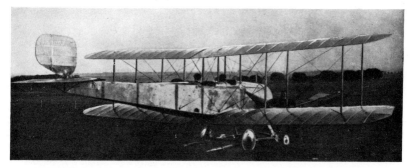

Early Bristol T.B.8 converted from Bristol Coanda Military Monoplane. (*Bristol Photo.*)

successful machine in its own right. A fairly long fuselage contained the two cockpits in tandem and carried normal equal-span, two-bay, unstaggered wings. The standard tail assembly and four-wheel main undercarriage unit of the monoplane were retained. The T.B.8s built, numbering fifty-three, were powered by various engines, including the 50 h.p. Gnome, 60 h.p. le Rhône, 80 h.p. Gnome, 80 h.p. le Rhône and the 100 h.p. Monosoupape Gnome. The T.B.8 was not a design which attempted anything spectacular or unusual in construction and used the conventional wire-braced and fabric-covered framework of the period, a style which, owing to its many merits, was to remain firmly entrenched for many years ahead.

The T.B.8 was evolved by Bristol to meet the Admiralty's order for a land-based biplane version of the Coanda Military Monoplane, to accompany the central-float biplane works number 120 which the Admiralty had contracted to buy if the machine passed its acceptance tests satisfactorily.

The landplane T.B.8 was produced by converting monoplane works number 121. Number 121 eventually became a seaplane taking the place of works number 120, and a fresh landplane was obtained by taking yet another monoplane—works number 144—and using it as the basis for the replacement T.B.8 biplane. This eventually made its first flight on 12th August, 1913, and entered naval service as No. 43. Through placing its order for the T.B.8 land-plane, the Admiralty was thus responsible to a considerable degree for the machine's existence as a design which its builders were then encouraged to develop. It was, perhaps, the earliest example of a British bomber aeroplane suitably equipped for its task, as far as the knowledge of design would permit at the time of its conception.

Naval interest in the promotion of flying had been at a level more or less parallel with that of the Army. Happy enough in the knowledge that the Royal Navy's might could meet and transcend all foreseeable danger, from whichever quarter it might appear and at any time, there was little sense of urgency to adopt the flying machine on any sizeable scale.

The first indication of an awakening of interest in flying in the Royal Navy came during July, 1908, with the proposal which was submitted to the First Sea Lord, Sir John Fisher, by Capt. R. H. S. Bacon, Director of Naval

21

Ordnance. This was for the construction of a rigid airship to be used by the Fleet for reconnaissance. The Committee of Imperial Defence debated the idea at a number of meetings and finally decided to go ahead with the design and construction of one example, the Admiralty to be responsible for supervising the entire project. Vickers, Son and Maxim were selected to undertake the work, which started during May, 1909, in Cavendish Dock at Barrow-in-Furness. After two years the Naval Rigid No. 1, popularly known as the *Mayfly*, emerged from its shed in May, 1911, to be taken in again, after four days at the mooring mast, to undergo modification. The airship was brought out once more on the following 24th September, but broke its back on the way to the mast and was wrecked completely. In January, 1912, the Court of Inquiry recommended the cessation of airship projects for the Navy, and the special section recently formed for airship work under Capt. Murray F. Sueter, Inspecting Captain of Airships, was disbanded.

This decision might have set back flying experience in the Royal Navy several years had the lighter-than-air sphere been the Service's only interest in aeronautics. Such, however, was not the case as, during the construction of the Naval Rigid No. 1, the aeroplane had come into the picture when four naval officers started their flying training at Eastchurch on 2nd March, 1911. Consequent upon the successful completion of their instruction was the setting up of the Navy's first flying school—also at Eastchurch—in December, 1911.

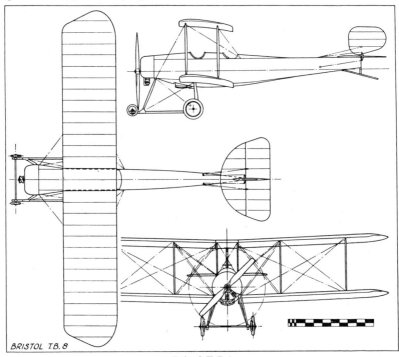

Bristol T.B.8

The Admiralty steadily became more alive to the potentiality of the aeroplane in offensive and defensive rôles, and a particular impression was made by the paper submitted by Lt. H. A. Williamson in January, 1912, to the Submarine Committee. This body had been constituted to examine measures which might be taken as defence against the submarine, a type of craft which —used by an enemy—could confront the Royal Navy with an extremely serious and awkward problem.

Lt. Williamson was a submarine officer and produced his suggestions in response to an appeal issued by the Admiralty to officers of the submarine service. His proposals for dealing with the under-water menace suggested that suitably equipped aircraft should be employed to detect and then attack hostile submarines. It was recommended also that the presence of aircraft overhead would force enemy submarines to remain well submerged when in the vicinity of the Fleet.

Experiments were therefore ordered to test Lt. Williamson's theories and took place at Harwich in June, 1912, and three months later at Rosyth in September, 1912. It was established that in normal visibility a seaplane was able to detect a submarine in diving trim on the surface and attack it with a bomb before a dive could be effected. As seaplanes capable of carrying out such attacks were not yet available for the Navy's use, it was obviously imperative that adequately equipped machines should be developed for service without delay. In addition to bomb-dropping gear, reliable wireless equipment was urgently needed.

The interesting task of performing the flying experiments necessary to the design of effective bomb-dropping gear and to obtain data on the characteristics of bombs when released in flight was allotted to Cdr. C. R. Samson, one of the most experienced and capable naval pilots then available. Samson carried out the tests at Eastchurch, and further valuable experimental work was conducted by a naval gunnery officer, Lt. R. H. Clark-Hall, who was detailed for armament duties with the Naval Wing in March, 1913. The work included carefully conducted trials in December, 1913, with floating explosive charges—the weight of which ranged from 2 to 40 lb.—detonated underneath seaplanes which flew overhead at set heights to ascertain possible effects on the aircraft. Analysis of the results produced the conclusion that a 100 lb. bomb with a 40 lb. charge inside could be released at 350 ft. altitude without damage to its carrying aircraft.

Numerous other tests were conducted in a steadily pursued programme with the commendable object of compiling as quickly as possible a useful fund of experience and data which could be embodied in the naval aviator's training schedule and put to immediate use should the need arise. Such determination and enthusiasm were injected into the task in hand that the Royal Navy's flying wing personnel soon gained an undisputed lead over the Military Wing in the art of bomb-dropping, so much so, in fact, that in January, 1914, the Admiralty permitted the data amassed to be transmitted to the Military Wing of the R.F.C.

Previous to this, in March, 1913, the Military Wing had constituted an

Experimental Branch under Maj. Herbert Musgrave with the express object of co-ordinating the results of the experimental work in which each of the four squadrons was engaged. At such an early stage in the formation of a new service with intended duties to be carried out in an entirely new element, a vast amount of inter-related work waited to be done, and the only logical step to take was the setting up of a central organization to sift and record the facts collected and to recommend methods of their application in the establishment of an effective and efficient force in return for the taxpayers' money voted in its favour.

A very broad field of investigation was covered by the Experimental Branch. Bomb-dropping was included among these tasks, which covered also artillery co-operation, ballooning, kiting, meteorology, photography and wireless telegraphy. In deference to the idea firmly held by those responsible for the direction of policy for the Military Wing, that the aeroplane would assist the Army by augmenting its facilities for reconnaissance, the Experimental Branch naturally concentrated its efforts in the direction of improved wireless equipment and performance so that the shortcomings prevalent in wireless telegraphy could be steadily removed. In this work Maj. Musgrave was assisted by two Royal Engineers, Lt. B. T. James and Lt. D. S. Lewis, and the three were able to advance the science profitably. Relatively little attention was devoted by the Experimental Branch to evolving techniques for bombing or developing equipment for fitting to aircraft, enabling them to act as effective bombers. Eventually, therefore, the situation existed whereby the Military Wing was well aware of its paucity of knowledge and practical experience and turned to the Naval Wing to assist it in remedying the defect in its proficiency.

Although the Military and Naval Wings of the Royal Flying Corps were ostensibly equal partners of the same Service, the deeply entrenched traditions and functional duties of both the Army and the Navy could never be subordinated. As the Senior Service, the Navy was soon asserting its spirit of virile independence in several ways, and the official title Naval Wing of the Royal Flying Corps was quickly supplanted in general usage by that of Naval Air Service. By the end of 1913, the headquarters of the Naval Wing had been established in the Central Air Office, Sheerness, at the close of a year which had witnessed the setting up of the first links in a chain of Naval Air stations around the British coast, following the decision to constitute them which was taken by the Admiralty in October, 1912. Eastchurch was the first of the new units, followed by those on the Isle of Grain, at Calshot, Felixstowe and Cromarty. Despite efforts made at a high level in Whitehall by the members of the Air Committee, the deep-seated basic differences between the Army and the Navy rendered compatibility impossible in the Royal Flying Corps, with the result that, on 1st July, 1914, the Naval Wing became a separate entity as the Royal Naval Air Service.

The torpedo formed a very significant and effective component of naval armament, so that, in addition to their work in developing bomb-dropping by naval aircraft, the naval technicians and pilots paid considerable attention to the airborne launching of torpedoes at enemy surface vessels.

By 1911 the potential offensive value of the addition to the Navy of aircraft capable of discharging torpedoes against enemy ships was beginning to be appreciated, at a period when the machines themselves were in a very early stage of development and barely able to maintain flight, let alone carry a passenger and a worthwhile load in addition to the pilot. In the course of 1911 the first release of a torpedo in the air was carried out from a Farman biplane by an Italian officer, Capt. Guidoni, who launched one weighing 352 lb.

The steady progress discernible in Britain in performance and reliability of both landplane and seaplane made it possible by mid-1914 to consider a practical demonstration of taking-off with a torpedo and launching it safely while airborne. The naval experiments of the last three years were leading towards the eventual employment of the airborne torpedo, the main obstacles to be overcome being those of the weight of the weapon, the provision of its launching mechanism and the endowment of the carrying aircraft with adequate range and navigation facilities. The final stimulus for the trial launch itself came during the Review of the Fleet held at Spithead from 18th until 22nd July, 1914, after which the First Lord of the Admiralty, Winston Churchill, questioned Sqn. Cdr. Arthur M. Longmore, then the Commanding Officer of Calshot Naval Air Station, about the progress being made there with airborne torpedoes and intimated that the work should be expedited. Flt. Lt. D. H. Hyde-Thomson had been concentrating on the mechanical aspect of the project and proceeded to develop the necessary release gear and to adapt the 810 lb. 14 in. torpedo for its new rôle. Sqn. Cdr. Longmore requested, and was granted, the use of one of the four Short Folder Seaplanes equipped with the fourteen-cylinder 160 h.p. Gnome engine, which had taken part in the Review, and Horace Short assisted with the design work involved in modifying the crossbars of the main floats to accommodate the weapon. The task of adaptation proceeded apace so that a few days later, on 28th July, 1914, Longmore was able to rise solo from the water without trouble and with the torpedo slung beneath the fuselage between the pair of floats. The release was accomplished successfully, but the achievement could only be regarded as a preliminary step in the evolution of the practical torpedo aircraft. The machine used was not designed from the outset to cope with the onerous task of transporting such a weight and, to do so, its fuel load was perforce restricted to allow about thirty minutes duration only. The accommodation of a second crew member was also out of the question. Nevertheless, the possibility of attack by air-launched torpedo had been proved conclusively by practical demonstration, and it remained simply for the concept to be methodically developed so that it could become an accepted form of attack as rapidly as possible.

While the naval authorities had been delving into the potentialities of the seaplane as a torpedo carrier, the idea had also occupied the thoughts of the Sopwith Aviation Company, one of the most prominent and capable of the pioneer British constructors. Accordingly, towards the end of 1913, the two-seat Sopwith Torpedo Seaplane Type C made its appearance. The machine was specifically designed for the duty of torpedo discharge, the weapon being carried in the optimum position between the main float units.

The Type C's general lines followed those of the 100 h.p. Anzani-powered Sopwith Tractor Seaplane supplied to the Naval Wing of the R.F.C. during July, 1913. Four-bay, unequal-span wings without stagger were used, and the primary floats were augmented by a small float at each lower wingtip and underneath the tail. Four strut-connected ailerons were embodied in the mainplanes and the 200 h.p. Salmson, cooled by tall vertical radiators installed on each side of the fuselage alongside the engine, transmitted its power to the two-blade wooden propeller through an extension shaft. Late in 1913 the Type C, with clipped wings, was at Calshot and was to be seen from March until July, 1914, taxiing on the water under test to develop its torpedo release gear and to check the reaction of the floats when running on the water with a load. These trials were often carried out by Lt. Robin P. Ross. Shortly afterwards a second Type C—fitted to carry an 810 lb. Whitehead 14 in. torpedo—was delivered to Calshot and flown successfully in practice runs on a target by Sqn. Cdr. Longmore prior to making his torpedo release from the Short Folder at the end of July.

A. V. Roe and Company constituted another of the British firms which, by 1912, had become firmly established in business as designers and constructors of aircraft which were of particular interest to Military and Naval customers. During March, 1914, a design was prepared for a two-seat bomber biplane mounted on twin main floats and a small tail float; the wings, tail surfaces and landing-gear were to be interchangeable with the units used on the Avro 510. The new project was given the type number 513 and was scheduled to be powered by two 80 h.p. Gnomes installed as pushers at mid-gap between the unequal-span folding wings. The crew of two would have been seated in tandem in the nose of the fuselage, but, eventually, the decision was taken not to proceed with construction of the Avro 513.

An objective appraisal, therefore, of British air power—if such it may even justifiably be termed—as it stood in mid-1914 produces a comparatively indeterminate and desultory scene. In the very short period of some five years a completely new force—capable of both offence and defence—had been made available well-nigh simultaneously to the Army and the Navy. In the minds of high-ranking officers of each service, men ultimately responsible for the deployment of personnel and material at their disposal, the aeroplane—operated from either land or water—still constituted relatively little in the way of a weapon capable of contributing anything of value in the conduct of a war. The effort and sacrifice on the part of manufacturers and pilots—private and officially-sponsored—demonstrated progress in performance, reliability and safety which was, in reality, remarkable when considered against the length of time elapsed.

In spite of the ominous signs portending that the peace of Europe might shortly be shattered, the admirable scheme of unifying both Military and Naval air strength in a single service lasted but little over two years. With the formation of the breakaway Royal Naval Air Service, the Royal Flying Corps became a purely military organization operating in conjunction with the Army. Acceptance of the aeroplane in either case was far from being wholehearted by those responsible for overall Army and Navy strategy and was limited to reconnaissance, despite the firm belief by individual enthusiasts in each service in a far greater potential in aircraft and their ability to undertake diverse duties. Endorsement as a major weapon of war was still a long way from being a fact, a situation which time and time again ordained that the British Services have been drawn into battle far from adequately prepared and at a cruel disadvantage from the outset of hostilities.

Apart from the basic differences of tradition and environment, the Army and the Navy possessed widely divergent ideas in selecting their sources of equipment. The Military Wing of the R.F.C. had turned mainly to the Royal Aircraft Factory at Farnborough for its aircraft, while the Navy actively supported the British private constructors in the procurement of its machines.

Although, in most categories, British aircraft designs were patently in advance of all others by 1914, the position was far less happy as far as that most important component—the engine—was concerned. Since 1909, the year in which it first appeared in Britain, the French-designed Gnome in its various models had justifiably gone from strength to strength and had contributed more than any other power plant towards making the aeroplane into a practical vehicle in so short a period.

The lack in Great Britain of a range of indigenous aircraft engines, capable of meeting varying requirements, was felt keenly, so that, on 30th September, 1909, a prize of £1,000 was put up by Patrick Y. Alexander for the best British aero engine to be produced. The rules of the contest, which was conducted at the National Physical Laboratory at Teddington, called for a run of 24 hours. Six units were entered, out of which three took part, but none was successful in keeping going for the stipulated period. A second competition for the same £1,000 award was held during December, 1911, this time at Farnborough. A Green engine was declared the winner after making two runs of 12 hours nonstop at 66 h.p. and 1,150 r.p.m.

Although the Green had fulfilled the requirements, it was not considered generally satisfactory, so the Royal Aircraft Factory staff were asked to set to work to design a competent unit. The suggestion, when first made, was rejected, but Col. Seely, the Minister for War, later agreed to the proposition with the result that, in 1913, the eight-cylinder, air-cooled 90° vee R.A.F.1 made its appearance, developing 100 h.p. This signified the start of the Factory's work in aero engine design, a phase which was to last for five years and brought into being a useful range of power plants. At the same time, the research work initiated later produced innumerable innovations in aero-engine technique and built up a vast pool of knowledge and experience of the greatest value. A start had been made in developing a suitable range of British aero engines, but, by mid-1914, relatively little progress had been made in filling the painfully obvious gap and in making up for lost time. Consequently, by the time that the aeronautical strength which Britain could muster was required for war, the aircraft available were—in the main—relying heavily on engines from abroad, an untenable position at such a critical time.

As the summer of 1914 moved steadily on, the last remaining weeks of an uneasy peace slipped away and tension on the continent of Europe mounted rapidly. Orders were issued to the R.F.C. and the R.N.A.S. to prepare men and machines for the inevitable action soon to come, and the small forces of aeroplanes on strength were groomed for their allotted tasks.

The tentative experiments indulged in over the previous few years had imparted a certain amount of proficiency in the subject to the Army and the Navy, but of properly-equipped bombers or torpedo-carriers there was none. The idea had been born, but had not so far received sufficient forthright recognition and encouragement in either Service to provide even a small force of aircraft capable of punishing the enemy either on land or at sea. Greater awareness at the right level in the War Office and in the Admiralty that the embryo of a potent new weapon lay waiting to be nourished and promoted to grow eventually into the mightiest force in warfare would have been of incalculable value in the conduct of successful operations. As it was, when the fateful first week of August arrived and both the R.F.C. and the R.N.A.S. were called to active stations, despite the excellent spirit prevailing in each Service and the amount of hard work put in by all personnel, the limited number of aircraft available were far from being ideal for decisive operational use, either in their general design or in their meagre specialized equipment.

The 1912 Military Trials had miscarried utterly in their avowed purpose of promoting the development of suitable equipment for British Service pilots, and two years passed before, during February, 1914, the War Office issued a memorandum listing three types of aeroplane considered to be necessary. The first machine specified was a single-seat light scout with an engine which could be started by the pilot. The speed range desired was 50 to 85 m.p.h., climb rate was to be 3,500 ft. in 5 mins., and sufficient fuel was to be carried to confer a range of 300 miles. The second type for which a requirement existed was in the two-seat reconnaissance category. A heavier machine, it was to have wireless telegraphy installed and to possess, with pilot and observer aboard, a range of 200 miles and be capable of a speed range of 35 to 60 m.p.h. In a wind not exceeding 15 m.p.h. the machine had to be able to stop within 100 yards of a 30 ft. obstacle. The third and last aircraft on the list was a heavy two-seat fighter, the gunner to have a machine-gun and sufficient ammunition and to be able to use his gun without obstruction in a field of fire up to 30° on each side of the line of flight. Enough fuel was to be carried for 300 miles and the machine had to be able to climb to 3,500 ft. in 8 mins. A speed range of 45 to 75 m.p.h. was demanded. The memorandum demonstrated a realization of the basic types of aircraft required, but still omitted any mention of a bomber or torpedo-carrier. The same shortcoming was noticeable in the minute from Winston Churchill on 26th October, 1913, which—a few months earlier—had contained a list of three types of aircraft for which openings existed in the Navy. The First Lord considered that both landplanes and seaplanes for tactical work were needed—'an oversea fighting seaplane to operate from a ship as base, a scouting seaplane to work with the Fleet at sea, and a home service fighting aeroplane to repel enemy aircraft, protect vulnerable points on our coast and to carry out patrol duties along the coast'. The monoplane ban of October, 1912, enforced in the Military Wing of the R.F.C. until February, 1913, was responsible for the concentration of design effort on the biplane, which was considered to be both stronger and safer.

The few squadrons of the R.F.C. in existence when the emergency came in 1914 were equipped primarily with Farnborough-designed B.E.2s and B.E.8s, Avro 504s, Blériots and Farmans, augmented by a variety of other odd types. The R.N.A.S. pilots were also flying the useful 504, together with a heterogeneous collection of alternative machines which included B.E.2s, B.E.8s, Bristol T.B.8s and Shorts.

Abroad, the outbreak of the 1914–18 War found the official attitude towards the use of the aeroplane in war to be broadly the same as that prevailing in Britain, namely a lack of appreciation of the vast latent offensive and defensive potential waiting to be exploited. In France, a generally lukewarm feeling on the part of the General Staff restricted the Army and the Navy to the small force of aircraft which each could muster.

Although the airship had claimed a major portion of development in Germany and automatically possessed the great advantages of range and capacity —particularly useful attributes for bombing—both the Army and Navy had systematically organized their own air arms so that, when the conflict blazed up, each was well forward in the ability to deploy its aircraft in some numbers.

Despite the fact that Italy had been quick a few years earlier to use her crude aircraft as bombers, little more had been done to build up a functional air force.

Belgium, immediately embroiled and to suffer greatly in the war, was also in the position of possessing a very small number of machines and personnel.

In each case, therefore, the combatants, destined to enter into, and to fight out, for the next four and a quarter years the greatest and most tragic war experienced until that time, owned air arms of varying sizes but were not experienced in exploiting them to the best advantage and were completely incapable of launching them into a battle so as to procure either a quick decision or any positive advantage at the outset.

The opportunity was there for several years before the final hour, but inertia and indecision had taken too great a toll of the best intentions where they existed. Nevertheless, once the armies were in motion, the new force in warfare rapidly drew to the forefront, starting its swift climb to indispensability, an ascent which eventually left the bomber aloft on its for-long-unassailed pinnacle as the transporter and agent of the mightiest and deadliest weapons yet devised.

Avro 504 biplane 878, one of the batch of six from which 873, 874 and 875, together with 179, were modified for the raid on Friedrichshafen on 21st November, 1914. (*Avro Photo.*)

CHAPTER TWO

BIRTH OF THE BOMBER

Throughout the centuries Europe's story has been one of unsettled peace, split asunder by intermittent wars of ever-increasing violence and extent. The twentieth century was destined to outstrip all of its predecessors in bloodshed and unimaginable terror as the outcome of the unprincipled machinations of irresponsible men of unbounded ambition and of unmitigated ruthlessness, but endowed with the misplaced power to send millions of their innocent fellow beings to unsought and undeserved premature death.

New weapons, born of the rapidly developing industrial and technological capacity of the civilized nations, released conflicts from the bounds which had encompassed them previously and brought for the first time the possibility of the hideous horror of total war to the blameless and the guilty alike.

Under Bismarck's hand Germany had been transformed at a rapid pace from a collection of small states which had existed for some six hundred years into a strong, co-ordinated country, of great power militarily as well as economically. Bellicosity towards neighbouring nations followed as a matter of course, with France left bleeding and humiliated and with hatred in her heart for the Germans and schemes in her head for revenge. To safeguard Germany's newly-won territory the Triple Alliance—comprising Germany, the Austro-Hungarian Empire and Italy—was formed. France countered this move by joining with Russia to constitute the Dual Alliance, and so the opposing factions drew together to stand facing, each warily watching the other in anticipation of the next move in the dangerous game of military chess.

Germany's policy of overseas expansion and aggrandisement was interpreted as a developing threat to the security of the British Empire, with the result that Great Britain was drawn towards alliance with France and Russia in the Triple Entente.

As the Edwardian era advanced through its single decade, the old order in Europe of centuries past was crumbling at an increasing rate. One by one the outmoded monarchs of an archaic system of the primitive and medieval past were being replaced, moves which were accompanied by a rise in nationalistic feeling. The surface of the Balkans rippled with discontent and intrigue, while Germany strove relentlessly to augment her position of power and wealth and outstrip her competitors at maximum speed until she could feel ready to challenge and dominate them. Her thorough preparations for war were manifold and evident in each direction, with particular attention being paid to staff organization and logistical support. The German Army was superior to its potential adversaries in strength and equipment, and in naval power the country was excelled by Britain only.

As one European crisis was succeeded by the next apprehension grew until, finally, on 28th June, 1914, in Sarajevo Gavrilo Princip pointed his gun at the Archduke Franz Ferdinand, heir to the throne of Austria, and fired the shots which killed the Archduke and his wife. The stage was set for the drama due to begin, the villains of the piece were ready and waiting to make their entry, and the curtain was about to rise on the first of the two great tragedies of the first half of the twentieth century.

Backed by Germany, Austria–Hungary presented her ultimatum to Serbia on 25th July, following the Emperor Franz Josef's decision to go to war. The Austro-Hungarian declaration of war against Serbia came on 28th July, the die was cast and there was no turning back. Nation by nation the principal combatants mobilized in accordance with their treaty obligations to undergo the nightmare which was destined to be theirs unceasingly for the ensuing four and a quarter years.

The first four days of August, 1914, were crowded with momentous events as Germany declared war on Russia on the 1st, on France on the 3rd and on the 4th told Belgium that she would be invaded forthwith.

At 11 p.m. on the 4th Great Britain entered the fray with her declaration of war against Germany following the German refusal to respect Belgian neutrality. On the day after, the 5th, Austria-Hungary declared war on Russia, and this announcement was followed on 10th August by France in turn declaring war on Austria-Hungary. Two days later, on the 12th, Britain also declared war on Austria-Hungary.

Alongside the relatively known quantities of the Army and the Navy, the Royal Flying Corps and the Royal Naval Air Service—both so far untried in combat—had mobilized for action immediately. For some weeks beforehand, both Services had been preparing themselves for the eventuality. During June, 1914, the Military Wing of the R.F.C. had undergone combined training at a Concentration Camp at Netheravon and had dispersed on 2nd July after the various elements engaged had indulged in practical exercises which embraced all aspects of their work. The Navy's turn had come shortly afterwards at the review and manoeuvres at Spithead and, soon after these were over, the Royal Naval Air Service received instructions on 29th July laying down the duties to be carried out by its aircraft in the impending emergency.

There was no delay in ordering the available units of the Royal Flying Corps to go to France once the conflict had started. Taking the field under Brig.-Gen. Sir David Henderson, the small number of squadrons so far formed crossed the Channel with their mixed equipment, ready to put into practice the theories of aerial reconnaissance in which they had been trained. At 9.30 a.m. on 19th August Capt. P. B. Joubert de la Ferté of No. 3 Squadron in a Blériot and Lt. G. W. Mapplebeck of No. 4 Squadron flying a B.E.2a took-off together from Maubeuge to undertake the first observation from the air of the advance and disposition of the enemy.

For the first two months of the War the original units—Nos. 2, 3, 4 and 5 Squadrons, backed by the Aircraft Park and their Headquarters—which had been dispatched to France immediately, remained the sole representatives in the field of the R.F.C. Although untried at the outset of hostilities, flying primitive aircraft without specifically developed defensive armament and running the risk continually of being fired at by friendly troops as well as by those of the enemy, the squadrons very quickly proved their worth and made themselves absolutely indispensable by their work. Complete and rapid enthusiastic acceptance of the aeroplane automatically brought the realization that, to carry on the task of reconnaissance and to expand the R.F.C.'s vital activities as a whole, fresh machines wedded to far better equipment were needed in large numbers at the greatest possible speed.

In the midst of this newly-won approbation, what of the bomber? The conflict itself had immediately assumed the age-old form of land warfare with, as was to be expected, the opposing armies advancing and retreating across a once prosperous and fertile landscape. Conducted on a far larger scale and at a greatly increased speed compared with any previous campaigns, a prodigious thirst arose for knowledge of the composition and location of the German forces—both mobile and static—in action and of their reinforcements. Consequently, all available new squadrons were pressed into the rôle of reconnaissance to fly over the troops entwined in bloody battle below on ground which quickly lost all semblance of its former peaceful, cultivated self.

In spite of experiments in firing machine-guns and quick-firers from Military and Naval aircraft which had been conducted prior to August, 1914, the R.F.C. and the R.N.A.S. went into battle without any formal armament fitted to their aircraft. The crews simply took with them their revolvers, augmented by rifles and shotguns. Of bombs, developed specifically for dropping with maximum effect from British aircraft, there was none. Similarly lacking was a bomb-sight, but this did not deter an R.F.C. pilot on 1st September, 1914, from dropping a pair of bombs on two columns of German cavalry when he flew over them near Villers-Cotterets, north-east of Paris, the explosions causing the horses to panic and stampede. In default of any bomb-dropping gear, the missiles had to be launched over the side of the fuselage from a low level to try to ensure a direct hit, a practice which had the primary and serious disadvantage of exposing a valuable aeroplane and its equally precious crew to the direct danger of point-blank fire from rifles and machine-guns on the ground. Every available aeroplane of the R.F.C. was required for unceasing duty on reconnaissance and artillery spotting in co-operation with the Army; consequently, little attention could be spared still to developing aircraft and techniques for tactical bombing.

The Admiralty, however, was differently placed. At the outbreak of war the defence of the United Kingdom was in the hands of the War Office, which, however, found immediately that, owing to its multifarious commitments both in Britain and in France, it was unable to supervise the establishment of adequate facilities for defence—which were at the time well-nigh non-existent. Lord Kitchener thereupon came forward with the suggestion that the Admiralty—not so heavily committed—should be asked to assume responsibility for the defence of the British Isles, and on 3rd September, 1914, the Navy took over.

Admiralty defence policy was based on the assumption that the Germans would undoubtedly employ their Zeppelins in bombing raids against Britain, the expectation being that heavy loads of explosive would be flown across the North Sea to rain down on British soil. Based on this premise, some considerable time before battle was joined, the decision was taken that counter measures against the Zeppelins were not to be merely passive but that—if practicable—the possible marauders were to be destroyed in their lairs.

Immediately the Admiralty donned the cloak of protector of the British Isles, orders were issued to implement this policy with the utmost speed and vigour. Already in Belgium was the Eastchurch Squadron of the R.N.A.S., commanded by the redoubtable bearded Sqn. Cdr. C. R. Samson and the most advanced in training of the R.N.A.S. units. The squadron had been sent to Ostend on 27th August to assist the Marines put ashore at the port, but remained there for three days only until the 30th, on which day the Marine Brigade withdrew; the *Astra Torres No. 3* airship on the squadron's strength was sent back to England and the aeroplanes of the unit flew to Dunkirk on 1st September. The Admiralty was therefore in possession of an advanced air base suitable for the dispatch of aircraft to seek and destroy the hangars housing the Zeppelins. A radius of 100 miles from Dunkirk was laid down as the arbitrary distance for the destruction of any new airship sheds which the enemy might construct, while those already known to exist at Cologne and Düsseldorf were to be attacked by bombing as soon as practicable. The Admiralty was more fortunate than the War Office at the time, for in August, 1914, as a result of its pioneer experiments in bomb-dropping, the Navy at least had stocks available of single and double bomb-carriers and 20 lb. impact-detonating Hale bombs, as well as the heavier 112 lb. Naval type of bomb. The smaller bomb had been designed by F. Marten Hale and had been in use by the R.N.A.S. at Eastchurch since 1913.

When, therefore, the Admiralty became responsible for United Kingdom anti-aircraft defence on 3rd September, it was immediately in the position of being able to execute without delay the plan to destroy the known Zeppelin sheds, as it already possessed the essential forward base on the Continent as well as the aircraft, crews and the bombs, albeit in small numbers. The R.N.A.S. force at Dunkirk was scheduled to be composed of three units with the designations Nos. 1, 2 and 3 Squadrons, each of which was to have twelve aircraft. In the event, Samson was able to muster a total of some twelve machines only which were employed immediately on reconnaissance. A raid on the Zeppelin hangars alongside the River Rhine was planned straightaway, and three machines of the unit known as No. 1 Squadron went back to Ostend on 3rd September to make ready for the attack which was to take place from Antwerp. A few days were required to prepare an airfield at Antwerp, so, in the interval, the aircraft were picketed at Ostend on the leeward side of the sand dunes. Before the raid could be mounted, it was thwarted by a storm on 12th September which hurled the aeroplanes along the sand, wrecking them completely. Meanwhile, the aerodrome at Antwerp was nearing completion, and a week after the Ostend squall two of the small R.N.A.S. squadrons moved up to Antwerp, while the third went to its new base at Morbecque, which was also to be the location of the headquarters of the unit from 19th September. Finally, all was ready for the first raid by British aeroplanes on Germany proper. On 22nd September, 1914, four machines took-off—two climbing in the direction of Cologne, with the other pair heading for Düsseldorf. A heavy mist blanketing the Rhine and Roer rivers served the enemy by frustrating the raid so that only Flt. Lt. C. H. Collett, attempting to reach Düsseldorf, was lucky enough to gain his objective. Arriving over the target at 6,000 ft., he glided down to 400 ft. and released three bombs. One exploded short of the shed and the two others failed to detonate, but may have landed on the target. Each of the four aeroplanes managed to make its way back to the aerodrome at Antwerp.

Preparations were made to repeat the operation as soon as possible with greater effect, but, before the second raid took place, Sqn. Cdr. A. M. Longmore arrived at Dunkirk on 27th September with reinforcements for the Eastchurch Squadron in the form of six other aircraft besides the R.E.5 which he himself flew over. Three days later, on 30th September, Longmore set off in his R.E.5, accompanied by Flt. Lt. E. Osmond as his passenger, to attack the railway junction at Cambrai. Their offensive load consisted of three improvised bombs of French manufacture which Osmond had to drop over the side of the cockpit when Longmore gave the agreed sign. The flight to Cambrai was made over cloud, but the R.E.5 descended through it to appear exactly over the target. Another machine, piloted by Flt. Lt. E. T. R. Chambers, was also sent out on a similar raid on the same day.

The R.E.5 flown by Sqn. Cdr. Longmore was one of the small batch of twenty-four only which were built by the Royal Aircraft Factory at Farnborough. Twenty-two of them were completed in 1914 with two more being constructed in 1915. Designed during 1913, the R.E.5 was a sturdy, well-proportioned tractor biplane of equal span with two-bay, staggered wings, and carried its crew of two in tandem. The type came under the Reconnaissance Experimental category, thereby being developed to be as stable as possible to perform its duty as an observation platform for the observer ensconced in the front cockpit. A flat-sided fuselage was surmounted by a fairly deep curved decking which afforded the crew adequate protection and, at the same time, enabled the Beardmore-built, six-cylinder, inline 120 h.p. Austro-Daimler engine to be fully enclosed, complete with the radiator installed to its rear. Cable-connected ailerons were fitted to each wingtip and an advanced feature for the time was the installation of streamline bracing wires, known as Raf-wires and specially developed by the Factory to replace the stranded wire cable hitherto used. The compact twin-wheel unit incorporated the popular pair of wooden skids. A four-blade propeller was fitted, and a silencer formed part of the exhaust manifold which ejected underneath the front cockpit. A few of the R.E.5s built were powered by original Austro-Daimler units. The type's layout was quite conventional, as was the wooden structure with its fabric covering. The twenty-four R.E.5s produced formed the first sizeable production run of a Factory design and were paid for out of £25,000 handed over to the War Office by the Admiralty when the Navy assumed the responsibility for lighter-than-air development in Britain on 1st January, 1914. The relatively short production sequence of the R.E.5 prevented any wide-scale use as a bomber, but two of those belonging to No. 7 Squadron, R.F.C., carrying three 20 lb. Hale bombs each, took-off from St. Omer on 26th April, 1915, accompanied by seven of No. 8 Squadron's B.E.2cs, to attack German troop trains steaming from Ghent.

By the first week of October, the Germans were pressing hard towards Antwerp, and it was but a few days before the town was bound to be taken. True to its great naval traditions, the R.N.A.S. continued to display the utmost spirit and zest for action. Under incessant German fire, as the airfield lay between the advancing enemy and Antwerp itself, preparations for another attack on Cologne and Düsseldorf went on, dogged also by appalling weather. The decision had been taken that the evacuation of Antwerp could no longer be delayed and that the town would be abandoned on 8th October, 1914. In spite of this, the R.N.A.S.'s two Sopwith Tabloids 167 and 168 were still made ready to carry out the raid while the withdrawal was under way.

Sqn. Cdr. Spenser D. A. Grey took-off at 1.20 p.m. on the 8th in 167 armed with two 20 lb. bombs and set course for Cologne. The atrocious weather had forced the departure to be delayed, but, finally, it was impossible to wait a minute longer, even though the weather was just as bad. Grey reached Cologne to find a heavy mist enveloping his objective and reduced his height to 600 ft., a manoeuvre which brought his tiny Tabloid under intense fire from the ground for the ten to twelve minutes during an unsuccessful search for the Zeppelin sheds. Grey finally gave up the quest and headed for the main railway terminal which was in the middle of Cologne and was crowded with troop-filled trains. Arriving overhead, he released his pair of twenty-pounders and flew his damaged machine back with all speed to Antwerp, arriving at 4.45 p.m.

Flt. Lt. R. L. G. Marix, destined for Düsseldorf in Tabloid 168, followed Grey into the air after ten minutes and found his objective with difficulty. A dive to 600 ft. followed, his two 20 lb. bombs hurtled down and exploded on their target. Searing flames soared to 500 ft., the hangar's roof disintegrated, and a new Zeppelin—Z.IX—which had only recently occupied the building, was entirely destroyed, together with the adjacent erection and machine shops. Marix's Tabloid came under damaging rifle and shell fire from the ground, but he managed to fly back towards his base at Antwerp before his fuel was exhausted some twenty miles from home. A forced landing could not be avoided, but the pilot was lucky enough to persuade a peasant to part with his bicycle which took him part of the way to Antwerp, the rest of the trip being accomplished by car.

The two Tabloids pressed into service as bombers to such good effect had been sent to reinforce Cdr. Samson's Eastchurch Squadron at Antwerp at the beginning of October. Prior to this, the R.N.A.S. possessed a single example only at the outbreak of the War. Although used in this way briefly as an early bomber, the Tabloid's primary rôle was that of a single-seat scout, for which purpose it had been evolved from the original side-by-side two-seater of 1913 and from the Schneider Trophy winner of 1914. The design was a very handy little wood-and-fabric single-bay biplane with wings of 25 ft. 6 in. equal span incorporating slight stagger. The machine's seven-cylinder 80 h.p. Gnome rotary engine was carried in the nose of the stubby fuselage and enclosed in a metal cowling which had a pair of horizontal cooling slots disposed on each side of the centre line. The twin-wheel main undercarriage unit was typical of the period with its forwards-jutting pair of wooden skids. The Tabloid's main claim to fame lay in the epic exploits of 167 and 168 as bombers in the hands of Grey and Marix.

The Navy's early essays into bombing encouraged further forays, and several attacks were carried out early in November, 1914, on Bruges, where the Germans were assembling U-boats which had been brought there in sections by rail. A Short seaplane was used on 3rd November to drop two 100 lb. bombs on the town's railway station. Both exploded—one adjacent to the canal and the other in a siding on the eastern side of the station.

These spirited incursions were not assisted by the poor weather prevailing at the time, and the withdrawal of Allied forces to Dunkirk, forced by the occupation of the Belgian coast by the enemy, brought about a limit to the important targets within striking range of the improvised bombers. Particularly urgent and inviting targets were the Zeppelin hangars alongside the Rhine, but there was no immediate possibility of reaching them with the available types of machine. Reluctantly, for the time being, they had to be abandoned as objectives, but the Admiralty searched for other centres of airship activity which were within reach and lighted upon the Zeppelin factory itself at Friedrichshafen, on the shores of Lake Constance, as a prime target for attention.

In full implementation of the agreed policy to attack the potential raiders in their lairs, orders were issued immediately instructing the R.N.A.S. to prepare for the adventure. The task itself was not going to be easy, involving as it did a flight over some 250 miles of hostile territory, terrain which was mainly of woods and mountainous country adjacent to the Black Forest. Arrangements went ahead apace in great secrecy and elaborate detail, the organization for the assault being placed in the resourceful hands of Lt. Noel Pemberton Billing, a name of some account in the pre-war development of British aviation and an inventive personage who had now joined the R.N.V.R. The most suitable point for launching the attack was determined to be Belfort, on the Franco-Swiss border, and Pemberton Billing arrived there on 24th October, 1914, having left England on the 21st, to make arrangements with the French commanding general for the use of the aerodrome and its facilities. The large airship shed there was ideal for housing the aircraft to be used, and, to combat the activities of enemy spies thought to be on the alert in the neighbourhood, arrangements were made for the crews of the machines to inhabit the hangar while they were in Belfort and also for the aircraft to be conveyed there by road during darkness. At the same time, Pemberton Billing obtained details of the layout of the Zeppelin factory and other relevant information, all of which he welded into instructions covering the route to be taken and the procedure for the raid itself.

Four days of strenuous work sufficed, and Pemberton Billing departed again for England on 28th October to conduct the next stage. During his absence men and machines had been gathered together at Manchester, the home of A. V. Roe and Company, whose 504s had been selected as capable of carrying out the raid. Four of the biplanes, numbered 179, 873, 874 and 875 and constituting the first of the type to be taken on R.N.A.S. strength, were formed into a special flight under the direction of Sqn. Cdr. P. Shepherd. The Avros' pilots were Sqn. Cdr. E. F. Briggs, Flt. Cdr. J. T. Babington, Flt. Lt. S. V. Sippé and Flt. Sub-Lt. R. P. Cannon. The Admiralty's disturbing habit during the period of taking the serial number of the first machine to be accepted of a specific type ordered was applied in the case of the 504 and led to it being known often in the Service as the Avro 179.

Together with eleven mechanics, the unit embarked at Southampton on 10th November for le Havre to arrive by special train in darkness at Belfort on 13th November for immediate detraining, uncrating and assembly. By 3.30 p.m. on 14th November, in under sixteen hours after arrival, all four 504s had been erected, loaded with fuel, bombed-up and had their 80 h.p. Gnomes tested.

The 504 had never been intended to operate as a bomber, but its constructors had risen to the occasion by designing and fabricating improvised under-wing racks for the four raiders, each machine being capable of accommodating four 20 lb. H.E. bombs and four incendiary type. The Avros and their impatient crews were forced by bad weather to stand by for a week until conditions improved early on Saturday, 21st November. Four of the 20 lb. Hale bombs were loaded on to each of the 504s, all of which were ready at 9.30 a.m. for final checking. Finally, at intervals of five minutes, three of the machines took-off—873 piloted by Briggs left first, 875 was next with

Babington, and Sippé left last in 874. 179, flown by Cannon, broke its tailskid and abandoned the attempt, but the others forged on to the north of Basle, then—at around 5,000 ft.—took the path of the Rhine until Lake Constance was reached. To avoid perception the three 504s lost height until they were only 10 ft. above the lake, then some 5 miles from their objective rose to 1,200 ft. and arrived over Friedrichshafen—practically together—at about midday, having flown a course involving several headings before making the run-in. The distance from Belfort to the objective had totalled some 125 miles by the devious route followed. After diving to about 700 ft. eleven of the bombs hurtled down into the main area of the target of 700 yds., two falling on to the sheds housing the Zeppelins. One severely damaged a new Zeppelin being built, while the other destroyed the gasworks by sending it up in colossal flames. The fourth bomb carried by Sippé's 874 failed to drop from its rack. Briggs's petrol tank was perforated by machine-gun fire and he was forced to land, but the other two returned safely to their base, although one of them had to land 35 miles south-west of Belfort. After their 250-mile flight the 504s were then dismantled, and the unit arrived back at Southampton on 26th November, well pleased with the destruction and consternation they had wrought.

The 504 had acquitted itself handsomely in its temporary offensive rôle as a bomber with but little change from the standard model. An all-wood and fabric, two-bay biplane seating two in tandem, it had achieved instant success and acceptance from its initial appearance in July of 1913, the first public showing taking place at Hendon in the second Aerial Derby two months later on 20th September. Production started in mid-1914 with a War Office order for twelve and an Admiralty order for a single example. The seven-cylinder 80 h.p. Gnome rotary was selected as the 504's standard power plant, and modifications incorporated in the fuselage of the production R.F.C. and R.N.A.S. machines included the sloping downwards, towards the rear, of the upper longerons as opposed to those on the prototype, which were horizontal. The 504 was designed to be flown from the rear seat, and its manoeuvrability was enhanced by the provision of cable-connected ailerons on each tip of the 36 ft. span staggered wings. Rubber cord springing in the main undercarriage legs took care of loads while taxying, and the typical Avro central hooked skid was a conspicuous feature of the type. A well-proportioned design of very pleasing aspect, the 504 did more than any other of the early Avro creations towards the sound establishment of its constructors and was destined to become a familiar sight in its various forms for many years ahead. Although used comparatively little for offensive work in either Service, the 504s' daring and successful raid on Friedrichshafen ensured the type of its own particularly glorious moment in the 1914–18 War.

Another instance of the 504 being used for bombing early in the hostilities was provided by the first one to be delivered to Cdr. Samson's Eastchurch Squadron. This had joined the unit on 27th November, 1914, and just over two weeks later—on 14th December—Flt. Lt. C. H. Collett took-off in it to attack the U-boat assembly depôt at Bruges. Bad weather thwarted

Collett in his effort to reach Bruges, so, instead, he dropped his four 16 lb. bombs on the railway line running to Ostend from the medieval canal-crossed town.

Among other 504 expeditions against the enemy, another raid of note was that mounted early in 1915 when five from No. 1 Squadron, R.N.A.S., piloted by Sqn. Cdr. I. T. Courtney, Flt. Lt. B. C. Meates, Flt. Lt. H. L. Rosher, Flt. Sub-Lt. B. L. Huskisson and Flt. Sub-Lt. F. G. Andreae left Dunkirk to attack the launching slips of the U-boat assembly depôt at Hoboken, not far from Antwerp, on 24th March. Taking-off in the morning mist, one 504 came down in Holland with engine trouble, two turned back owing to the bad weather, but the other pair pressed on to drop their four 20 lb. bombs each in the ship-yard, the first machine releasing from 350 ft., followed by the second 504, one of those which had performed so well in the previous November's raid on the Friedrichshafen Zeppelin hangars. Both returned safely to Dunkirk. A further raid on the Hoboken objective was carried out successfully on 1st April, 1915, by another 504 from the same squadron, and again the load consisted of four 20 lb. bombs.

Cdr. Samson's renowned Eastchurch Squadron had three Bristol T.B.8s on strength while it was stationed in France. One, 153, was of earlier type with modified undercarriage and tailskid and fitted with the old-style semi-cowling over the Gnome, while the two later machines were from the batch of twelve improved versions, incorporating four ailerons replacing the out-moded wing-warping for lateral control, a full engine cowling of circular form and destined originally for the R.F.C. under a War Office order of 4th August, 1914. The first few were completed on 26th September, but, of this batch, all twelve were absorbed instead by the R.N.A.S. bases at Eastchurch and Gosport and numbered from 1216 to 1227.

One of Samson's new T.B.8s was used as a raider on 25th November, 1914, when it took-off from Dunkirk and successfully bombed the German gun batteries at Middelkerke. The German batteries installed to the south of Ostend were treated to a fine example of the audacious and buccaneering Samson's spirit when on 21st December, 1914, making the War's first flight at night, he took-off in the dark to bomb the U-boats ensconced in Ostend harbour. His Maurice Farman was loaded with eighteen 16 lb. bombs which he unleashed on the enemy's gun emplacements after being unable to sight the submarines. The furious Germans let fly at the intrepid and aptly-named Samson with a devastating barrage, but, with only a Very pistol and his torch, he landed safely in the night on the sand at Dunkirk.

This advance Christmas present for the Germans heralded a spectacular, daring and carefully-planned R.N.A.S. raid which took place on 25th December, 1914, and was launched against the Zeppelin hangars at Nordholz, south of Cuxhaven, and had the double purpose of reconnoitring the enemy shipping and installations at the mouth of the River Elbe, in the Schillig roads and at Wilhelmshaven. Nine seaplanes were transported in three carriers, the *Empress*, *Engadine* and *Riviera*, escorted by the light cruisers H.M.S. *Arethusa* and H.M.S. *Undaunted* and a protective force of eight destroyers of the Third Flotilla and submarines which departed from Harwich at 5 a.m. on 24th December. By 6 a.m. on Christmas Day the expedition was some twelve miles north of Heligoland. Just after 7 a.m., in very cold weather, seven out of the nine aircraft took-off from the calm water and headed for Cuxhaven. The remaining two aircraft failed to rise and were again taken aboard the carriers. The supporting ships cruised about awaiting the return of the seven seaplanes so that they and their crews could be picked up, but it was not until 10 a.m. that three of the machines returned. Able to linger no longer, the main force headed homewards, but three more of the awaited pilots were later rescued by *E.11* one of the British submarines. The fourth machine had alighted on the water, and the pilot was held for a while in Holland after rescue by a Dutch trawler. It transpired that heavy fog and mist had combined to prevent the Zeppelin sheds being located, but the machines had instead dropped their bombs on ships and gun emplacements at Wilhelmshaven and had brought back valuable details of the concentration of German shipping in the area.

Among the floatplanes employed in the raid were three Shorts, Admiralty Type 74—811 flown by Flt. Lt. C. H. K. Edmonds, 814 Flt. Sub-Lt. V. Gaskell-Blackburn and 815 Flt. Cdr. D. A. Oliver. Short Brothers gave the type the designation Improved S.41, but its Admiralty Type 74 came from the initial serial of the first production batch.

Although the designation implied a direct connection with the S.41 of 1912, there was little to support any such contention of relationship, the 100 h.p. Gnome constituting the main common factor. The 1913 Short Admiralty No. 42 showed a far more direct resemblance to the Type 74, a number of which had joined the Navy by the summer of 1914 before the start of the War. This latest Short floatplane's appearance suggested that it was much sturdier than its predecessors from the same firm. The unequal-span, three-bay wings were unstaggered and had the fuselage mounted direct on to the lower pair. The overhang of the upper planes was strut-braced, split pairs of wide-span ailerons without balance cables being incorporated also only in the top surfaces. The crew were accommodated in tandem in cockpits without the benefit of a deck coaming. The Type 74's main under-carriage consisted of a pair of unstepped pontoon floats, supplemented by a tail float and a cylindrical air-bag under each lower wingtip.

Included also among the seven aircraft which took-off to attack Cuxhaven on 25th December were two Short Folder Seaplanes—Nos. 119, flown by Flt. Cdr. R. P. Ross, and 120, pilot Flt. Lt. A. J. Miley. Generally reminiscent of the Type 74, the first Folders built had two-bay wings of 56 ft. upper span, but later examples appeared with an upper span of 67 ft. and three bays. These last versions embodied facilities for folding the wings from the cockpit. A 160 h.p. Gnome was installed as the standard power plant, and the float arrangement followed that of the Type 74. Some of the Folders were equipped with crutches accommodating a 14 in. Whitehead torpedo, and external racks carried the bombs.

The two other Short seaplanes which, together with the three Type 74s

Short Folder Seaplane. (*Short Photo.*)

and two Folders, made up the force which attacked Cuxhaven on Christmas Day, 1914, were Admiralty Type 135s, Nos. 135 and 136. Evolved from the 160 h.p. Gnome Folder, design work on 135 started late in 1913 following the order from the Admiralty in September, 1913. The machine's unequal-span, 54 ft. 6 in. upper and 40 ft. lower, folding wings utilized two-bay bracing with struts supporting the generous upper extensions, and a rounded decking conferred a refinement on the previous stark style of slab-sided fuselage. No. 135 appeared in 1914 for delivery to the R.N.A.S. before the War began, powered by the Swiss-designed single-row, water-cooled 135 h.p. Salmson radial. 136, the second Type 135 constructed, was given the extra power of the two-row, fourteen-cylinder Salmson which developed 200 h.p. 135's engine was cooled by a massive rectangular radiator mounted vertically on the fore-deck ahead of the front cockpit and was surmounted by a small lip-type portion of curved cowling.

In the attack on Cuxhaven Flt. Cdr. C. F. Kilner piloted No. 136, accompanied by Lt. Erskine Childers as his observer, both officers being particularly successful in the value of their reconnaissance reports made as a result of the raid.

Within the first five months of the outbreak of the 1914–18 War, therefore, the fighting spirit of the Royal Navy—unmatched over the preceding centuries by that of any other country and already infused deeply into its off-spring, the Royal Naval Air Service—had demonstrated vigorously that bombing of the enemy was a completely practical and rewarding new element in warfare. Circumstances—in particular the fact that destruction of the Zeppelin sheds to forestall German raids on the United Kingdom had sensibly constituted Admiralty policy on being charged with the defence of the British Isles—had ordained that the R.N.A.S. should pioneer strategic bombing.

The presence of naval flying units based on the French coast and adjacent to the Western Front encouraged increased activity in bombing and torpedo-dropping by the R.N.A.S. squadrons. The success which attended their initial forays and the plethora of targets waiting to be attacked stimulated naval interest in developing their aircraft, equipment and techniques to the highest levels for the prosecution of the war against the enemy.

During August, 1914, three Short Folder Seaplanes, equipped to carry torpedoes, had been assigned to the carrier *Engadine*, one of three 22 kt. cross-Channel steamships acquired by the Admiralty on the outbreak of war. The other two were the *Empress* and the *Riviera*, and all three had been fitted out in Chatham Dockyard to accommodate four seaplanes each. The object of providing these carriers was to give the Fleet the means to deploy aircraft when necessary while at sea and to get the most out of the restricted range of which the machines were then capable. These three small vessels were found in turn to be limited in their range for work with the Grand Fleet, so, in September, 1914, the Cunard liner *Campania* was taken over by the Admiralty and passed to Cammel Laird for conversion into a suitable seaplane-carrier with a 120 ft. flying deck over the forecastle and space aboard for ten or eleven seaplanes. The *Campania* was commissioned in May, 1915.

On 4th August, 1914, the strength of the R.N.A.S. was about 130 officers and about 700 petty officers and men, equipped with 39 landplanes and 52

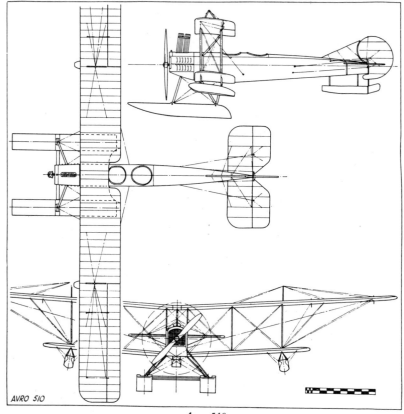

Avro 510

42

Short Admiralty Type 166 with arched spacers between floats to carry the torpedo. (*Short Photo.*)

seaplanes. About 50% were serviceable and ready for immediate use. Another 46 seaplanes were at that time on order for the Service. The involvement straightaway of the R.N.A.S. in offensive operations brought a sharp increase in demand for more aircraft and for new types able to undertake the many and varied tasks now confronting it. The opening months of the conflict had seen the R.N.A.S. concentrating a great proportion of its available resources on its avowed objective of destroying the ability of the German airship service to operate its Zeppelins effectively.

The fact that the Germans intended to raid the British mainland was brought home on 21st December, 1914, when a single enemy aeroplane crossed the water and released two bombs which fell in the sea by the Admiralty Pier at Dover. A few days afterwards, on 24th December, Dover once more received a visit from a hostile aircraft, resulting in the first enemy bomb to be dropped on to the British Isles. The following day, on Christmas Day, an enemy seaplane managed to fly up the Thames from Sheerness to reach Erith before turning back and escaping.

Sqn. Cdr. Longmore's success with releasing a torpedo at Calshot from the adapted Short Folder just prior to the commencement of hostilities had provided convincing proof of the practical possibilities of such a technique. Short Brothers thereupon put in hand a development of the Admiralty Type 135, the new design being evolved specifically for the carriage and launching of a torpedo.

In common with the second Type 135 No. 136, the Admiralty Type 166— as the newcomer came to be known—retained the 200 h.p. Salmson engine, cooling of which was by a prominent radiator block mounted on the foredeck. Little alteration was visible in the fuselage, but revision had taken place in the support of the upper extensions of the two-bay wings. The previous bracing struts had been discarded and replaced by kingposts and wire. To provide additional lift for transporting the extra load of a torpedo, the wings of the Type 166 were increased in area, the upper span reaching 57 ft. 3 in. The very large fin, which had by now become a prominent characteristic of Short seaplanes, was evident at the tail and provided support for the top of the balanced rudder. The convenience of wing-folding was retained, and the undercarriage system used the standard layout of two main and one rear pontoon floats, together with wingtip cylindrical air-bags. A water-rudder was hinged to the tail pontoon, and the steel tube spacers bracing the main floats were curved upwards to take the 14 in. 810 lb. torpedo. Six only Type 166s—Nos. 161–166—were built by Short Brothers; a second batch—Nos. 9751–9770—was produced during 1916 by the Westland Aircraft Works at Yeovil, differing from the parent firm's version in omitting the arch in the floats' horizontal struts so that a torpedo could not be accommodated. Instead, the Westland-built Type 166 carried three 112 lb. bombs, and the observer was provided with a Lewis machine-gun.

During mid-1914 an initial order for twelve floatplanes of a new design was placed with Short Brothers, half of which were to be powered by the 135 h.p. Salmson, while the other half were to receive the more powerful water-cooled eight-cylinder vee 150 h.p. Sunbeam Nubian. The Admiralty designations applied were Type 827 to the Nubian version and Type 830 to the Salmson model. There was basically little difference in the Types 827 and 830 from the Type 166, one of the main alterations being a reduction in span to 53 ft. 11 in. The compound taper of the 166's ailerons was abandoned in favour of straight taper on the 827 and 830, while the newly-adopted kingpost-and-wire bracing of the overhanging upper wingtips was embodied once again. The two-bay wings incorporated folding as a standard feature, but no provision was made for a torpedo as a missile. Underneath the fuselage, however, bomb-racks were installed.

While the R.N.A.S. had thus stepped into the lead in promoting bombing of the enemy early in the war, the R.F.C. had, perforce, to pursue a rather different course. The meagre force of four squadrons and their supporting units, numbering 105 officers and 63 aeroplanes, had engaged immediately in intense activity in their recognized duties of reconnaissance for the Army and, from 6th September, 1914, were assigned to assist the I and II Corps in tactical work, proving of the greatest value throughout the Battles of the Marne, the Aisne and Ypres. On 7th October welcome reinforcement arrived in the form of No. 6 Squadron, R.F.C., which, after only a week at Bruges, was compelled to withdraw to Poperinghe.

Such excellent and well-appreciated results had accrued from the R.F.C. squadrons' work over the opposing troops that the demand for their services

Short Admiralty Type 830. (*Short Photo.*)

44

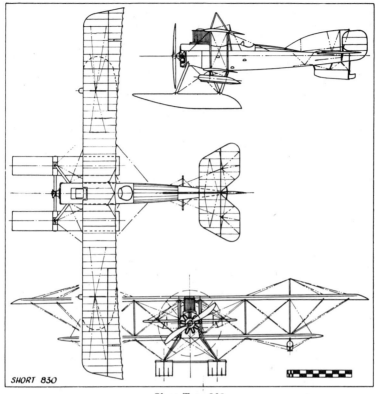

SHORT 830

Short Type 830

as the mobile and versatile eyes of the army commanders rose sharply. To assist in exploiting the potential of the squadrons to the greatest advantage, the units were reorganized on 29th November, 1914, a procedure which resulted in their decentralization into two Wings, Headquarters and H.Q. Wireless Unit.

By early 1915 the scout aircraft, with either one or two seats, was receiving due attention as a type to be developed specifically for its specialized duties and was also being evolved to carry machine-gun armament. Relatively little was being done to evolve new machines solely as bombers for the R.F.C., and those which were employed for the purpose were still adaptations of existing designs rapidly becoming obsolete.

In the Battle of Neuve Chapelle which started at 7.30 a.m. on 10th March, 1915, for the first time bombing formed a part of the plan for the conduct of such a ground operation. By attacking from the air the trains carrying re-inforcements to the enemy's army formations, it was expected that a con-siderable amount of delay would ensue to the Allies' benefit. A number of raids were carried out with various aircraft against rolling stock and the railway system with excellent results.

45

Among the machines used was the B.E.2a. Developed from the B.E.2 two-seat biplane of 1912, the B.E.2a was adapted to carry an offensive load of a single bomb or an equivalent load of smaller bombs and was used in considerable numbers. The type appeared late in 1912 as an improved version of the B.E.2, embodying a new fuel system installed inside the curved decking which had been added to the rear of the 70 h.p. Renault engine. As a result, the gravity tank mounted previously in the centre section had been discarded. The B.E.2a's unstaggered two-bay wings were equal in span, measured 35 ft. 0·5 in. from tip to tip and retained warping for lateral control. Structurally, no advance was visible on the standard fabric-covered, wire-braced frameworks in vogue. Those taken across to France at the commencement of the War had faithfully taken-off time and time again on their important reconnaissance work for many weeks, but, eventually, the B.E.2a found itself pressed into service as a bomber when three from No. 4 Squadron, R.F.C., set off on 11th March, 1915, to attack the rail junction at Lille. The railway station at Courtrai received attention from 2nd Lt. W. B. Rhodes-Moorhouse's B.E.2a of No. 2 Squadron, R.F.C., on 26th April, 1915, a 100 lb. bomb falling on the line near by. The exploit resulted in the posthumous award of the Victoria Cross to Rhodes-Moorhouse, the first to be won by either the R.F.C. or the R.N.A.S.

During 1913 E. T. Busk, one of the experimental pilots at the Royal Aircraft Factory, commenced trials in an endeavour to endow the B.E.2a with improved stability. His findings were embodied in a new version designated B.E.2c, the first of which took to the air in June, 1914. It was based on the fuselage and undercarriage unit used in the B.E.2b, but fresh wings, incorporating four cable-connected ailerons and stagger, made their appearance. A rounded coaming extended fore and aft of the pair of tandem cockpits, and steel tube framing was introduced into the fin and rudder. The 70 h.p. Renault was retained to power the early production B.E.2c, and the Factory had succeeded well in imbuing the machine with great natural stability, a factor then thought to be greatly advantageous to the aircraft in its expected rôle of reconnaissance. Later, however, this fallacy was to be exposed and heavily emphasized in combat when the resulting lack of manoeuvrability put the B.E.2c in a position of grave disadvantage on operations over the Western Front. As well as being deficient in this respect, the location of the observer in the front cockpit placed a markedly severe restriction on his ability to wield a machine-gun when such armament was eventually brought into play as a defensive measure.

To enable the B.E.2c to operate as a bomber, it was flown as a single-seater, and one of its first exploits as an offensive weapon took place on 10th March, 1915, when Capt. L. A. Strange of No. 6 Squadron, R.F.C., flew his to Courtrai railway station to drop three 25 lb. bombs which disrupted movements by rail over three days. Another B.E.2c raid was carried out on 19th April, 1915, when the sheds housing German airships at Gontrode were attacked by Capt. Lanoe G. Hawker, who dropped three bombs on them. The B.E.2c normally housed its bomb load in racks beneath the fuselage and

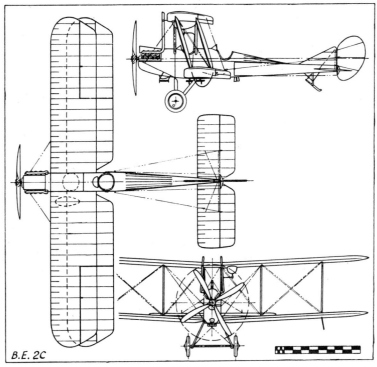

B.E. 2C

B.E.2c

inboard under the lower wings, but those built for the R.N.A.S. and equipped with the R.A.F.1a as the engine were often fitted with a rack, capable of accommodating three bombs, in an unusual position below the engine's sump. In some cases the R.N.A.S. bomber B.E.2c had its front cockpit faired over. The B.E.2c was also notable as the first to carry out a night raid by the R.F.C. which was made by two of the type on Cambrai aerodrome on 19th February. Numerous other bombing operations were to stand to the credit of the B.E.2c, an aeroplane pressed by the exigencies of war into performing duties for which it had not been developed. Consequently, despite the greatest gallantry displayed by the crews who flew the B.E.2c on operations, the type was castigated owing to the heavy losses which it suffered through being allotted tasks on active service which were never intended to be its *métier*.

Another of the early Royal Aircraft Factory designs which found itself adapted as a bomber soon after the start of the war was the B.E.8, a well-proportioned two-seat, two-bay, equal-span biplane with 39 ft. 6 in. staggered wings and the 80 h.p. Gnome as its engine. The first prototype was started during 1912, but the Factory built three examples only of the design, the ensuing fairly small production run being undertaken by Bristol, Coventry Ordnance Works and Vickers to contracts placed in 1914. Last of the Factory's B.E. designation to employ the rotary style of power plant, the

47

B.E.8 sported a rounded cowling over the upper portion of the unit. The three prototypes were turned out without a fin, but this was added to the tail units of the production models. These also were given ailerons on the upper wings in place of the prototypes' all-warping system. In common with the majority of the early machines adapted as vicarious bombers in the first few months of the conflict, the B.E.8 was flown solo when loaded with its single 100 lb. missile, and this was the case when four 'Bloaters' from No. 1 Squadron, R.F.C., launched their attack against the railway bridge at Douai on 12th March, 1915.

Within a very brief space of time from the middle of 1914, the fortunes of the fledgling British aircraft industry had undergone a significant and far-reaching metamorphosis for the better. Viewed at first as a frail novelty with capabilities as yet unproved in full-scale warfare, the aeroplane had nevertheless immediately made plain its unique qualities and shown itself to be an invaluable asset in the field. Any lingering doubts about the advisability of investing money in it as a weapon of war were swept aside overnight.

Orders, previously for very small batches quite incapable of making good inevitable attrition in action, were placed for far more realistic quantities. Perforce, these were at first for existing designs, but, at the same time, development of new designs went ahead at the greatest possible speed. Experience of wartime operations pinpointed sharply and immediately shortcomings in available equipment and dictated the procurement of types for which a particular demand was seen to exist.

Among the new types to appear in the course of 1915 was the A.D. Seaplane Type 1000, the result of an Admiralty requirement for a floatplane to operate as a bomber or a torpedo launcher. The design of the 155 ft. span biplane, the largest British-built machine at the time of its conception, was the work of Harris Booth of the Air Department of the Admiralty. J. Samuel White and Company were commissioned to build the massive machine, of which seven appear to have been ordered under the designation A.D. Type 1000 derived from the first serial number allocated. 1358 was the sole example to emerge eventually from the Cowes works. The Type 1000 represented a gigantic leap forward in size from previous British seaplanes and accordingly demanded relatively high power, being given three 310 h.p. Sunbeam engines. These were disposed as two tractors—one each in the nose of the pair of fuselages forming a prominent feature of the design—and a pusher installed at the rear of the centrally situated cabin for the crew, whose quarters contained a lavish amount of glazing. The twin fuselage frames were simple rectangular-section structures lacking any attempt at refinement, the same feeling being expressed by the angularity evident in the cowlings shrouding the Sunbeams. The upper planes overhung the lower surfaces, and the fuselages terminated at the rear in well-rounded twin fins and rudders. To support the heavy machine on the water, twin floats were employed both at the front and at the rear. Success was not forthcoming for the A.D. Type 1000, and 1358 is believed to have been abandoned at Felixstowe after its sojourn at the East Coast marine aircraft base during 1916. As a design the machine

8081, a Short Type 184. (*Short Photo.*)

embodied a comparatively novel layout and represented an essay into the field of very large aircraft at an early period of evolution and at a time when engines of advanced power ratings, coupled with attendant reliability, were not forthcoming. These factors and a lack of manoeuvrability may well have militated against acceptance of the Type 1000 as an aircraft suitable for use in war, a situation to be encountered many times in the future by designs which made a radical departure from conformity.

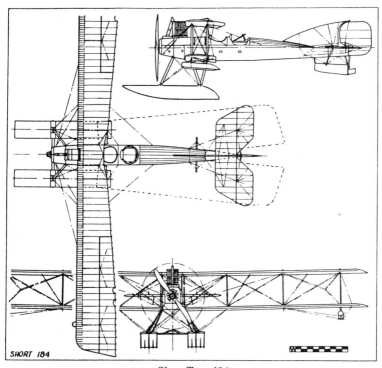

Short Type 184

49

The assiduous pursuance of the Navy's aggressive bombing policy brought in its train a steady demand for the means of delivery both of bombs and of torpedoes. Voice was given by Commodore Murray F. Sueter, head of the Air Department at the Admiralty, to requests for new machines to be developed, capable of taking the war to the enemy ever more effectively. The torpedo constituted a most potent weapon for dealing with enemy shipping, and it was considered that an improved version of the Short Type 166 would prove a worthwhile investment. Horace Short was consequently approached by Commodore Sueter to evolve the new torpedo-carrier to take the 14 in. weapon.

The result, the Short Type 184, was destined to become one of the most ubiquitous and successful in its category during the 1914–18 War. In appearance the new machine perpetuated the established lines of Short seaplanes, with three-bay, equal-span, unstaggered wings attached to the typical style of fuselage set by its predecessors. Folding wings had become an integral feature of the larger shipborne types and were applied automatically to the Type 184. The prototype 184 underwent several modifications to its lateral control system. Ailerons were fitted at the outset, but in unbalanced form to the upper planes only. They were eventually given the benefit of a balancing cable, then finally superseded by cable-connected ailerons on all four wingtips, a feature carried on through the production machines. The prototype 184 flew with the 225 h.p. Sunbeam engine driving a two-blade propeller and fully cowled. The rectangular box-style radiator occupied its usual view-obscuring position ahead of the pilot on the fore-deck. The standard three pontoon floats made up the undercarriage, augmented by wingtip cylindrical air-bags. The Type 184 carried its torpedo suspended beneath the arched spacers connecting the main floats and its bomb load borne in a rack mounted on the underside of the front portion of the fuselage. On operations the Type 184 achieved its greatest success in the Dardanelles when one of three which had arrived there in the seaplane-carrier *Ben-my-Chree* took-off on 12th August, 1915, piloted by Flt. Lt. C. H. K. Edmonds and sank a Turkish steam vessel with its 14 in. torpedo. To the Short Admiralty Type 184 thus went the honour of being the first aircraft to sink a ship by air-launched torpedo in action. Five days later, on 17th August, Flt. Lt. Edmonds repeated his success by sinking another Turkish ship from an increased range. Encouraged by these successes, another Type 184 attack in the Dardanelles was made on 17th August, this time by Flt. Lt. G. Bentley Dacre, resulting in the sinking of a Turkish tug. These first-class results, obtained at such an early stage in the torpedo-carrier's career, were not achieved easily. The Type 184 was not by any means endowed with a surfeit of power and was able to lift its torpedo only when flown solo from calm water with the assistance of a breeze and with a reduction in fuel aboard. These shortcomings inevitably led to a lower rate of use of the machine as an operational torpedo-carrier, but the Type 184 performed valiant service as a bomber, particularly in the Dardanelles, the Mediterranean, in raids on the Belgian coast and on patrol against U-boats. A solitary Type 184, 8359, piloted by Flt. Lt. F. J. Rutland, achieved

N1091, a Short Improved 184. (*Short Photo.*)

Short Type D/184, 8103. (*Short Photo.*)

N1098, a Short Dover Type 184. (*Short Photo.*)

prominence as the aircraft which reconnoitred the German warships for the British Grand Fleet in the Battle of Jutland on 31st May, 1916.

It was natural that, in the course of its production life, modifications should be made to the Type 184. 8103 appeared as the Type D, a single-seat bomber seaplane with the original front cockpit area transformed into an internal bomb-bay housing nine 65 lb. bombs stowed vertically. The 250 h.p. Rolls-Royce Eagle displaced the Sunbeam engine in 8104, and 8105 was perched

51

9306, first of the initial production batch of Short Bombers, with short fuselage. (*Short Photo.*)

some distance above its main floats on extended undercarriage struts. A good view for the pilot had not been a strong point in the Type 184, but a decisive improvement was effected in the Dover Type equipped with the 260 h.p. Sunbeam cooled by a frontal radiator in place of the obstructive box-style unit hitherto installed on the coaming. Total production of the Short Type 184 in its various forms reached over six hundred and fifty.

In pursuance of its vigorous policy of attacking the enemy by bombing, the Admiralty promoted a contest in 1915 to select a landplane bomber in which Short Brothers entered an extensively modified adaptation of their Type 184. 3706, the prototype, retained the 225 h.p. Sunbeam in a normal 184 fuselage but had the crew positions reversed. The pilot was transferred to the rear cockpit so that the observer could stand up to fire the single Lewis gun installed above the upper centre-section. 3706 received unequal-span wings with two bays and extensive overhang of the upper tips, for which kingpost-and-wire bracing was provided. Wings of ample area were fitted with the express object of conferring adequate weight-lifting qualities on the machine. The undercarriage was a somewhat complex arrangement containing four wheels, the front pair of which were of slightly smaller diameter than those at the rear. The two-bay wings were shortly replaced by new surfaces of increased span and three-bay bracing. The Short Bomber was sufficiently successful in its trials for a production order to be placed with Short Brothers and four sub-contractors, eighty-three examples being built. Those produced

Short Bomber for the R.F.C. 9315 with long fuselage. (*Short Photo.*)

by Mann, Egerton, Parnall, Phoenix Dynamo and Short were fitted with the 250 h.p. Rolls-Royce Eagle, but Sunbeam installed their own lower-power 225 h.p. Sunbeam engine. Other changes in the production versions included the substitution of side radiators for the prototype's awkward upper-nose unit, the armouring of the fuel tanks and the transfer of the observer to the rear cockpit, where he was provided with a set of controls and a Lewis gun. Later production Short Bombers were drastically altered by a con-

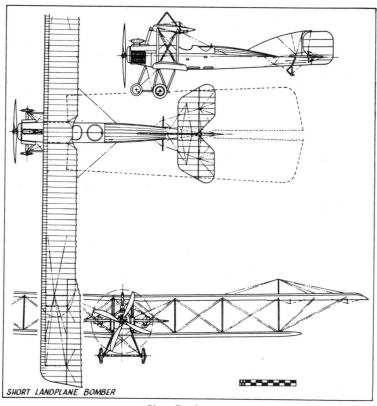

SHORT LANDPLANE BOMBER

Short Bomber

siderable extension of the length of the fuselage, but the machine still retained its characteristic feature of a generous curved fin. Racks beneath the lower wings housed the bomb load, normally an alternative of four 230 lb. or eight 112 lb. missiles.

Short Bombers went into service in the closing weeks of 1916, and No. 7 Squadron, R.N.A.S., the first unit to receive them, sent four from Coudekerque on their initial sortie during the night of 15th November, 1916, to bomb Ostend with eight 65 lb. bombs apiece. For the ensuing few months, the naval pilots continued to mount attacks against the enemy with their large 85 ft. span Shorts until the arrival of even more effective equipment.

Contemporary with the Short Bomber were two other two-seat tractor biplanes designed as bombers for the Admiralty—the Grahame-White Type 18 and the Wight Bomber. Designed at Hendon during 1915, the Grahame-White machine embodied a similar fabric-covered wooden framework type of construction but was given a greater degree of refinement than others of the period. The single prototype Type 18 also was fairly large, with four-bay equal-span wings attached to a basic rectangular-section fuselage which was faired to an oval section. Power was provided by the twelve-cylinder vee 285 h.p. Sunbeam Maori, designed by Mons. Louis Hervé Coatalen—the Sunbeam Motor Car Company's talented chief engineer—which was cooled by a deep frontal radiator and drove a two-blade airscrew. Folding was incorporated in the mainplanes, which lacked the support of normal centre-section struts, their place being taken by the inner pair of interplane struts on each side. The Type 18's normal two-wheel undercarriage, attached to the fuselage by strong struts, was augmented by a small nosewheel. Under-wing racks accommodated the machine's bomb load, and the observer was armed with a machine-gun carried on a ring-mounting.

Far less prepossessing in aspect than the Grahame-White Type 18 was the angular and ungainly Wight Bomber N501, which was completed in 1916 as a single prototype by J. Samuel White of East Cowes. In general layout the Wight product resembled the Short Bomber to a degree. Three-bay, unequal-span wings, 65 ft. 6 in. upper and 55 ft. lower in spread, were fitted to a simple flat-sided slim fuselage, surmounted by a curved decking, which housed two cockpits in tandem and a 275 h.p. Rolls-Royce Eagle in the nose. N501's wings could be folded, incorporated the double-camber section originated by the firm's designer Howard T. Wright and carried the four 112 lb. bombs in racks beneath the innermost interplane struts. A Lewis machine-gun on a Scarff ring was provided for the observer in the rear cockpit.

Among the machines from J. Samuel White and Company which achieved quantity production was the Wight Admiralty Type 840 seaplane, a two-seat tractor biplane fitted with the 225 h.p. Sunbeam. The 61 ft. span, four-bay, folding wings possessed a moderate amount of overhang of the upper planes, in which were incorporated the long-span ailerons. The wing section embodied the double-camber idea with its depression in the upper curve of the aerofoil. Twin main floats were attached to the simple type of fuselage by a complex arrangement of struts; as a torpedo-carrier the cross-braces between the floats were arched, but later examples which were not intended to launch a 14 in. torpedo appeared with straight cross-struts. The Sunbeam received its cooling through twin radiators, one of which flanked the engine on each side. The Type 840 was employed at a number of R.N.A.S. coastal stations, but was unable to match the lustre which attached to its contemporary, the Short Type 184.

A landplane version of the Wight Type 840 was constructed using, among other modifications, a nosewheel main undercarriage reminiscent of the Grahame-White Type 18.

The Royal Aircraft Factory at Farnborough had been fully committed since the start of hostilities and on 7th April, 1915, received a message of encouragement addressed to its employees from Lord Kitchener. After working day and night nonstop for twelve months the Factory closed on 6th August, 1915, for three days to allow the workers a rest from their labours.

Among the designs to make their début at the Factory during 1915 was the R.E.7, a two-seat development of the R.E.5, which was evolved into a fairly useful bomber for the R.F.C. despite an ungainly, unprepossessing appearance. The deep fuselage housed a 120 h.p. Beardmore in the nose, and the unequal-span, two-bay wings were slightly staggered. Ailerons were mounted in the upper wingtips, the overhang of which was braced by a pair of parallel struts. In the absence of a centre-section, the upper wing panels met at the centre-line at the apices of the centre-section struts. The relatively short moment arm dictated the provision of tail surfaces of large area. The R.E.7 was mounted on oleo main legs preceded by a small nosewheel set well to the fore. Basically the machine utilized a conventional wooden frame with fabric covering; the fuselage, however, was formed from steel tubing in the front matched to a wooden structure to the rear of the cockpits. Another unusual feature for an aircraft of the period was the inclusion on a number of R.E.7s of airbrakes in the form of panels hinged vertically to the fuselage sides a little to the rear of the engine.

The R.E.7 was introduced at a time when the importance of adequate defensive armament was just being appreciated. In spite of this, the observer was placed in the front cockpit, where it was well-nigh impossible for him to wield his Lewis machine-gun with any effect. This drawback was eliminated in the small number of R.E.7s which were converted to contain a third cockpit, to the rear of the pilot, which was surmounted by a Nieuport ring-mount for a single Lewis gun. Several alternative engines were installed in the R.E.7, and the machine was able to carry either a single R.A.F. 336 lb. bomb or two 112 lb. bombs, supplemented by a quantity of 20 lb. bombs. Superseded comparatively soon by aircraft endowed with superior qualities, the R.E.7 was flown on the Western Front for some seven months, chiefly by No. 21 Squadron, R.F.C., the sole unit to be equipped with the machine and which had arrived in France on 23rd August, 1916.

The first half of 1915 witnessed a growing appreciation by the Allied commanders of the value of bombing, resulting in an increased demand for the R.F.C. to execute more raids against enemy targets. However, the use for such purposes of the limited number of aeroplanes available meant automatically a reduction in the number of reconnaissance flights which could be made. Observation had so far been considered the main task for the R.F.C.'s aircraft and had been exploited fully, but the whole-hearted acceptance of the value and versatility of their work brought ever-increasing demands for their services. Nevertheless, little had so far been done to equip the machines to enable the maximum results to accrue from the dangerous forays which their courageous crews willingly undertook. The many aerodynamic advantages which the tractor type of aeroplane possessed compared with the pusher had by now been more or less fully appreciated, but the lack of an interrupter or synchronizing gear for the pilot's gun made him still dependent in a two-seater upon his observer to fight back with whatever type of bullet-firing armament the crew had taken aloft with them. The time was not too distant, however, when the pilot would have a machine-gun under his direct control.

The need for a reliable and efficient bomb-sight was also evident to replace the rough and ready method so far practised of flying as low as possible over the target and trusting to the judgment of the eye for release, often in the face of intense ground fire. This deficiency was recognized at first hand by the pilots in the field, many of whom attempted to devise improvements in their equipment. Notable among them was Lt. L. A. Strange of the R.F.C., with whom 2nd Lt. R. B. Bourdillon co-operated in France towards the close of 1914 in contriving a primitive form of bomb-sight This was considered sufficiently promising for Bourdillon to be posted to the C.F.S. at Upavon in December, 1914, to develop the device into a sight for the use of the R.F.C. and the R.N.A.S. This became known as the C.F.S. bomb-sight and was successful enough to be put into production for both Services, making its operational début in mid-1915 to stay as standard equipment until the beginning of 1918.

The adoption of a practical bomb-sight became all the more a matter of urgency by the disclosure made in the summer of 1915 when, during a lull in the fighting around Neuve Chapelle and Festubert, the results of bombing by R.F.C. squadrons between 1st March and 20th June were analysed. The extremely disappointing revelation was made that in only three raids out of one hundred and forty-one carried out to disrupt the movement of enemy forces by attacking railway stations and other targets had there been any appreciable success. A new policy of concentrated direction of available Allied bombing power, from which maximum return might be expected, was therefore immediately decided upon, with cessation of the previous style of sporadic raids on scattered targets.

In the course of 1915 the Supermarine Patrol Seaplane was designed for use as a general-purpose shipping escort. The pusher layout followed normal three-bay biplane lines with the crew of two seated in tandem in a nacelle suspended at mid-gap between the slightly-staggered wings, the observer occupying the front cockpit with a Lewis machine-gun. The bomb load was intended to be suspended beneath the lower centre-section, and the tail unit was to be carried in the conventional manner on four booms. A certain amount of progress was made with the design of the Supermarine Patrol Seaplane, but confirmation is lacking of the completion of a prototype.

A 1915 design which was produced for R.N.A.S. service in small numbers was the Sopwith Admiralty Type 860, a two-seat tractor seaplane capable of carrying the 810 lb. 14 in. torpedo. Powered by the 225 h.p. Sunbeam engine cooled by a frontal radiator, the Type 860 had equal-span, three-bay, folding wings incorporating cable-connected ailerons on each surface. The machine's pilot occupied the rear cockpit. Pontoon main floats, each with a single step and sprung, were accompanied by a tail float and one at each wingtip. A

Sopwith Admiralty Type 860. (*Hawker Photo.*)

version of the Type 860 was constructed with wings of unequal span, king-posts and wire supporting the upper overhanging tips; ailerons were in the top wings only.

Another of the seaplane designs of 1915 was the comparatively unusual Blackburn T.B. biplane which was completed in August of that year. The T.B.'s main contribution to unconventionality lay in its duplicated side-by-side fuselages, each of which housed a 100 h.p. Monosoupape Gnome in the nose in 1510, the first prototype. 1517, the second example, received a pair of 110 h.p. Clerget rotaries. The main purpose behind the design was to meet an Admiralty need for a machine capable of climbing above marauding Zeppelins and attacking the quarry with steel darts, the total load of which was to be 70 lb. The two members of the crew were carried one in each fuselage, the wings were of unequal span, and the pairs of main and rear pontoon floats were mounted independently. An essential requirement of the task which the T.B. was proposed to accomplish was a high rate of climb to achieve interception of its high-flying objective, a performance feature which could not be subject to compromise. The T.B., however, was a

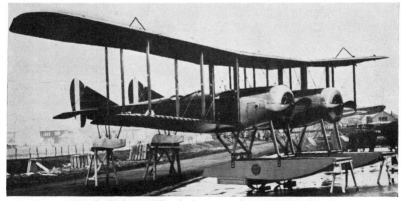
1517, the Blackburn T.B. twin-fuselage seaplane. (*Blackburn Photo.*)

relatively large and unwieldy machine, the climb performance of which was not assisted by the comparatively low power of the engines selected. Although tested by the R.N.A.S. at the Isle of Grain, no production ensued.

Frederick Koolhoven's F.K.3 design for Armstrong Whitworth arose out of the firm's disinclination to undertake production of the Royal Aircraft Factory's B.E.2c and the company's conviction that its own designer could evolve a superior machine. The project was started in August, 1913, and the machine emerged as a two-seat tractor biplane of conventional appearance. A fair amount of stagger was incorporated in the equal-span, two-bay wing cellules; the fuselage contained two tandem cockpits with the pilot occupying the rearmost. The 90 h.p. R.A.F.1a engine drove a four-blade propeller, and the undercarriage embodied a long central skid.

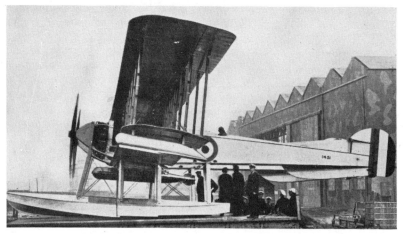

1451, the third Wight Twin Seaplane, with 18 in. Mk. IX torpedo.

The F.K.3's performance in its trials brought a substantial order for the production version which was modified to have the pilot seated in front of the observer in a large single cockpit. The 105 h.p. R.A.F.1b was installed as an alternative power plant, and the observer was equipped with a single Lewis gun on a pillar mounting. Several different sizes of bomb—16 lb., 100 lb. or 112 lb.—could be carried externally, but, when engaged in such a rôle, the F.K.3 was often flown solo to enable it to lift its bomb load.

During 1914 Howard T. Wright designed a large Wight biplane with a span of 117 ft. and powered by two 200 h.p. Salmson radial engines mounted as tractors in a pair of side-by-side fuselages attached to the lower wings. The machine's crew were carried in a nacelle placed on the lower centre-section between the engines. The wings, braced in five bays, incorporated folding; a pair of radiators for cooling the Salmson radials were installed on the flanks of each fuselage at the trailing edge of the wings. After modifications had been made to the somewhat complicated tail unit, the Wight biplane crashed.

The twin-fuselage concept, however, was retained in the seaplane version, also of 117 ft. span, which followed the earlier landplane design. The first prototype Wight Twin, 187, was equipped to launch a single 18 in. Mk. IX torpedo which it bore beneath the lower centre-section. The central nacelle for the crew was discarded, and they were accommodated in each of the pair of fuselages. Support on the water was provided by a pair of long main floats supplemented by a cylindrical one at each lower wingtip. The two 200 h.p. Salmson engines were cooled by vertical side radiators and transmitted their power through extension shafts to two-blade wooden propellers.

Two additional torpedo-carrying Wight Twin seaplanes, 1450 and 1451, were completed in September, 1915, differing from 187 in having modified fins and rudders and extended undercarriage struts. Using the same 200 h.p. Salmsons, both machines were found under test to lack sufficient power for their great size and to be incapable of leaving the water armed with a torpedo and with full tanks. Under such conditions the type was unable to accomplish its set task and development ceased.

The Admiralty's well-founded and wholly admirable policy of taking the offensive and punishing the enemy by bombing was responsible to a great degree for initiating the development of the Handley Page series of large bombing aircraft. Within the first few months of the start of the war the Admiralty had realized that, to implement such a scheme to the fullest extent, an aircraft was needed which could carry a worthwhile bomb load on patrol over water coupled with good endurance. A requirement was drawn up and issued in December, 1914, for a twin-engine two-seater capable of a minimum top speed of 72 m.p.h. and to carry six 112 lb. bombs.

Frederick Handley Page was already firmly convinced of the superiority of the large aircraft for load-carrying and was soon able to submit for the Admiralty's consideration a design for a sizeable biplane with a pair of 120 h.p. Beardmores. The proposal was received with enthusiasm, with such warmth in fact, as to draw from the worthy and uninhibited Director of the Air Department, Commodore Murray F. Sueter, his classic and uncompromising demand for a 'bloody paralyser' of a bomber. The challenge was accepted with alacrity by Handley Page and his fellow-designer George R. Volkert, who redesigned the original layout as the H.P.11 designated O/100. Two 150 h.p. Sunbeam engines and a span of 100 ft. were specified. No time was lost in constructing the machine, which was ready in less than a year from receipt of the order.

Coincident with this activity in the Handley Page factory at Cricklewood was that in the Rolls-Royce works at Derby, where two new engines, eventually to become renowned as the Eagle and the Falcon, were being evolved specifically for aircraft use.

A pair of Eagles, each developing 250 h.p., were chosen for the O/100 and were installed as tractors in armoured nacelles. The cabin for the crew of 1455, the first prototype, was given bullet-proof glass and armour-plate as extra protection. The load of sixteen 112 lb. bombs was carried vertically internally in the centre part of the flat-sided, rectangular-section fuselage, which was constructed in three portions. To enable the O/100 to be housed

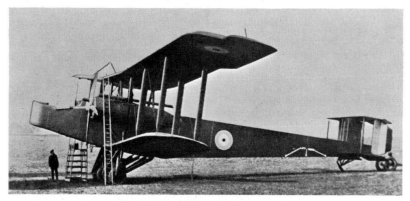

Handley Page O/100. (*Handley Page Photo.*)

in a hangar the wings were designed to fold. Of three-bay form, the upper tips overhung considerably and were braced with the usual kingposts and wire. A biplane tail was used, and the main undercarriage consisted of twin pairs of wheels.

The O/100 was most impressive in appearance and looked every inch the deadly bomber which it was intended to be. As soon as 1455 was completed

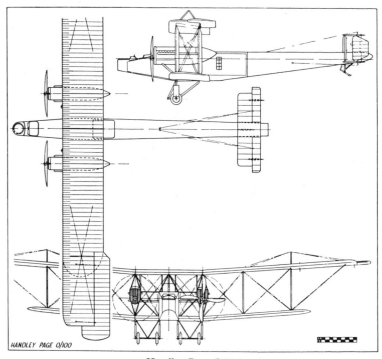

HANDLEY PAGE O/100

Handley Page O/100

it was taken by road in strict secrecy at night on 17th December, 1915, the short distance to Hendon for its first flight. Assembly was carried out rapidly within a few hours, so that, at 1.51 p.m. on 18th December, the O/100 was able to make a successful take-off piloted by Flt. Cdr. J. T. Babington. The attempt to provide improved crew comfort on long flights by the inclusion of the cockpit enclosure was short-lived, as the structure broke up in flight and was subsequently discarded. The major portion of the armour-plating around the crew was also taken away. No armament was fitted to the first few prototype O/100s, but those ordered to equip the R.N.A.S. were modified to incorporate a Scarff ring in the nose and upper and lower positions for Lewis guns in the fuselage to the rear of the wings.

Training in the use of the fine new bomber began at Manston, Kent, in September, 1916, and two months later, in November, the 5th Wing of the R.N.A.S. took delivery of its first O/100s at Dunkirk. After being employed on daylight coastal patrol and bombing for a few months, the O/100 was transferred to bombing during the hours of darkness, an operation in which it was increasingly successful despite a shortage of the machines.

Another manifestation of the Admiralty's determination to adhere to its policy of keeping the R.N.A.S. on the offensive came with its order for the Type 9700 from Sopwith. The prototype, 3686, was completed at Kingston in mid-December, 1915, and emerged as a single-bay staggered biplane with equal-span wings of 33 ft. 6 in.

The designation Type 9700 lapsed into obscurity immediately, as the appearance of the newcomer brought the name of 1½-Strutter, by which it was to be known ever afterwards. The unusual appellation is generally conceded to have arisen from the use of pairs of short and long centre-section struts. A second noteworthy feature of the 1½-Strutter lay in its introduction of the urgently-needed and long-awaited synchronizing gear to allow a front gun—in this case a single Vickers machine-gun—to fire ahead through the propeller arc. Two further innovations in the 1½-Strutter were the ability to adjust in flight the incidence of the tailplane and the incorporation of airbrakes in the trailing edge of the lower wings' centre-section. These consisted of a pair of panels hinged to turn upwards in opposition to the airflow. The 1½-Strutter was without any particularly radical features in its design and followed the firmly established Sopwith style of a well-proportioned conventional layout, a practice which had already demonstrated itself as a sound formula for success in the majority of projects.

Success was certainly to attend the 1½-Strutter in its career, both in the R.N.A.S., which ordered one hundred and fifty initially, and in the R.F.C., which subsequently took the machine into its ranks. The R.N.A.S. received its first Type 9700s in the early part of 1916 and immediately put them to use as bombers and bomber-escorts. As was often the case with the early two-seaters, the 1½-Strutters were at times flown solo to enable a reasonable load of bombs and fuel to be carried. The early naval versions utilized the Scarff–Dibovski gear to synchronize the pilot's Vickers, but, later on, both Ross and Sopwith–Kauper gears were installed. The observer defended the machine

Two-seat Sopwith 1½-Strutter built by Westland. (*Westland Photo.*)

with the usual Lewis gun, at first on a Scarff pillar mounting and subsequently on Nieuport and Scarff No. 2 rings.

The 1½-Strutter was regarded with enough favour by the Admiralty for a special single-seat version to be developed as a long-range bomber. The machine was flown from the front seat and the load of up to twelve bombs was housed in a compartment to the rear of the pilot. Occasionally, a single Lewis gun was mounted on the upper centre-section in addition to the standard Vickers on the nose. 1½-Strutters were responsible also for carrying out many patrols against U-boats.

Among the machines pressed into service by the R.F.C. as a bomber was the Martinsyde G.100, originally employed as an escort for other types engaged in bombing and reconnaissance. The machine's relatively large size militated against it as a fighter, but it came into its own as a single-seat bomber carrying a 112 lb. bomb, particularly in the hands of the pilots of No. 27 Squadron, R.F.C. The G.100 was powered by the 120 h.p. Beardmore, but a later version designated G.102, which made its appearance during 1916, was given the increased power of the 160 h.p. Beardmore and found itself popularly called the Elephant. The G.102 was able to transport two 112 lb. bombs or one 230 lb. bomb. In addition to its use on the Western

N5504, a single-seat R.N.A.S. bomber Sopwith 1½-Strutter. (*Hawker Photo.*)

Front, the Martinsyde Elephant performed valiant and effective service as a bomber in the Middle East.

In the course of 1915 the specialists at the Royal Aircraft Factory had actively pursued their various paths, and two useful results of their labours were the evolution of P.C.10 fabric dope to resist deterioration from the effects of actinic light rays and the development of a corrected bombsight.

One of the designs of indeterminate purpose but of appearance strongly suggestive of being intended as a bomber was the Avro Type 519 biplane of

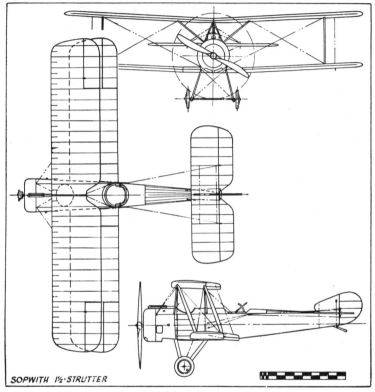

SOPWITH 1½-STRUTTER

Sopwith 1½-Strutter

early 1916. Two prototypes—1614 and 1615—were ordered for the R.F.C. and a further pair—8440 and 8441—for the R.N.A.S. Unequal-span, two-bay, unstaggered wings were mated to a normal style of fuselage with two cockpits in tandem. Mounted in the nose was the 150 h.p. Sunbeam Nubian, and aft of the cockpits—which were set well back and embedded in the deep curved decking—there was a large curved fin. The pilot's view was not assisted by the bulky radiator installed above and to the rear of the Nubian. 8441 appeared as a folding-wing single-seater flown from the rear cockpit, that at the front being faired over, and a typical Avro-style single skid was incorporated in the undercarriage. The Type 519 was singularly

63

undistinguished in appearance, and no progress was made with the design beyond the prototype stage.

Following the successful début of his D.H.2 single-seat fighter, Geoffrey de Havilland turned his talents in the direction of the D.H.3, the first prototype of which was completed at the beginning of 1916. The new machine was notable as the first of many twin-engine de Havilland designs and was powered by a pair of 120 h.p. Beardmores at mid-gap between the folding three-bay wings. Extension shafts bore the two-blade pusher propellers behind the trailing edges. The fuselage was mounted so that its major portion was below the lower wings, resulting in the use of a short main undercarriage supplemented by a pair of wheels set well forward beneath the nose. Defensive positions were provided for two Lewis guns, one in the nose and the other at mid-fuselage.

D.H.3 with two 120 h.p. Beardmore engines. (*de Havilland Photo.*)

7744, a modified D.H.3 designated D.H.3A, was also constructed. Alterations made included provision of two 160 h.p. Beardmore engines still driving pusher propellers but with four blades and without extension shafts. Instead, the trailing edges of the upper and lower wings received cut-outs to accommodate the blades. Other minor revisions were forwards-sloping exhaust pipes above the fronts of the cowlings and a slight increase in the area of the rudder's balance portion.

On test the three-seat D.H.3A showed every promise of proving a most capable and efficient bomber, and production was started on an order for fifty when cancellation was made while the first example, A5088, was under construction by the Aircraft Manufacturing Company—Airco.

Contemporary with the Airco D.H.3 and D.H.3A was the twin-engine tractor Dyott Bomber, developed by G. M. Dyott from his pre-war project for a large biplane evolved for exploring in South Africa. Construction of each of the Dyott designs actually built—his monoplane of 1913 and the Bomber—was carried out by Hewlett and Blondeau. 3687, the initial prototype to the order of the Admiralty, was completed in 1916 with two 120 h.p. Beardmore engines installed as tractors between the equal-span wings. The crew numbered three, the gunners manning Lewis machine-guns disposed in the nose and in a cockpit in the top decking to the rear of the wings. Independent single-wheel undercarriage units were mounted between pairs of skids and struts beneath each engine, and the lengthy tailskid was balanced by a large nosewheel under the front cockpit. Second thoughts about the design brought cowlings to cover the hitherto bare engines, together with frontal radiators and a fore-deck of increased depth. Much heavier armament was fitted in the form of four Lewis guns disposed around the nose cockpit and a fifth carried in the cockpit amidships.

3687 arrived at Hendon on 17th August, 1916, and 3688—the second prototype—underwent R.N.A.S. trials at Dunkirk. The Dyott Bomber's promising appearance, however, was not to result in a production order.

By early 1916 it was evident that the worth of the aeroplane as an instrument of war had been fully appreciated and recognized. As far as British bombing policy and procurement were concerned, the Admiralty had patently led the way. Eventually, the lethargy and obduracy of the Army had been dissipated by the force of events, and by December, 1915, the idea had taken hold of concentrated attacks on targets carried out by larger numbers of aircraft, the crews of which dropped their loads on seeing their leader do so over the objective.

During March, 1916, Noel Pemberton Billing, as Member of Parliament for East Herts., gave vent to his feelings and attacked the organization and administration of the Royal Flying Corps and of the Royal Aircraft Factory, asserting that 'the officials who were responsible for deciding types of machines . . . failed either by ignorance, intrigue or incompetence to provide the best machines that this country could produce.'

Without a doubt the R.F.C. and R.N.A.S. had entered the war with unequalled personnel but handicapped in the usual miserable, dreary way by the dangerous parsimonious policies in procurement of arms which resulted in their equipment being too little and too late.

On 7th May, 1916, the Secretary of State for War announced that a committee under Mr. Justice Bailhache was to undertake an inquiry into the administration and command of the R.F.C.

A few days later, on 12th May, 1916, came the report of the committee under the chairmanship of Sir Richard Burbidge which had been set up to inquire into the affairs of the Royal Aircraft Factory and 'Whether within the resources placed by the War Office and the limits imposed by the War Office Order, the origin and management of the Factory are efficient, and to give the Army Council the benefit of their suggestions on any points of the interior administration of the Factory which seem to them capable of improvement.' The findings of the Burbidge Committee recommended, *inter alia*:

(i) A stricter observance of the original terms of reference of the Factory, namely that it should foster the research and development aspects of aeronautics, rather than engage in production aspects, even of an experimental prototype nature.

(ii) The Factory should be under the direction of a single superintendent possessing special business experience and administrative capacity.

(iii) Col. Mervyn O'Gorman, having completed his term of seven years

Avro 523 Pike with two 160 h.p. Sunbeam pusher engines. (*Avro Photo.*)

and rendered eminent public service in the design and construction of aircraft, to be appointed consulting engineer to the Director General of Military Aeronautics at the War Office.

A few months afterwards, on 21st September, 1916, O'Gorman was succeeded as superintendent of the Factory by Henry Fowler, until then chief mechanical engineer of the Midland Railway.

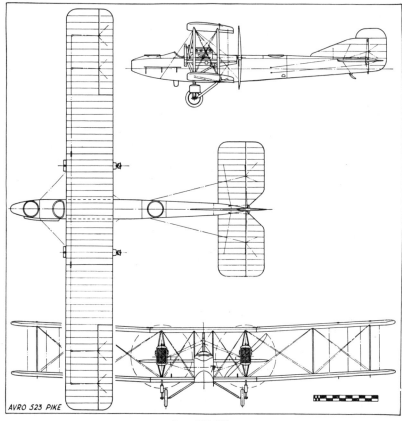

Avro 523 Pike

66

By 1916 the concept of the multi-seat, twin-engine type had been assessed and accepted as the next inevitable stage in the evolution of the bomber. A. V. Roe made a determined but unsuccessful attempt to enter the field with the Type 523 Pike which was completed in May, 1916, being assembled at Hamble. Roy Chadwick was responsible for the design, and the three-seat Pike was of note as the first Avro type with twin engines, in this case a pair of 160 h.p. Sunbeams mounted at mid-gap as pushers driving two-blade propellers. As a short-range bomber for use by day or night, the bomb load was carried internally and horizontally in the fuselage. The flying surfaces—equal-span, non-staggered, three-bay wings and tail unit—were of typically Avro shape, and the machine was supported on separate undercarriage units beneath the engines. Extension shafts ensured propeller clearance of the trailing edges, and there were rectangular frontal radiators. Cockpits for defensive Lewis machine-guns on rings were installed in the nose and amidships. The Type 523 underwent Admiralty trials on the Isle of Grain.

A second prototype, designated Type 523A and powered by two tractor-mounted, rear-cooled 150 h.p. Green engines, emerged from the erecting shops at Hamble in August, 1916. Despite apparently excellent prospects of adoption as a very useful bomber, neither version of the Pike was ordered, and projected variants—the Sunbeam-powered Type 523B and Rolls-Royce-powered Type 523C—did not materialize.

May, 1916, saw the first flight of a new two-seat bomber and reconnaissance biplane, the Armstrong Whitworth F.K.8 designed by Koolhoven. A compact, clean design, it was to remain relatively little publicized and yet performed well and reliably on active service. A neatly-cowled 120 h.p. Beardmore, flanked by upright radiators which slanted inwards to meet at the upper centre-section, was installed in early F.K.8s, but greater power was available from the 160 h.p. Beardmore which was fitted subsequently. Stagger was built into the equal-span two-bay wings, and the undercarriage at first followed the style of the F.K.3 with a central skid. In the course of its production career various alterations were made, including the adoption of a simpler main undercarriage unit. No. 35 Squadron, R.F.C., was the first to go into action with the F.K.8, popularly called the Big Ack, taking them to France on 24th January, 1917.

Another two-seat bomber making its début in 1916, but one which was destined to make its mark among the most successful and significant British aircraft of the 1914–18 War was Geoffrey de Havilland's outstanding D.H.4, to the design of which A. E. Hagg made a considerable contribution.

By this period the basic requirements of performance had brought a fairly definite degree of rationalization and standardization in bomber layout, and the new Airco product followed without deviation the two-seat tractor biplane formula in meeting the requirement for a new advanced day bomber. The disappointment felt at the lack of progress made towards acceptance of the D.H.3 was quickly forgotten in the certain knowledge that in the D.H.4 the team at Hendon were evolving a winner. An excellent appearance characterized the well-proportioned machine which made its initial flight piloted by Geoffrey de Havilland, accompanied by Maj. G. P. Bulman, in the middle of August, 1916.

The 160 h.p. Beardmore was scheduled in the first instance as the D.H.4's engine, but advantage was taken of the new unit being developed simultaneously by F. B. Halford and which emerged as the 230 h.p. Beardmore–Halford–Pullinger. The new B.H.P. was installed in the prototype D.H.4, but delays in production of the six-cylinder inline B.H.P. led to the more-powerful and first-class twelve-cylinder vee 250 h.p. Rolls-Royce Eagle being used for the early production D.H.4s.

The basic design earned high praise in its official trials, those of the prototype being conducted from 21st September, 1916, until 12th October, 1916, by the Central Flying School's Testing Flight. In every way, the D.H.4 justified the high hopes of its creators and was taken to France on 6th March, 1917, for its first active service with No. 55 Squadron, R.F.C. No time was lost in developing the basic design through minor airframe modifications and in fitting engines of progressively higher power. Eventually, with the 375 h.p. Eagle VIII, the D.H.4's top speed reached 133·5 m.p.h. at 10,000 ft., and an absolute ceiling of 23,000 ft. was achieved. Apart from its virtues in allied rôles, the D.H.4 was unrivalled as a day bomber in its time and played a great part in taking the war to the enemy. Armament generally comprised a pilot's Constantinesco-synchronized ·303 Vickers mounted to port on the decking and a ·303 Lewis on a Scarff No. 2 ring for the observer. The basic offensive load, in racks beneath the lower wings, consisted of two 230 lb. or four 112 lb. bombs or their equivalent. Very successful use of the D.H.4 was made also by R.N.A.S. squadrons.

Although, as a general design layout, the pusher type of aircraft carrying its tail unit on booms had largely been eschewed by the middle of the 1914–18 War, it was still considered effective enough to be employed in the two-seat A.D. Navyplane which Supermarine built in 1916 for the Air Department of the Admiralty. Overall, the 36 ft. span biplane resembled strongly the Supermarine Patrol Seaplane. R. J. Mitchell and a fellow Supermarine designer, Richardson, co-operated in the project with the Admiralty's Harold Bolas, whose product the design was. The single prototype, 9095, employed two-bay, unstaggered wings of 36 ft. equal span, in the centre of which a light-weight monocoque nacelle with tandem seats was supported by struts. A flexibly-mounted Lewis gun armed the observer's cockpit. Twin pontoon main floats were augmented by a smaller pair borne at the rear by the booms.

9095's first engine, with which Lt. Cdr. J. W. Seddon conducted the Navyplane's first flights during August, 1916, was the ten-cylinder, single-row 150 h.p. Smith Static radial. This was later replaced by the 150 h.p. Bentley A.R.1 rotary in which form 9095 underwent further trials in May, 1917, but its relatively low overall performance precluded its production as a reconnaissance or bomber aircraft.

Blackburn entered the field of torpedo-carrying, patrol-bomber design during 1916 with the advent of their two large three-seat biplanes, the G.P. and the S.P. One only of each was built—1415 the G.P. with two 225 h.p.

D.H.4 supplied to the Royal New Zealand Air Force. (*R.N.Z.A.F. Photo.*)

Sunbeam engines and 1416 the S.P. using two 250 h.p. Rolls-Royce Falcons. The 74 ft. 10·25 in. upper wings overhung the lower planes by 21 ft. 9·75 in. and were made to fold. Apart from the power plants used, there was comparatively little to distinguish the machines from each other. Both were mounted on independent main pontoon float units with a single float at the tail, but the S.P. incorporated ailerons in its lower wings also. 1415 was put

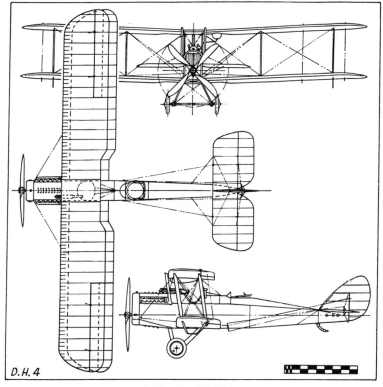

D.H.4

de Havilland D.H.4

69

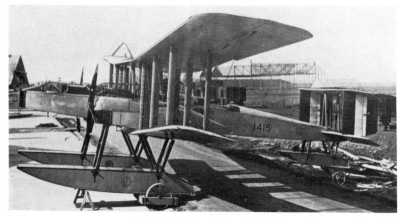

1415, the Blackburn G.P. seaplane.

through its Admiralty trials at the Isle of Grain, but those of 1416 were undertaken at Brough; in the event, neither was ordered for service.

To augment its strength of Short 184 patrol seaplanes during 1916, the R.N.A.S. bought ten Mann, Egerton Type B aircraft. The Type B was produced by the Norwich firm as their improved version of the Short 184, which they were making as sub-contractors. To a great extent, the Type B incorporated parts of the 184 and used the 225 h.p. Sunbeam as its power. However, Mann, Egerton departed from the basic 184 layout by fitting wings with greatly extended upper surfaces overhanging the lower planes. The batch of two-seat Type Bs produced were numbered from 9085 to 9094.

The feature of extensive upper wings' overhang was perpetuated in another single-engine seaplane of 1916, the Short 320, which was intended to launch the 18 in. Mk. IX 1,000 lb. torpedo. Two prototypes—8317 and 8318—were built, and the 320 was ordered into production for the R.N.A.S., being fitted with the Sunbeam Cossack engine of either 310 h.p. or 320 h.p. The pilot

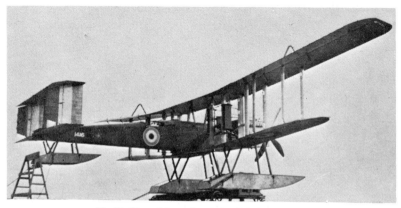

The Blackburn S.P. seaplane 1416. (*Blackburn Photo.*)

70

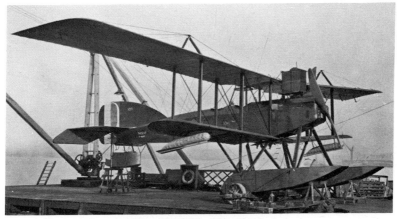

Short 320 N1397. (*Short Photo.*)

was accommodated in the rear cockpit, a fact which accentuated the difficulty of the observer in using his Lewis gun to advantage. To enable him to do this, the bizarre expedient was resorted to of mounting a strut-supported Scarff

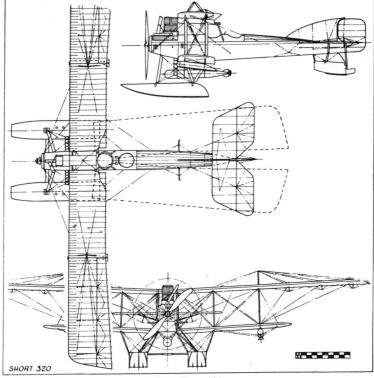

SHORT 320

Short Type 320

71

Early prototype D.H.6 with curved fin and rudder. (*de Havilland Photo.*)

ring in line with the upper centre-section, from which the unfortunate gunner was expected to fire his Lewis by climbing out of his seat to stand in the cockpit. In addition to acting as a torpedo-carrier, the Short 320 was employed on reconnaissance and anti-submarine patrol, its bomb capacity being two of 230 lb. each.

Among the least prepossessing in appearance of the diverse prototypes of the period was N525, the solitary Beardmore W.B.I two-seat, long-range bomber intended for the R.N.A.S. An inordinately ungainly and cluttered tractor biplane using the 230 h.p. Beardmore Adriatic as power, the W.B.I was designed by G. Tilghman Richards in 1916. The 61 ft. 6 in. three-bay wings were equal in span and were heavily staggered. The cumbersome undercarriage consisted of two main units, each of which contained a pair of large rear wheels and a pair of smaller front wheels. The W.B.I was designed to carry six 110 lb. bombs and have an endurance of 7·3 hrs. Aiming and release of the bombs was the duty of the observer from his rear-set cockpit. As an alternative to the Beardmore engine, the 240 h.p. Sunbeam was tested in the W.B.I which was delivered to the R.N.A.S. Station, Cranwell, on 8th June, 1917, subsequently being involved in an accident there following a landing by Wg. Cdr. R. E. C. Peirse. Projected only was a revised version of the W.B.I, the W.B.IA, which would have used the 500 h.p. B.H.P. Atlantic engine to carry a crew of two.

Following successful use of the F.E.2b as a night bomber during November, 1916, No. 100 Squadron, R.F.C., was sent to France on 24th March, 1917, equipped with the pusher, specifically modified with a simplified under-carriage, for bombing the enemy by night. Results were so good that, although accepted as outmoded for daytime operations, the F.E.2b was put into production again to equip a further six squadrons for nocturnal attacks over the Western Front.

Geoffrey de Havilland's outstanding versatility as a designer was fully demonstrated in the course of the 1914–18 War as—in turn—he evolved fighters, bombers and trainers. It was as a trainer that the extraordinarily angular D.H.6 was designed and served mainly. Alternatively powered by the 90 h.p. R.A.F.1A, 90 h.p. Curtiss OX-5 or the 80 h.p. Renault, according to availability of supplies, the two-seat, two-bay biplane was never to be considered as endowed with enough power. Consequently, when the D.H.6 was adapted early in 1918 for anti-submarine patrol around the coast of the British Isles, it was at a disadvantage from the start and was perforce flown solo to enable it to carry a single 100 lb. bomb or the same load of smaller missiles. Despite modifications carried out from March, 1918, with the object of improving the performance of the D.H.6 to make it more effective against U-boats, all that was achieved was a slight increase in top speed, but the machine was unable to improve its bomb-carrying ability.

Among the results of the work of the Royal Aircraft Factory in the course of 1916 were the issue in November of A.P.970, a six-page pamphlet which formulated *Design Requirements for Aeroplanes,* and Professor A. H. Gibson's pioneer work for two years on air cooling of engines which investigated the depth, thickness and spacing of cooling fins and effects of airflow.

Further Admiralty sponsorship of the long-range bomber was evident in 1916, when two developments of the Avro 523 Pike were ordered as the prototypes 529 and 529A. Both machines were constructed at Manchester and erected on the South Coast at Hamble, the 529 being completed in April, 1917, and the 529A six months later in October.

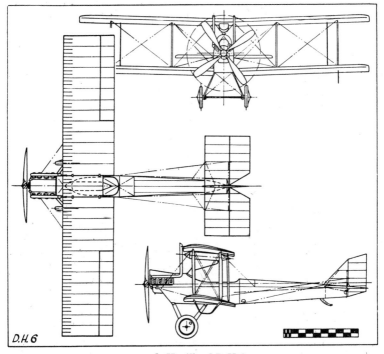

de Havilland D.H.6

73

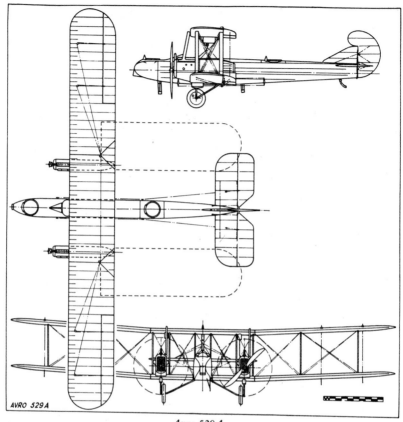

Avro 529A

3694, the 529, was slightly the smaller of the pair with a span of 63 ft. as opposed to the 64 ft. 1 in. spread of 3695, the 529A. Each followed the same basic layout of the Pike, receiving three-bay unstaggered wings which could be folded to the rear. In place of the earlier design's square tips, however, those of the new machines were rounded. The three cockpits were disposed similarly to those of the Pike in the same style of fuselage but in one of slightly greater length. A significant difference between the 529 and the 529A lay in their engines; 3694 was equipped with a pair of 190 h.p. Rolls-Royce Falcons mounted without cowlings at mid-gap, fed with fuel under pressure from a single large tank to the rear of the pilot, while each of the two enclosed 230 h.p. B.H.P. engines of the 529A, mounted on the lower wings, received its fuel independently from its own nacelle-mounted tank by way of a gravity tank installed on the underside of the upper planes. Scarff rings fitted in both gunners' cockpits facilitated the use of the Lewis guns, and a set of controls in the amidships cockpit enabled the gunner to take over in an emergency. The 529A's offensive load of twenty vertically-stowed 50 lb. bombs was housed inside the fuselage and was released by the front gunner—who doubled as bomb-aimer—from a prone sighting position in the nose. Despite this second attempt by Avro at producing a competent twin-engine, long-range bomber and the good overall handling reports earned by each machine, the effort expended on the 529 and the 529A was in vain and neither was destined for production.

By the autumn of 1916, British defence successes against raiding Zeppelins had forced the Germans to reconsider the ultimate value of such attacks. The conclusion was that the evolution of the aeroplane in its diverse forms had forged ahead of the lighter-than-air weapon, thereby steadily reducing the airship's potency, and that bombing of the United Kingdom by strong forces of bomber aircraft was the next logical and potentially effective step.

On 25th May, 1917, heavy German raids were made in daylight on towns in Kent, and again on 5th June when both Kent and Essex were bombed. On 13th June, 1917, a formation of Gothas dropped their lethal loads on London at midday, and another attack took place against the capital three weeks later on 7th July. An immediate revision of the country's defence system was effected.

Another swift reaction to these attacks was a demand for a rapid increase in the number and the quality of British bombers. Large orders were placed for the successful D.H.4 and, at the same time, plans were drawn up for a successor—the D.H.9. The promise inherent in the D.H.9 was such that it was decided to order it in place of the D.H.4s for which contracts had just been let. A D.H.4—A7559—was immediately taken into the shops at Hendon and modified so as to become the prototype D.H.9. In its new guise A7559 made its first flight at Hendon in July, 1917, powered by the 230 h.p. B.H.P.

In most respects the new machine was identical with its predecessor, the main exterior differences being the new shape of nose, with the exposed cylinders of the engine, the retractable radiator on the underside of the fuselage just ahead of the undercarriage, and the alteration of the pilot's cockpit to a rear position adjacent to the gunner. This new location of the

C6051, first of the initial production batch of D.H.9s built by Airco. (*de Havilland Photo.*)

D.H.9 of the Royal New Zealand Air Force. (*R.N.Z.A.F. Photo.*)

pilot's position removed two of the main adverse criticisms of the D.H.4 namely the inordinate distance between the cockpits, resulting in poor communication, and also the placing of the pilot between the main fuel tank and the engine—a situation far removed from any pilot's liking.

Nevertheless, in spite of the promise at first displayed by the D.H.9, the programme ran into trouble through selection of the B.H.P. engine, with which unit the machine was unable to equal the performance of the illustrious Rolls-Royce-powered D.H.4. Notwithstanding, plans for the production of the B.H.P.-powered D.H.9 were too far advanced by the time that the unfortunate facts were known for any further alteration in engine selection and, by the end of 1917, the first production examples had been completed. The main obstacle in the way of success for the D.H.9 was its lack of performance at higher altitudes. It was incapable of carrying its bomb load at a steady 15,000 ft. and often was unable to exceed 13,000 ft. altitude. To reach its target, therefore, the D.H.9 had, perforce, to fight its way through enemy fighters, which found little difficulty in reaching the bombers' operational level and thereafter conducting affairs to a great extent their own way.

The D.H.9 went into action during the spring of 1918, working particularly as part of the Independent Force. Persistent engine failure contributed its share to the troubles of the D.H.9 squadrons on the Western Front, and

D.H.9 of the Belgian Aviation Militaire. (*Musée Royal de l'Armée et d'Histoire Militaire Photo.*)

D.H.9 151 of the South African Air Force, fitted with Jaguar engine. (*S.A.A.F. Photo.*)

losses during the summer of 1918 were such that cogent doubts eventually arose about the type's status as a first-line aircraft. Attempts to improve the performance of the D.H.9 by testing airframes fitted with alternative engines, among them the 230 h.p. and 290 h.p. Siddeley Puma, the 250 h.p. Fiat A-12 and the 430 h.p. Napier Lion, fared badly, little progress being made in

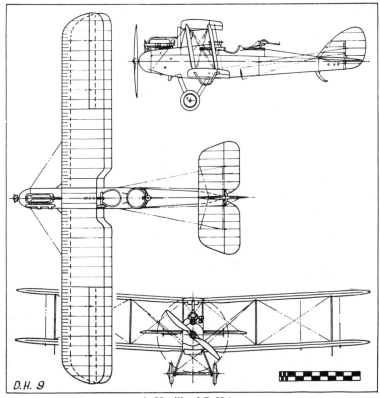

de Havilland D.H.9

Early version of Sopwith 2.B.2 Rhino using ailerons equipped with horn balances. (*Hawker Photo.*)

bestowing a worthwhile performance on the machine, the experimental Lion installation turning out to be the most rewarding.

1917 witnessed the advent of several prototype bombers of various categories, none of which made the grade as production entities. Among them were one Sunbeam and two Sopwith designs.

The single-seat Sunbeam Bomber came from a firm which had been producing Shorts and Avros to meet Admiralty orders during the war and eventually decided to design its own bomber for the R.N.A.S. The result was the inauspicious single N515, a two-bay 42 ft. span biplane fitted with the 200 h.p. Sunbeam Arab engine. The pilot was located mid-way along the fuselage and was armed with one synchronized Vickers gun well out of his reach on the fore-decking; the bomb load was borne externally. The proportions of the Sunbeam Bomber did little to inspire confidence in the

Sopwith 2.B.2 Rhino X8 with plain ailerons. (*Hawker Photo.*)

machine and, although tests were carried out in 1917 at Castle Bromwich and during the following year at Martlesham, it failed to earn a production order.

The Sopwith 2.B.2 Rhino was a Kingston prototype of 1917 intended as a two-seat day bomber. A return was made to the triplane formula in the design which consisted of equal-span, single-bay wings mounted on a fuselage, the fore portion of which was particularly deep in order to form an internal bomb-bay. X8 was the sole example constructed and carried the 230 h.p. B.H.P. engine in its nose, flanked by low-set radiators. The ponderous and ungainly Rhino relied on the ground on a tiny undercarriage unit which further contributed to the machine's unlovely appearance.

One redeeming and laudatory feature, however, in an otherwise uninspired design lay in the Rhino's self-contained bomb-pack, which was calculated to reduce rearming time between raids. The pilot's cockpit was situated immediately above the bomb-bay, and the pack was lifted into place by hoisting gear fitted inside his cockpit. The pack contained alternative loads of four 112 lb., nine 50 lb. or twenty 20 lb. bombs; armament for the pilot consisted of a single forwards-firing Vickers, while that of the observer to his rear was a Lewis gun on a pillar mounting, later exchanged for a Scarff ring. In the course of its existence an alteration was made to the ailerons of the Rhino. Carried on all three planes, the first surfaces were horn-balanced, but these were later superseded by the same number in plain form, still retaining the upper wire and lower strut connections between them.

The prefix of the X8 serial number of the Rhino, granted under Licence No. 14, indicated that the machine was entirely a Private Venture but which was considered as a design project showing sufficient promise for the parent firm to be granted permission to proceed to construct a prototype at a time when materials and labour were at a premium.

Tests performed with the Rhino during February and March, 1918, failed to promote the machine's chances of adoption, and the design was ultimately abandoned.

Although by 1917 the concept of the multi-seat bomber was accepted generally, the advantages inherent in the small, faster single-seater were still not neglected. Sopwith set to work to design a competent single-seat bomber, and the result emerged in the spring of 1917 as the B.1 B1496, a shapely two-bay, equal-span biplane fitted with the 200 h.p. Hispano-Suiza engine in a clean cowling. To endow the pilot with a good view for conducting his bombing attacks, the cockpit was set well forward between the centre-section struts. The bomb load of 560 lb. was borne internally and hung vertically in the fuselage bay which extended from the rear centre-section struts to the lower wings' trailing edge. Armament for the B.1's pilot consisted of a single Lewis gun mounted centrally to fire forwards from the top of the engine cowling. The first-class results obtained in the B.1's tests of April, 1917, prompted service trials with the 5th Wing of the R.N.A.S. at Dunkirk. The original promise shown by the B.1 was not, however, rewarded by subsequent production.

Sopwith Cuckoo built by Blackburn. (*Blackburn Photo.*)

The Sopwith Aviation Company had shown an early interest in the torpedo-carrying aeroplane, and, at the instigation of Commodore Murray F. Sueter in his capacity as Superintendent of Aircraft Construction at the Air Department of the Admiralty, T. O. M. Sopwith discussed with him in October, 1916, the idea of designing a machine with an endurance of four hours and the

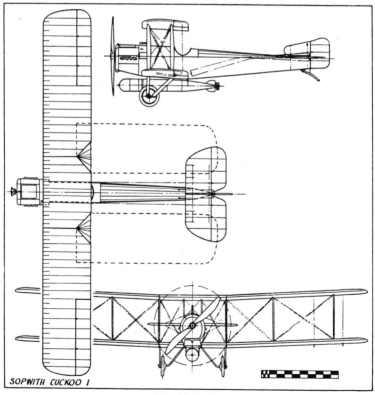

Sopwith Cuckoo

capacity to transport one or even two torpedoes, taking into account the possibility of catapult launching from ships.

For the period, the assignment was a tough one, but, shortly, the Kingston firm came forth with the Sopwith T.1 design. The layout envisaged was that of a single-engine biplane carrying a pilot only. Authority was given to proceed with construction of a prototype, but with Sueter's departure from the Air Department in January, 1917, the fire went out of the project as far as official circles were concerned and was not revived until the partly completed airframe was noticed at Kingston during February, 1917, by Wg. Cdr. A. M. Longmore, who managed to press for its completion.

The T.1 N74 was finished on 6th June, 1917, and—although somewhat greater in span—bore the strongest possible resemblance to the B.1. Three-bay folding wings were incorporated, the pilot sat in line with the trailing edges, and separate main undercarriage units enabled the 18 in. 1,000 lb. Mk. IX torpedo to be accommodated in the optimum launching position. The nose housed the 200 h.p. Hispano-Suiza engine under a circular cowling.

Trials with N74 were satisfactorily carried out from the Isle of Grain during July, 1917, and were followed in August by an order for one hundred T.1s to be produced by the Glasgow firm of Fairfield Shipbuilding and Engineering Co. Ltd. The name Cuckoo was applied to the T.1, and modifications were drawn up for the production aircraft. To counter the shortage of Hispano-Suiza engines the 200 h.p. Sunbeam Arab was specified, an enlarged tailskid was fitted to ensure sufficient clearance for the torpedo while on the ground, and minor alterations were made to the tail unit.

The Cuckoo's passage into production was far from smooth, however. Delays occurred, particularly in developing the Arab into a satisfactory operational power plant, and the entire programme lagged. Eventually, the first squadron was ready to take its place with the Fleet some three weeks before the Armistice, but it was too late then for the Cuckoo to be used operationally. As the Mk. I's Arab engine was so fractious, a Mk. II version of the Cuckoo was prepared using the 200 h.p. Wolseley W.4A Viper, and October, 1919, saw yet another version—using the 275 h.p. Rolls-Royce Falcon III—under test.

Numerous patrol seaplanes performed valiantly for long periods over cold, unfriendly expanses of open water in the course of many months of bitter and relentless struggle for supremacy at sea during the 1914–18 War. Among the lesser-known types employed by the R.N.A.S. was the Wight Converted Seaplane, an adaptation on floats of the unsuccessful Wight Bomber N501 of 1916. 9841 served as the prototype seaplane conversion and appeared in 1917 mounted on a pair of lengthy floats, supplemented by the usual wingtip floats which were—on the Wight—fitted flush beneath the lower wings without connecting struts. Apart from the 275 h.p. Rolls-Royce Mk. II engine normally used, the Wight was—in a few cases—powered by the 265 h.p. Sunbeam Maori. Production totalled thirty-seven, a relatively short run. The bomb load of the Wight Converted Seaplane was carried on racks fitted beneath the fuselage, and defensive armament consisted of a Lewis gun on a

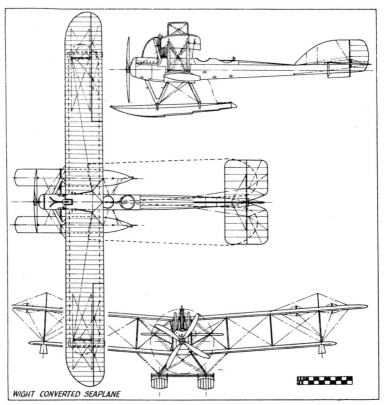

WIGHT CONVERTED SEAPLANE

Wight Converted Seaplane

Scarff ring for the observer in the rear cockpit, a position giving him a fairly broad field of fire.

Most prolific producers of seaplane designs during the war, Short Brothers built two examples—N66 and N67—of the N.2B patrol-bomber, their final floatplane to appear before the Armistice. A far tidier design than were most of those emanating from Rochester in the course of the 1914–18 War, N66 made its bow on 22nd September, 1917, powered by a neatly-cowled 275 h.p. Sunbeam Maori. Although the N.2B was cleaner than its predecessors, one of the less happy aspects of the design was that of the considerable gap which separated the two cockpits—already established clearly as a bad feature in a multi-seater.

The N.2B departed from previous Short practice in several respects. Although it retained the usual unequal-span, two-bay wing cellules, bracing of the upper tips' overhang was by a pair of splayed struts instead of the wire and kingpost arrangement employed hitherto. A frontal radiator took the place of the customary view-obstructing box type so often installed on the fore-decking before the pilot. Flush-fitted wooden floats served under the

N66, the first Short N.2B. (*Short Photo.*)

wingtips instead of the old style of wrinkled air-bags, but the main floats followed the normal pattern of flat-sided pontoons. Those fitted to N66 were shaped with one step and concave undersides, but N67 received a pair with unbroken bottoms. The N.2B's offensive load consisted of two 230 lb. bombs stored beneath the fuselage; a Scarff ring around the rear cockpit held the observer's Lewis gun.

Another Short floatplane design which remained simply a prototype was the S.364, a two-seat, two-bay, equal-span biplane which represented a complete breakaway from the usual intricate type of seaplane layout which had succeeded design after design from Rochester. Remarkably clean folding wing cellules, with a straight trailing edge and elliptical tips, housed upper and lower ailerons, and the 200 h.p. Sunbeam Afridi engine and its frontal radiator were neatly cowled into the fuselage of simple lines. The centre-section struts were exceedingly slim and encompassed the pilot's cockpit. His observer sat some way aft of the trailing edges in a cockpit surmounted by a Scarff ring-mounting for his Lewis gun. The S.364 was out of the factory in March, 1917, but made no headway towards a production order, despite its promising appearance.

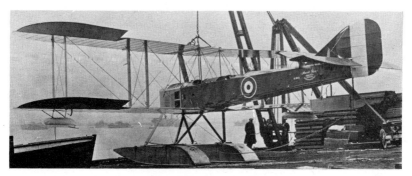

Short S.364. (*Short Photo.*)

83

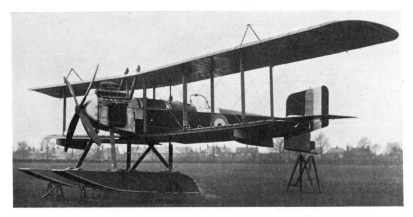

N1000, the first Fairey F.16 Campania. (*Fairey Photo.*)

The Fairey Aviation Company was destined to have long and close associations with the Royal Navy in the supply of its aircraft, the foundations of which were laid early in the 1914–18 War. Following production of a batch

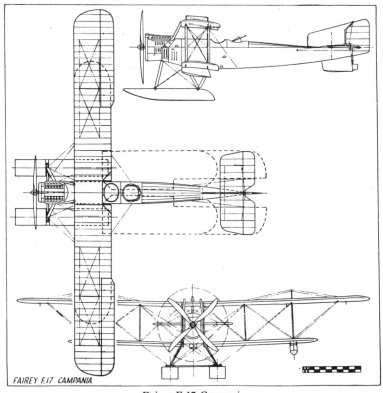

FAIREY F.17 CAMPANIA

Fairey F.17 Campania

of Short Admiralty Type 827 seaplanes under sub-contract, the firm turned
to designing its own aeroplanes. The F.2 long-range fighter was its first
attempt at the art, and this was succeeded by a two-seat patrol seaplane
designed in 1916. Of special importance was that the machine should be
stowed aboard the seaplane carrier *Campania*, from which the seaplane was
to take its name.

Allotted Fairey airframe number F.16, the first prototype N1000 was
fitted with the 250 h.p. Rolls-Royce Mk. IV engine. In overall appearance
the Campania—and succeeding Fairey seaplane designs—were far neater and
less cluttered than their counterparts of the period from Short Brothers. The
Fairey designs did not indulge in the frustrating habit of mounting the

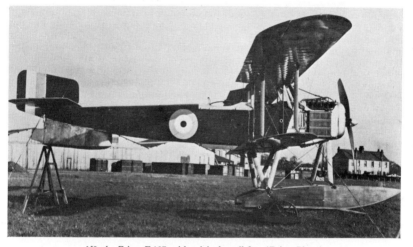

N9, the Fairey F.127, with original small fin. (*Fairey Photo.*)

radiator block in front of the pilot to the great detriment of his view forwards.
Side-mounted radiators cooled the Campania's engine, and the twin exhausts
were taken up through the centre-section. Flush-fitting wingtip floats were
used, accompanied by pontoon-style main and rear floats. Folding wings
were mandatory, and those on the Campania utilized two-bay bracing with
kingposts and wire support for the upper wings' overhang.

Second thoughts were evident in the second Campania F.17 N1001, resulting in various alterations. Increased power appeared in the form of the 275
h.p. Rolls-Royce Mk. I incorporating a frontal radiator The wings embodied an improved aerofoil section, and a cut-out in the upper centre-section
aided the pilot's field of view. Revision of the tail surfaces had taken place,
and the tip floats were suspended on short struts. Under-fuselage racks
carried the Campania's bomb load, and the observer's Lewis gun was
installed on a Scarff ring.

In its F.17 form the Campania passed into production during 1917. From
F.22 N1006, the 250 h.p. Sunbeam Maori II engine was also used, owing to
a shortage of the Rolls-Royce units brought about by the demand for such an

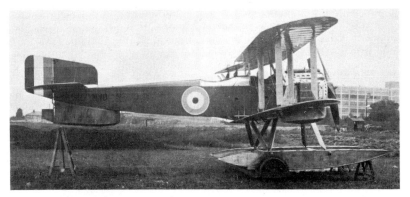

Fairey F.128 III N10, first of the Fairey III series. (*Fairey Photo.*)

Fairey IIIA. (*Fairey Photo.*)

Fairey IIIC on skis after conversion from IIIA N2876. (*Fairey Photo.*)

excellent engine. Later on, the Campania was equipped with the 345 h.p. Rolls-Royce Eagle VIII, as yet another alternative, and served well in both F.17 and F.22 versions.

By 1917 Fairey enthusiasm for seaplane development was well entrenched, and during the year the two-seat 190 h.p. Rolls-Royce I-powered F.127 N9 to Admiralty Specification N.2(a) made its appearance at Hayes. Designed for seaplane-carrier operation, the single-bay wings folded and incorporated the Fairey Patent Camber Gear in full form; both upper and lower trailing edges were arranged as lift-increasing flaps. Radiators flanked the engine on each side, and the short-span lower wings were without tip floats. N9's armament consisted of a Scarff-mounted Lewis gun in the rear cockpit. No production ensued, but the F.127 served a useful purpose as the guinea-pig in experiments with the Armstrong catapult installed in H.M.S. *Slinger*. To withstand the stresses associated with this type of launching, N9 was strengthened for the purpose and performed with complete success.

Following the F.127 during 1917, there came the Fairey F.128 N10 two-seat patrol seaplane, as an alternative design to Specification N.2(a), bearing also the designation Fairey III to head the subsequently long list of III-series to emanate from Fairey for nearly two decades. Upper-wing overhang had been discarded in favour of equal span, and the machine was fitted with the 260 h.p. Sunbeam Maori II cooled by side radiators. The two-bay wings embodied the firm's useful Camber Gear and were mounted on a fuselage matching that used on the F.127. Apart from a larger fin, the F.128's tail unit was the same as that of the F.127. As a seaplane the F.128 did not go into production, but, towards the close of 1917, N10 was stripped of its floats and equipped with a landplane undercarriage of straightforward V-strut type. The Maori's radiator became a single frontal block. Fifty of the landplane, redesignated Fairey IIIA, were ordered for shipboard use with the R.N.A.S., commencing with F.220 N2850. External racks housed the bomb load, and the single Lewis gun for the observer formed the IIIA's armament.

Designed to the Admiralty Specification N.2(b), the next Fairey product was the IIIB two-seat bomber seaplane. Powered by the 260 h.p. Maori II and using the same fuselage, tailplane and elevators as its predecessors the III and the IIIA, the folding wings of the IIIB were increased in area by the addition of generous upper surface extensions which carried the pair of ailerons; a larger fin and rudder were also fitted. The Camber Gear was retained and the bomb load of about 600 lb. was slung from under-fuselage racks. The production run of the IIIB was relatively short, only twenty-five coming from Fairey.

Still embracing the same two-seat seaplane category, the IIIC was next in the line of Fairey products. Using the same fuselage and float unit of the earlier III designs, the IIIC changed back to equal-span for its two-bay wings and embodied the IIIB's tail surfaces. The mixture of two different types resulted in an excellent general-purpose aircraft with a performance enhanced by a first-class engine—the 375 h.p. Rolls-Royce Eagle VIII.

Fairey IIIB N2240. (*Fairey Photo.*)

Increased fuel capacity gave an endurance of six hours, and side radiators were fitted. N2246 was the IIIC prototype and was completed in September, 1918. The IIIC's pilot was provided with a synchronized Vickers gun, and his observer was armed with the usual Lewis on a Scarff ring. The IIIC's bomb load was borne in under-fuselage racks. By the time that production

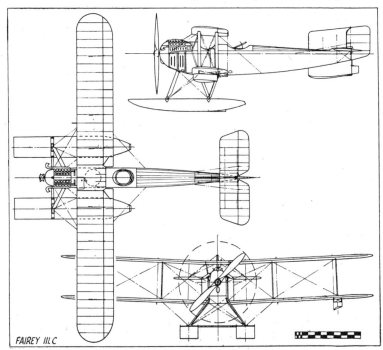

Fairey IIIC

was under way November, 1918, had arrived, and the IIIC was too late for active service in the 1914–18 War.

Modifications during 1917 of the basic Handley Page O/100 bomber, made by George Volkert, resulted in a new designation—H.P.12 O/400—being applied. The main alterations were the removal of the nacelle fuel tanks and their transfer to the fuselage and the rearwards position adopted for the fin. The general shortage of Rolls-Royce engines made alternative power plants essential, substitutes being found in the 250 h.p. Sunbeam Maori and the 260 h.p. Fiat A-12bis. Cricklewood was the venue for the initial flight of the first O/400.

The adoption of the day bomber in quantity was responsible during mid-1917 for the Air Board decision of 23rd July to defer placing orders for new heavy bombers. Opposition to such a policy was such that only a week later —on 30th July—the matter was re-examined, with the result that O/400s— to the tune of one hundred—were ordered on 14th August, 1917.

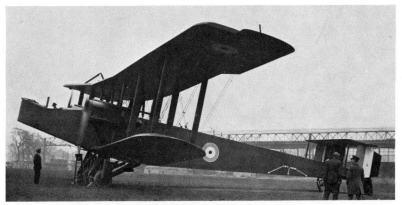

3138, the prototype Handley Page O/400. (*Handley Page Photo.*)

Production Handley Page O/400 with Eagle engines. (*Handley Page Photo.*)

89

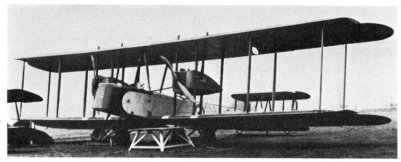

Vickers F.B.27 Vimy prototype B9952 with original elevators fitted with horn balances.
(*Vickers Photo.*)

H5066, second of twenty-five Westland-built Vickers F.B.27A Vimys. (*Westland Photo.*)

F9569, the prototype Vickers Vimy Mk. IV. (*Vickers Photo.*)

Meanwhile, proof had been forthcoming of the efficacy of night bombing, and the O/400 orders were increased substantially. By the spring of 1918, the O/400 had begun to appear in reasonable quantities and, for the succeeding months until the Armistice, made its name operating with the Independent Force of the Royal Air Force in long-range attacks on targets in Germany.

A further result of the decision of the Air Board on 30th July, 1917, to reverse its policy and to proceed again with development of the heavy night bomber was that contracts were placed forthwith for prototypes of new machines with Vickers and Handley Page. R. K. Pierson undertook the design of the Vickers bomber, three of which were ordered on 16th August, 1917, and which was designated F.B.27.

Pierson retained in the three-seat biplane the basic layout which he had earlier shown to Maj. J. S. Buchanan of the Air Board, and in under four months the prototype B9952 was ready. Twin tractor 200 h.p. Hispano-Suiza engines were mounted at mid-gap between the three-bay, equal-span wings, and the fuselage terminated in a biplane tail. The bomb load was accommodated inside the fuselage about the lower centre-section. Defensive armament was in the form of one Lewis gun in the nose position and another in the cockpit amidships. Four horn-balanced ailerons of generous area provided lateral control.

B9952's first flight was at the Vickers aerodrome at Joyce Green on 30th November, 1917, piloted by Capt. Gordon Bell. B9953, the second prototype F.B.27, used a pair of 260 h.p. Sunbeam Maoris as power and exhibited several alterations compared with B9952. Two 300 h.p. Fiat A-12bis engines were fitted to B9954, the third F.B.27. Official trials were satisfactory, and the Vimy, as the F.B.27 was eventually called, was put into full-scale production, falling in the category of R.A.F. Type VII Short Distance Night Bomber. One Vimy only had reached the Independent Force in France before the war ended, and the type was never able to fly operationally against Germany.

In the course of 1917 a landplane development of the Blackburn G.P. and S.P. seaplanes came into being. Apart from the substitution of divided wheel units for floats, the Kangaroo's airframe differed little from those of the G.P. and the S.P. Under test, the slim fuselage drew adverse criticism; it was found to lack rigidity and was deficient in comfort for its crew. Two 250 h.p. Rolls-Royce Falcons powered the Kangaroo, which carried four 230 lb. bombs inside the fuselage and a further four on external under-fuselage racks. One Lewis gun position was installed in the nose, and there was another mid-way along the fuselage. Very limited production of the Kangaroo ensued, and it served until the end of the war mainly on anti-submarine patrol from Seaton Carew.

A Handley Page project of 1917 which remained on paper only was the H.P.13 P/350. This would have been a single-engine bomber of broad span, powered by a 350 h.p. engine and weighing loaded 4,380 lb.

Blackburn Kangaroo B9970. (*Blackburn Photo.*)

91

One of the more unusual developments in the evolution of British heavy bombers was provided by the Kennedy Giant of 1917, an enormous biplane with a span of 142 ft. and powered by four 200 h.p. Salmson engines mounted in tandem pairs between the mainplanes. The aptly-named Giant was constructed jointly at Hayes by Fairey and by the Gramophone Company Ltd. to the design of C. J. H. Mackenzie-Kennedy. Kennedy's aeronautical experience in Russia prior to the 1914–18 War, culminating in his close association with Igor Sikorsky in the designing of the Russian's Il'ya Mourom'etz, showed up strongly in the British machine, construction of which was authorized by the War Office following representations by Kennedy. The early serial number 2337 was allocated to the machine, but the aircraft's components were not ready for assembly until the close of 1916. Northolt was selected as the best place for erecting the huge, square-cut bomber which had to be put together in the open in the absence of a hangar large enough for it. The Giant's remarkably deep fuselage rested on the shorter lower wings, and its constant depth extended to about mid-way along its length, at which point the lower longerons slanted upwards to provide slight taper in elevation. The crew members were fully enclosed and liberally provided with windows extending to the tail.

Unable to obtain the powerful engines which the Giant needed, the designer had to be content with the low-powered Salmsons, the combined 800 h.p. of which proved completely unequal to the task of lifting the machine from the ground at Northolt when Lt. F. T. Courtney attempted to fly it towards the end of 1917. Thereafter, the Giant was abandoned.

During the last year of the 1914–18 War several prototypes in various categories were tested and rejected as service aircraft. In 1918 the Grahame-White firm at Hendon completed the E.IV Ganymede, a long-range, three-engine biplane day bomber of unconventional layout. Two 270 h.p. Sunbeam Maori engines were mounted as tractors in the front of twin fuselages, while a third similar engine was installed as a pusher in the rear of the central nacelle provided for the crew. Three main Lewis gun positions were located in C3481, the sole Ganymede completed—one was in the nose of the nacelle and there was one in each of the pair of fuselages. In addition, each fuselage had a gun-firing opening in the underside towards the rear. Although the Ganymede had been scheduled to use 400 h.p. Liberty engines, these were not forthcoming and its performance suffered accordingly.

A requirement was formulated at the close of 1917 for a single-seat torpedo-carrying aircraft able to launch the 1,400 lb. Mk. VIII torpedo, a heavier weapon than that borne by the Cuckoo. Two firms—Blackburn and Short—built prototypes, three of each being ordered.

The Blackburd N113 was the first Blackburn machine and was particularly distinctive with its fuselage of constant depth from front to rear. Powered by the 350 h.p. Rolls-Royce Eagle VIII engine and fitted with equal-span, unstaggered wings, the Blackburd accommodated its missile between split undercarriage units and was designed to land on skids after jettisoning its wheels before launching its torpedo. N113 carried internal flotation gear in

Blackburn Blackburd. (*Blackburn Photo.*)

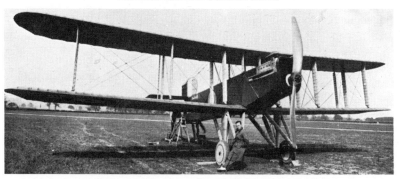

N113, the first prototype Blackburn Blackburd. (*Blackburn Photo.*)

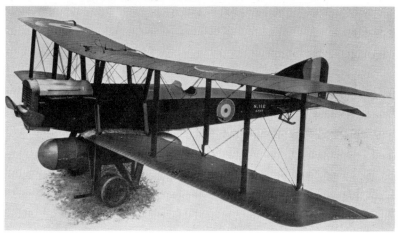

N112, third prototype Short Shirl. (*Short Photo.*)

D.H.9As of No. 39 Squadron in 1926. (*de Havilland Photo.*)

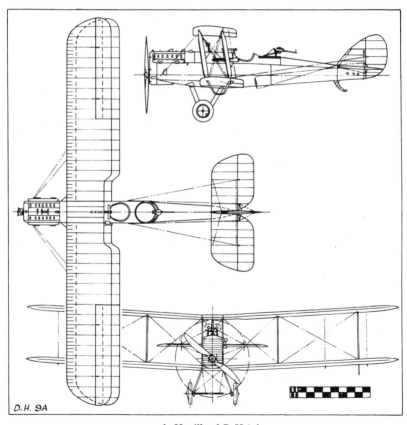

de Havilland D.H.9A

case of a forced landing on water, but the second prototype N114 was fitted with small floats for the purpose beneath the lower wings.

The Short answer to the single-seat torpedo-carrying requirement was the Shirl, N110 being the first prototype flown initially in mid-1918 by John Lankester Parker. The Shirl was far more conventional in appearance than the Blackburd. Two-bay, folding, equal-span wings were fitted to a slim fuselage, the nose of which housed the 345 h.p. Eagle VIII. In place of the simple V-type undercarriage of N110, N111—the second Shirl—received a complicated structure incorporating skids, together with swept-back wings; the third prototype—N112—differed once again in its landing-gear.

Under test, both the Blackburd and the Shirl were found to be inferior to the Cuckoo, and development of each ceased with the war's end.

Current shortage of Eagle engines to meet the demand for such a first-class unit was responsible for the decision to use the American Liberty engine as the power plant in a development of the D.H.9 day bomber, the design of which was undertaken by Westland to become the D.H.9A. Larger wings than those of the D.H.9 were used, and the prototype D.H.9A—B7664— made its début with the 375 h.p. Eagle VIII installed, complete with frontal radiator. Eventually the 400 h.p. Liberty 12 arrived on the D.H.9A scene in C6122.

Despite pressure from the Front, the first D.H.9A squadron—No. 110— was unable to reach France until 31st August, 1918. Teething troubles with the Liberty were eventually overcome so that the D.H.9A was evolved into a steady and reliable machine for its job. The aircraft's offensive load consisted of a maximum of 660 lb. of bombs carried beneath the fuselage and lower wings, and its armament comprised a Constantinesco-synchronized Vickers for the pilot and either one or two Lewis guns for the observer.

A new twin-engine bomber, the D.H.10, was completed at Hendon at the beginning of 1918. The newcomer revived the layout of the 1916 D.H.3 but

D.H.10 Amiens Mk. II C8659. (*de Havilland Photo.*)

was slightly longer. The first prototype of four ordered was C8658, designated Amiens Mk. I, which made its first take-off on 4th March, 1918, powered by a pair of pusher 230 h.p. B.H.P. engines. The next machine, the Amiens Mk. II C8659, was equipped with two 360 h.p. Rolls-Royce Eagle VIIIs installed as tractors and first flew on 20th April, 1918. C8660, the third machine and designated Amiens Mk. III, received a pair of tractor 400 h.p. Liberty 12 engines. The fine performance of the Liberty-powered Mk. III resulted in this version being selected for production, and four hundred and fifty were ordered on 10th March, 1918. The Mk. IIIA version was equipped also with the 400 h.p. Liberty 12 but attached to the lower wings, while the Mk. IIIC used a pair of 375 h.p. Eagle VIIIs, likewise mounted on the lower planes. An excellent bomber design, the D.H.10 arrived too late to play any part in the war.

Another bomber which would, like the Amiens, have acquitted itself well had hostilities lasted a little longer, was G. R. Volkert's massive Handley Page H.P.15 V/1500 which was ordered and designed in 1917 and completed during 1918. The first prototype, B9463, was constructed by Harland and Wolff at Belfast and was fitted with four 375 h.p. Eagle VIIIs mounted in tandem pairs between the 126 ft. span wings. The intended power plants were Rolls-Royce Condors, but delays in development led to the use of the Eagles. Two-blade tractor and four-blade pusher propellers were installed. B9463 was assembled at Cricklewood and made its first flight there during May, 1918, in the hands of Flt. Lt. V. Busby. Modifications were made as a result of early test flights, but the first V/1500 crashed later in June, 1918.

The intention was that the gargantuan V/1500 should serve in squadrons based in England and be able to make the return flight to bomb Germany. In the event, by the Armistice, only three V/1500s were in service—with No. 166 Squadron at Bircham Newton—and the machine was never able to demonstrate its power against Germany. The V/1500's maximum load consisted of thirty 250 lb. bombs, and its armament comprised Lewis guns in the nose, amidships and in the tail.

The termination of the 1914–18 War on 11th November, 1918, found Great Britain the possessor of the most powerful air force in the world. The development of the aeroplane under steady pressure and its employment over the battlefields and against an enemy's homeland had wrought the greatest possible change in attitude towards air power until, finally, it was established as an indispensable part of a country's armed strength.

From the start of the conflict, the R.N.A.S. had led the way as the strong protagonist of the bomber as a strategic weapon of worth until, eventually, the R.F.C. arrived at the same indisputable conclusion. Ultimately, on 1st April, 1918, both Services combined to form the Royal Air Force to prosecute the war to the greatest advantage. Inspired Admiralty sponsorship of the bomber and the torpedo-carrier had contributed a great deal towards their development.

Throughout the war, the biplane had held first place in bomber design with little practical incursion being made into its supremacy by the mono-

D.H.10A Amiens Mk. IIIA F1869. (*de Havilland Photo.*)

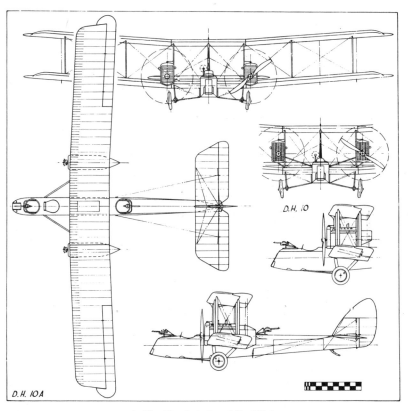

de Havilland Amiens Mk. IIIA

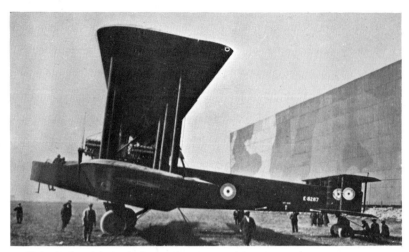

E8287, the first of the batch of twenty H.P. V/1500s built by Beardmore. (*Beardmore Photo.*)

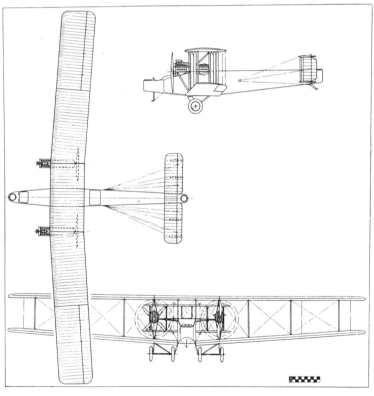

Handley Page V/1500

plane, triplane or quadruplane. During the four and a quarter years of production of warplanes for the British Air Services the materials employed for aircraft construction changed but little. Designers retained the all-wood airframe almost exclusively with an occasional blending of steel tubing in the fore-part of the fuselage. Doped fabric served as a covering together with an increasing use of plywood around the fuselage nose areas.

As great a change as any came in the realm of power plants. From an almost total reliance on French engines at the start of the war, the pendulum had swung strongly towards the use of excellent British-designed units, particularly those of Rolls-Royce and Sunbeam. Although the rotary held its own as a light-weight fighter engine for the course of the conflict, it was discarded relatively early by the designers responsible for the bombers and torpedo-carriers being developed. In their new projects they turned to the water-cooled, inline units to provide the power needed to propel the ever-larger aircraft being evolved in the pursuit of both range and load-carrying ability.

From a very small force which went to France and Belgium in August, 1914, the Royal Flying Corps with 105 officers, 755 other ranks and 63 aeroplanes, and the R.N.A.S., consisting of 20 officers, 80 other ranks and 10 aeroplanes, had, in the Royal Air Force by the Armistice, reached the enormous total of 27,333 officers, 263,837 other ranks and, on 30th November. 1918, 22,647 aeroplanes and seaplanes together with 103 airships.

Relentlessly, as reliance on air power grew inexorably over the span of the First World War, the influence of the bomber increased until—as the final curtain fell in Europe—the bomber and its ability to destroy stood paramount as the very soul of air power, a force which had emerged from among the traditional weapons also used to fight the war as a new and terrifying one which—once born—was not to die but to increase implacably, until finally it took its place as the primary weapon in the planning of wars to come.

The Bristol Braemar Mk. II C4297. (*Bristol Photo.*)

CHAPTER THREE

PROJECTS, PROTOTYPES AND PARSIMONY

Spawned under the impetus of a titanic life-or-death struggle, the mighty power of the Royal Air Force in men and machines was short-lived after the Armistice of November, 1918. Demobilization of personnel took place at a rapid rate, and a corresponding reduction was made in the number of aircraft on charge.

Despite the fact that, technically, both the Army and the Navy had been deprived of their air wings with the founding of the Royal Air Force, neither felt inclined to accept and recognize the new Service as anything more than a wartime expedient. The conflict was over, the Allies were victorious, so why the need for the continued existence of a new-born force which, by the advent of peace, was but seven months old? The heads of the older Services were well aware of the tussle before them to gain sufficient financial allocation from the Treasury for their own needs without having to combat the third hand presented on behalf of another—and far junior—Service. Both the Army and the Navy, in their indisputable seniority, could muster strong arguments and bring heavy influence to bear in the fight for funds. The Royal Air Force was extremely fortunate in having Air Marshal Sir Hugh Montague Trenchard as its Chief of Air Staff with a personality and strength of character ideally suited to ensure that not only would the R.A.F. remain in being but that it would also receive the necessary nourishment to enable it to maintain a steady rate of growth.

The aeroplane's place in warfare had been established swiftly and undeniably by the major conflict in Europe, and there was absolutely no possibility that, as a weapon, it would lose the position which it had ultimately won in the arsenals of many nations. Aircraft had served in many rôles during the war, but, despite the fair number of bombing raids carried out and the various machines developed for the purpose, bombing itself had still not superseded other methods of attack as the main means of defeating an enemy nor, during the period in which it had been practised in the later stages of the conflict, had it demonstrated convincingly that this might be a possibility. The pilots and observers engaged in bombing attacks in the course of the hostilities had displayed the greatest tenacity and gallantry in their duties, but, in spite of this, the technique of level bombing had still not managed—judged by ultimate results—to establish priority and superiority in its own right. The same situation obtained regarding torpedo attack from the air.

In both fields, the techniques and types of aircraft applicable to each had been developed substantially but not to the point where universal acceptance and recognition of the value of bombing in warfare had been established fully. Attacks on German airfields from 1915 until 1917 had inflicted only minor damage and produced little effect in the way of restricting enemy air activity. The primary reason for this failure was that the attacks were spread thinly over many objectives instead of being concentrated on a small number of the most important aerodromes. When this was eventually realized and a few airfields were subjected to attacks by a heavy, well-organized force of bombers supported by fighters an immediate improvement resulted in the damage achieved.

By the time that the Royal Air Force had come into being and the Independent Force was becoming effective operationally the 1914–18 War was in its closing stages. Much was expected of the Independent Force's attacks on Germany, but, despite the successes which its aircraft did achieve, the formations' raids had only a minor effect on German war potential. Had the war lasted for another six months, the new bombers, able to fly much farther with far heavier loads, would have been in action and established the real power of bombing to the detriment of the Germans in the eyes of all. The loads which British bombers were carrying by the Armistice consisted of high-explosive, cast-iron-cased bombs of various weights from about 20 lb. up to 550 lb., approximately 30% of which was explosive. Larger bombs were evolved late in the war, to a maximum weight of 3,360 lb. As well as dropping normal high-explosive bombs which detonated on contact, the magnesium-case incendiary bomb was developed and was used successfully by British bombers during the 1914–18 period. These ranged in weight from some 2·5 to 20 lb. The steady increase in operational height of bombers until the end of the war, which took place in an endeavour to avoid enemy ground defences and fighters, inevitably brought in its train the demand for a bomb-sight capable of operating accurately at high altitudes. With heights of nearly 20,000 ft.

101

being used for approach to the target, the error introduced by drift assumed major proportions. New sights of open type, generally mounted on the fuselage flank, were evolved to ensure the greatest accuracy possible by incorporating longitudinal and lateral levels and a drift-wire, together with facilities for setting the airspeed, operating height and the trail-angles of the bombs. As well as the High Altitude Drift Sights, alternative High and Low Altitude Drift Sights, the Course Setting Sight and Negative Lens Sight were employed.

The need, therefore, to prosecute the war by every possible means had given impetus to the evolution of bombing and torpedo-dropping techniques with the final result that, by the war's end, a specialized aeroplane in several forms existed for the tasks, and various missiles had been developed as weapons together with the related release equipment. Then, suddenly, at the peak of all of this effort the Armistice abolished overnight the need for its employment. The small group of firms which, in mid-1914, had constituted Britain's aircraft industry had expanded enormously during the war to meet the urgent demands made for airframes, engines and associated equipment. With the Armistice came the severance of these firms' arteries—the orders which had kept them alive since August, 1914. For the duration of the war, civil aviation had been non-existent in the United Kingdom, and there was nothing to turn to immediately to take the place of the cancelled orders for many thousands of aeroplanes and their power plants. The lean years were indeed upon the manufacturers, and not a few were forced to go out of business directly. A handful of firms endeavoured to stay alive by producing prototypes of new civil aircraft and by converting surplus wartime machines in anticipation of a post-war boom once restrictions on commercial flying were lifted. In the majority of cases their hopes were dashed swiftly, and, inevitably, still more companies closed their doors. In some cases the larger firms were able to remain in being by engaging in manufacturing activities of a nature far removed from aviation.

It was these few companies which were thus in a position to accept the thin trickle of orders for reconditioning existing aircraft when they eventually came and were also able to submit tenders for construction of prototypes to the requirements which the Air Ministry finally issued. That the Royal Air Force contemplated replacing its obsolescent aircraft with newer types became obvious when the Service continued to occupy its place alongside the Army and the Navy and survived the attempts made by the two senior Services to annihilate it. The fact that the R.A.F. remained in existence as a separate entity was owing largely to the astuteness and courage of Trenchard and his advocacy in 1920 of the use of the R.A.F. in keeping order in the mandated territories of the Middle East, thereby bringing about a reduction in the costly Army forces and expeditions hitherto employed. Greatly in its favour, also, were the aeroplane's speed of operation—enabling it to reach trouble spots far more swiftly—and its accompanying element of surprise. Events contrived, therefore, to give the bomber a new lease of life at a time when funds for financing the R.A.F. were at a very low level indeed. The basis of the air control which came into being was the employment of the bomber to quell any trouble-makers who disregarded a preliminary demand that they should surrender peacefully to the law. In the event, the system worked extremely effectively over a period of many years.

During the immediate post-war era the R.A.F. was compelled to keep its few bomber squadrons operational with D.H.9As, O/400s, D.H.10s and Vimys.

In the course of the closing months of the 1914–18 War a number of new advanced bomber aircraft were under construction as prototypes and were completed soon after the Armistice. In the West Country during October, 1917, Capt. F. S. Barnwell at Bristol spent some time on a scheme for a large triplane bomber with folding wings and a crew of six. The machine was designated B.1 and was prepared to possess a minimum range of 1,000 miles to enable it to bomb Berlin. Its capacity was to be such that it would carry internally six bombs of 250 lb. each.

Technically, the design was of particular interest, as it envisaged the embodiment of a concept which had been considered a number of times previously by other designers, namely the use of a power plant situated in the main fuselage and coupled to wing-mounted propellers. In this case four engines were scheduled for installation in a central engine-room from which gears and shafts would drive a single tractor four-blade propeller on each side of the engine bay. Preoccupation with his fighter design work made it impossible for Barnwell to devote further time to the B.1, so the layout was transferred to W. T. Reid for development. The practicability of the original centralized power-plant scheme was never put to the test by Bristol, as, once on Reid's drawing-board, considerable revision and simplification took place. The triplane wings were retained, the central planes acting as bearers of a pair of tandem engines on each side. The design was submitted soon to the Air Board, resulting in an order for three prototypes being placed on 26th February, 1918.

Once the project was accepted, construction of C4296—the first Type 24 Braemar Mk.I—went ahead rapidly so that a successful initial flight was made by F. P. Raynham on 13th August, 1918. The shortage of 360 h.p. Rolls-Royce Eagle engines for which the four-seat Braemar was designed, meant that substitutes had to be found to fly the machine. Four 230 h.p. Siddeley Pumas were selected, but the total output was considerably lower than that with which the Mk. I was intended to show its paces. Nevertheless, the big 81 ft. 8 in. span triplane performed very creditably in its official trials at Martlesham during September, 1918.

Sweepback was incorporated in the three-bay wings outboard of the centre-section, the cellules being mounted on a conventional fuselage with slab sides. The main undercarriage consisted of four wheels installed beneath the lower wings' centre-section in tandem pairs. Horn-balanced ailerons were incorporated in the centre and upper planes, and the tail unit used biplane horizontal surfaces and triple fins and rudders.

The second Braemar to be built, the Type 25 Mk. II C4297, was completed

C4296, the Bristol Type 24 Braemar Mk. I. (*Bristol Photo.*)

early in the following year, making its maiden flight on 18th February, 1919, with Capt. C. F. Uwins at the controls. The Mk. II, fitted with four Liberty 12 engines giving 400 h.p. each, was able to reach a top speed of 125 m.p.h., nearly 20 m.p.h. faster than the Braemar Mk. I. Consideration was given to converting the Mk. II to carry a torpedo beneath its fuselage, but towards the end of 1921 the machine was written off following an accident at Martlesham prior to taking-off.

The third Braemar prototype was completed in the spring of 1920, not as a bomber but as the Pullman civil transport with a fuselage accommodating fourteen passengers. In its bomber form the Braemar was scheduled to carry six 230 lb. bombs and to be armed with five Lewis guns.

When the Armistice came in November, 1918, the Aircraft Manufacturing Company at Hendon was part of the way through the construction of the

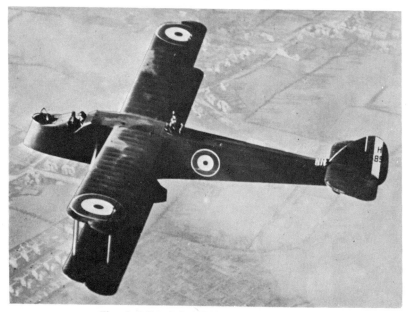

The sole D.H.11 Oxford H5891. (*de Havilland Photo.*)

D.H.11 Oxford prototype H5891, a three-seat, long-distance day bomber designed by Geoffrey de Havilland in 1918 around a pair of 320 h.p. A.B.C. Dragonfly engines. The arrival of peace inevitably brought a slowing-up in completion of H5891 so that its first flight did not take place until January, 1920.

The Oxford was a significant step forward in bomber design, being notably cleaner aerodynamically than its contemporaries. Centre-section struts were eliminated in the three-bay biplane wing cellules by deepening the shapely fuselage so that it filled the gap between upper and lower planes; this feature

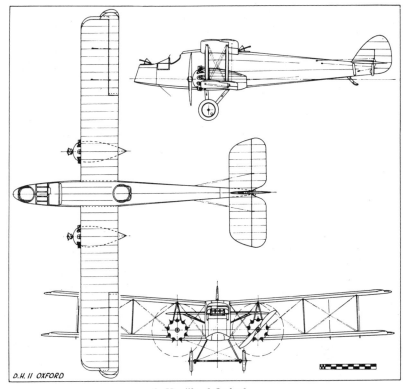

de Havilland Oxford

automatically made it possible to give the mid-upper gunner adjacent to the trailing edge a 360° field of fire in the upper hemisphere and enabled him to reach both the pilot's and front gunner's cockpits via a catwalk between all three positions. Another unusual feature in a twin-engine layout was the use of a single main undercarriage unit with transverse axle instead of the divided twin pairs of wheels normally placed one under each engine. The pilot, seated to starboard in a broad cockpit occupying the full width of the fuselage, was endowed with an excellent view. The two gunners' cockpits were equipped with a Scarff-mounted Lewis gun each and the bomb load—of some 1,000 lb. total weight—was borne inside the fuselage.

105

The Oxford was yet another in the sizeable list of British aeroplanes which were designed with high hopes around the air-cooled nine-cylinder radial Dragonfly, an engine conceived during 1917 by Granville Bradshaw and of which 11,050 were ordered in 1918. In spite of all good intentions behind the programme for the engine, its primary feature of high power for light weight was not achieved, and its several other shortcomings also had widespread repercussions among the many new aircraft for which it was scheduled as the power plant. Nevertheless, the Oxford Mk. I flew with its Dragonflies, mounted in neat nacelles fitted to the lower planes of the unstaggered 60 ft. 2 in. span wings.

As an insurance against the recalcitrance of the Dragonfly units, an unbuilt project—designated Oxford Mk. II—was drawn up around a pair of 290 h.p. Siddeley Puma high-compression engines. H5891 remained the solitary example constructed, as H5892 and H5893—the two other prototypes—were not proceeded with.

Still another projected derivative of the D.H.11 was the D.H.12, which, had it been built, would also have used twin Dragonflies but would have had the mid-upper gunner in what was considered to be an even more effective gun position between the main spars of the upper wings.

Following some experience with Horatio Barber's Aeronautical Syndicate Ltd. at Hendon prior to the start of the 1914–18 War, a youthful J. D. North had in a short period designed several successful biplanes for the Grahame-White concern at the same aerodrome from 1912 until 1914. A period of two years, from 1915 until 1917, was spent as superintendent of the aircraft works of the Austin Motor Company before North joined the Boulton and Paul aircraft department as their chief engineer. The firm had entered the aircraft industry in 1915 with the successful production of a batch of F.E.2bs, followed by larger orders for F.E.2ds, Sopwith Camels and, eventually, Sopwith Snipes. In the course of 1917 the decision was made to establish an office for the preparation of original designs. Under John North the P.3 Bobolink C8655 and P.6 X25—both prototypes only—were completed in 1918.

The company then proceeded to initiate work on its first twin-engine design, a fast reconnaissance day bomber designated the P.7 Bourges, of which three examples were ordered by the Air Ministry. Basically three-seat, three-bay, unstaggered biplanes, each differed in detail. F2903, the first prototype, was scheduled to receive a pair of the 320 h.p. Dragonfly engines in which so much hope resided. Delays with the radial Dragonfly found F2903, the P.7 Bourges Mk. IA, complete but for its engines. Rotaries, in the form of two cowled 230 h.p. Bentley B.R.2s, were therefore installed at mid-gap in the equal-span wings, the four ailerons of which were of plain type. The use of alternative engines, to enable the machine to fly in 1918, brought a revised designation of Bourges Mk. IIA for F2903, the suffix A denoting the conventional upper centre-section supported across the fuselage by struts. Eventually, F2903 received its Dragonflies, installed complete with large-diameter, bluff spinners; the four cable-connected ailerons were altered to include horn-balances, thereby increasing the span from 54 ft. to 57 ft. 4 in. Reverting to its

F2904, the second prototype Boulton and Paul P.7a Bourges Mk. IB. (*Boulton Paul Photo.*)

F2905, the third prototype Boulton and Paul P.7b Bourges Mk. II. (*Boulton Paul Photo.*)

originally intended Mk. IA designation, F2903 was not satisfactory with its spinners, which were removed, nor with its cowlings, which had to be revised.

F2904 the second prototype—the P.7a Mk. IB—introduced several significant modifications, the most important being the incorporation of gulled upper wings inboard of the engines—sloping down to connect direct with the top longerons, the tailplane mounted at a considerable dihedral angle to match that of the gull section of the upper wings, the installation of the Dragonflies direct on the lower wings, the increase in rudder area and the reduction in the size of the fin. The lowering of the engines dictated an increase in height of the undercarriage; the object of adopting the gull portion of the top wings was to improve the field of fire for the dorsal Lewis gunner. The front Lewis gun was mounted in the extreme nose and the bomb load was carried internally.

The third Bourges prototype, the P.7b F2905, reverted to the original straight, strut-supported, upper wings' centre-section and received greatly increased power with its pair of water-cooled 450 h.p. Napier Lions using frontal radiators, four-blade propellers and mounted on the lower wings. Its first take-off was made in December, 1920, tests resulting in a very creditable top speed of 130 m.p.h. at 10,000 ft.

Another version of the Bourges, the Mk. III with two 290 h.p. Siddeley Puma engines, remained a project only, but F2903, F2904 and F2905 gained a great deal of publicity through their speed and phenomenal degree of manoeuvrability. Boulton and Paul retained the services of Capt. F. T. Courtney as test pilot, and it was in his capable and skilled hands that the

F3493, the Avro 533 Manchester Mk. I.

remarkable reputation of the Bourges in aerobatics was established. These outstanding qualities were demonstrated for the delight of the public by F2905 at the 1923 R.A.F. Pageant at Hendon when, in a mock dogfight with a pair of Nieuport Nighthawk single-seat fighters, the comparatively large Bourges showed the assembled thousands that it could loop, roll and spin with speed and ease. John North's memorable Bourges design remains noteworthy as among the first of the twin-engine aircraft with which aerobatics could be safely performed.

The disappointing behaviour of the A.B.C. Dragonfly affected A. V. Roe as two 320 h.p. Dragonfly I engines had been selected as the units around which the Avro 533 Manchester fast day bomber was designed in 1918. Basically, the three-seat Manchester—which was built at the Hamble, Hants., factory—was a revision of the 523 Pike and the 529 biplanes. In general aspect, the new machine was cleaner aerodynamically than its lineal predecessors and was slightly smaller both in span and in length.

The Manchester was to suffer initially in precisely the same way as the other prototypes scheduled to use the Dragonfly; in its own case a pair of water-cooled 300 h.p. high-compression Siddeley Pumas in deep nacelles were chosen as substitutes. These enabled F3492, the 533A Manchester Mk. II, to take to the air early in December, 1918, following the completion of its airframe a few weeks before in October.

A year later, in December, 1919, the Dragonfly engines arrived at Hamble and were installed in F3493, the machine being allotted its original designation of 533 Manchester Mk. I. Revised tail surfaces accompanied the fitting of the Mk. I's Dragonfly power plants. F3494, the Manchester Mk. III, was completed as far as the airframe but was not fitted with its intended pair of 400 h.p. Liberty 12 engines. The Manchester's bomb load was to be 880 lb.; defensive armament comprised two Lewis guns—one in the nose and the other amidships. The Manchester was generally comparable with the Bourges, but its

108

greater size and weight gave it a relatively lower general performance than the Boulton and Paul product. Even so, the Avro machine was still very manoeuvrable and capable of aerobatics.

The feature of naming after cities or towns various of the bombers designed late in the 1914–18 War to use a pair of Dragonflies, applied to an unusual triplane conceived by H. P. Folland in 1918 for the Nieuport and General Aircraft Company. Called the London, the machine's rôle was that of night bomber, and H1740 was finished and marked accordingly. Originality, combined with practicability, was to be expected in full measure in any design originating with Henry Folland. Six Londons were ordered, but only two—H1740 and H1741—were constructed; the remaining four—H1742–H1745—were cancelled during November, 1918, before being built.

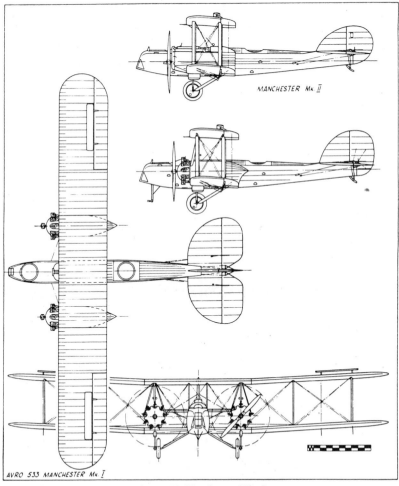

Avro 533 Manchester Mk. I

H1740, which made its initial flight at Acton on 13th April, 1920, and H1741, flown for the first time in July, 1920, were remarkable examples of structural design. The London was of wood throughout, its framework being joined together by simple means. The extraordinary covering medium of $\frac{1}{4}$ in. thick match-board, with tongue and groove fitting, was resorted to for enclosing the starkly utilitarian square-cut fuselage. The three sets of two-bay wings were equal in span, unstaggered and equipped with six horn-balanced ailerons. The movable portions of the tail unit were exceedingly angular, about the only streamlined aspect of the London Mk. I being the elegant cowlings and tapered nacelles attached to the Dragonflies mounted at mid-gap in the inner bays between the centre and lowest mainplanes. Following H1740's early flights, the ailerons on the centre and upper wings were discarded, as those on the bottom wings were found to be sufficient to ensure adequate lateral control. Divided single-wheel undercarriage units were mounted beneath the wings and underneath the engines. Insurance against possible non-availability of the Dragonfly engines was made with an alternative layout for a Mk. II version to use a pair of 290 h.p. Pumas. The London was defended by a pair of Lewis guns on a Scarff ring in the nose cockpit; its bomb load was designed to be nine 250 lb. bombs or an equal amount.

Representative also of the temporary incursion at the end of the war into the realm of the triplane as a formula for a three-seat bomber was the Sopwith Cobham. Sopwith had been the main exponent of the triplane in Britain, with five other triple-wing designs to their credit prior to the appearance of the 54 ft. span Cobham. Three were ordered and built—H671, the Mk. II with two 290 h.p. Siddeley Pumas, and H672 and H673, Mk. Is both fitted with a pair of 360 h.p. A.B.C. Dragonfly IA engines.

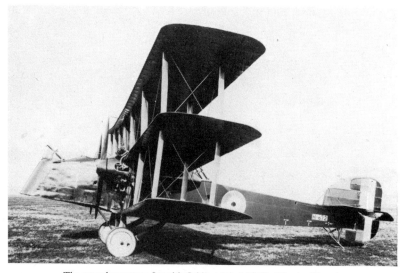

The second prototype Sopwith Cobham Mk. I H672. (*Hawker Photo.*)

J6858, the Siddeley Sinaia Mk. I. (*Armstrong Whitworth Photo.*)

Besides being the largest of the Sopwith triplanes, the Cobham was also of note as the only machine with two engines to be built by the company. The power plant around which the Cobham was designed was the ill-starred Dragonfly and, in common with several other designs scheduled to receive it, development delays were circumvented by fitting the Cobham H671 with Pumas and changing its designation from Mk. I to Mk. II. The cowlings of the water-cooled Puma installation occupied completely the gap between the centre and lowest wings, which were unstaggered, while the uppermost planes were set a short distance to the rear. Cable-connected ailerons were incorporated in all six wings, and the tail surfaces retained the typical Sopwith outline. The Cobham's fuselage was set between the centre and lowest wings. The pilot's cockpit was just ahead of the leading edge; the gunners used a Lewis gun in the nose cockpit and another in a position immediately aft of the wings.

When H672 was completed with its Dragonflies as the Mk. I some modifications to the airframe were apparent. The rudder was considerably larger in area, and its extension—complete with a second horn-balance—below the fuselage necessitated a longer tailskid to ensure ground clearance. The nacelles for the Dragonflies fitted flush beneath the centre wings and the top mainplanes were rigged with a little forwards stagger.

The Siddeley 103 Sinaia, designed by Maj. F. M. Green and built by the Siddeley-Deasy Motor Car Co. of Coventry, was yet another of the prototype bombers conceived early in 1918 but which lapsed into obscurity after making its initial flight on 25th June, 1921, in the hands of Capt. F. T. Courtney. Basically a conventional twin-engine biplane of 86 ft. 10 in. span, the Sinaia Mk. I J6858—the sole example constructed out of four prototypes ordered— was striking in the way in which its gunners were disposed on each side of the fuselage in long extensions to the rear of the engine nacelles. A third gunner occupied the nose portion, with the pilot's cockpit just behind. The Sinaia's

111

Testing the six Napier Lions of the Tarrant Tabor.

wings folded and carried cable-connected, horn-balanced ailerons on all four surfaces. The machine was evolved around a pair of water-cooled twelve-cylinder vee 486 h.p. Siddeley Tiger engines which were installed on the lower wings and drove four-blade propellers. Unbuilt projected versions of the Sinaia were the Mk. II with two 600 h.p. Rolls-Royce Condors and the Mk. III, which would have had a pair of 500 h.p. Beardmore Atlantic engines.

Designed during the closing months of the 1914–18 War with the object of operating on bombing raids against Berlin from England, the gargantuan Tabor F1765 was built by W. G. Tarrant Ltd. of Byfleet, and exceeded in immensity even the enormous Handley Page V/1500, evolved for the same purpose.

Apart from its great size, the overall appearance of the Tabor was of exceptional interest. Largest of the group of bomber triplanes which had suddenly sprung into popularity as prototypes, the Tabor was the possessor of a beautifully conceived circular-section monocoque fuselage which was suspended between the centre and lowest mainplanes. The top and bottom wings were 98 ft. 5 in. in span, but those in the centre measured 131 ft. 3 in. from tip to tip and carried the machine's pair of ailerons. The elegant fuselage terminated in a biplane tail unit which incorporated twin fins and rudders.

The Tabor was scheduled to be fitted with four water-cooled Siddeley Tiger engines, from which it was hoped to obtain 600 h.p. each, but un-expected development problems with the new power plants dictated the use of an alternative type. The engine selected was the Napier Lion, six of which—at 450 h.p. each—would provide the necessary thrust to fly the colossus. The Lions were installed as two tractors at mid-gap between the upper and centre wings and as two pairs in tandem mid-way between the centre and lowermost wings. Two-blade 12 ft. 6 in. propellers were used on the four tractor engines, while the pair of pushers turned four-blade 10 ft. 7·25 in. propellers. The undercarriage units, each with three wheels abreast, were installed under the bottom wings and in line with the power plants. The R.A.E. had co-operated with W. G. Tarrant in the course of construction of the Tabor, and the com-ponents were eventually brought together at Farnborough in the balloon shed there, in which they were assembled, so that the Tabor was completed in the spring of 1919. When finished the length was 73 ft. 2 in., and the height reached 37 ft. 2 in. By May, 1919, all was ready, and the 26th of the month was chosen for the maiden flight. The two pilots aboard were Capts. F. G. Dunn and P. T. Rawlings, who, after the usual taxying tests had been carried out satisfactorily, prepared to take-off. The opening up of the upper pair of Lions during the initial run was followed by a sudden rise of the tail past the horizontal so that the Tabor tipped up on to its nose, which was crushed as far back as the wings. Both pilots, seated well forward in the pointed nose, died after the crash. As a design feature for Service aircraft the triplane—despite its good weight-lifting qualities—was thereupon abandoned so that the biplane was still to hold its own for the next fifteen years or so before it was forced to give way to the monoplane.

At the tail end of Airco's exemplary wartime performance in construction of production and prototype aircraft to Geoffrey de Havilland's designs, there came two final biplane bombers. The two-seat D.H.14 Okapi day bomber, of which three prototypes were ordered, was in the process of being designed before the Armistice was declared, but construction was carried on at a slower rate after the end of 1918. The intention was that the new machine should take over from its predecessors from Airco, the D.H.4, D.H.9 and D.H.9A, which it resembled, but on a larger scale.

The Okapi was given two-bay wings of equal span, set with moderate positive stagger and was designed around the Condor I, a powerful new water-cooled, twelve-cylinder vee engine from Rolls-Royce which developed 525 h.p. The nose incorporated a frontal radiator, and the engine drove a four-blade propeller; the necessary ground clearance for the blades made a relatively lengthy undercarriage mandatory. The crew were seated in adjacent tandem cockpits mid-way along the fuselage. Both were armed—the pilot with a Constantinesco-synchronized Vickers set in the coaming and the observer with a pair of Scarff-mounted Lewis guns. Eight 112 lb. bombs

The incomplete D.H.14 bomber modified as the D.H.14A. (*de Havilland Photo*.)

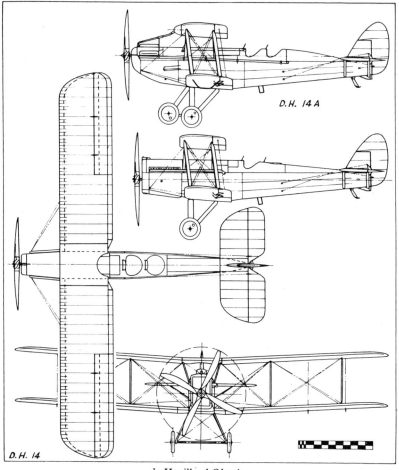

de Havilland Okapi

formed the Okapi's load, being carried internally by storing six inside the lower wings and two in the fuselage beneath the pilot.

Reduction, immediately post-war, of interest in developing new bombers curtailed the rate of completion of Okapis J1938 and J1939, but J1940 was finished late in 1919 in a modified form as the D.H.14A high-speed, long-range mail-carrier G-EAPY powered by a 450 h.p. Napier Lion. A second pair of wheels was added to the undercarriage ahead of the original main wheels prior to the London-to-Cape Town flight which was attempted by F. S. Cotton and W. A. Townsend, who took-off on 2nd February, 1920. A forced landing in Italy at Messina resulted in the D.H.14A turning over and, during the subsequent repairs, the extra wheels were discarded.

The two military Okapi prototypes were completed later at Stag Lane by the newly-formed de Havilland Aircraft Company, J1938 in September, 1920, followed by J1939. Official trials were conducted with both machines at Martlesham, whither they went in the spring of 1921, but no further development ensued.

Of the pair of D.H.15 Gazelles—J1936 and J1937—which were ordered, only J1937 was constructed. The airframe was that of a conventional D.H.9A, but was given extra power by installing the water-cooled, twelve-cylinder vee 500 h.p. B.H.P. Atlantic developed by the Galloway Engineering Company through combining two 230 h.p. B.H.P. engines on a single crankcase. The Liberty-style frontal radiator was still used, and the Gazelle was equipped with the standard D.H.9A armament of a Vickers gun for the pilot and a Lewis on a Scarff ring for his observer. The main purpose behind the conversion to D.H.15 form was the testing in flight during 1919–20 of the new engine.

The commencement of the twenty years period of peace from the end of 1918 was marked by a great deal of activity in the field of record-making flights, for the execution of which bomber aircraft came into their own by virtue of their already excellent range, which could be increased relatively easily by the installation of additional fuel tanks.

At a time of drastic contraction of the Royal Air Force, the name of the Vimy, in particular, was to be brought dramatically to the notice of all through three magnificent flights at a period when long-distance attempts were in their infancy. The first great feat was that of Capt. John Alcock and Lt. Arthur Whitten Brown, who flew their Vimy across the Atlantic 1,890 miles from St. John's, in Newfoundland, to Clifden, in Co. Galway, Ireland, in 16 hr. 12 min. on 14th to 15th June, 1919. Five months later another Vimy was in the news when, at 8 a.m. on 12th November, 1919, G-EAOU—piloted by Capt. Ross Smith and navigated by his brother Lt. Keith M. Smith, who were accompanied by Sgt. J. M. Bennett and Sgt. W. H. Shiers as mechanics—left Hounslow for Australia, arriving at Port Darwin just under a month later at 4.10 p.m. on 10th December after flying 11,130 miles.

Wg. Cdr. Pierre van Ryneveld and Flt. Lt. C. J. Quintin Brand, together

J1937, the D.H.15 Gazelle. (*de Havilland Photo*.)

Bristol F.2B supplied after the 1914–18 War to the Belgian Aviation Militaire for army co-operation duties. (*Musée Royal de l'Armée et d'Histoire Militaire Photo.*)

with a pair of mechanics, formed the crew of a third Vimy—G-UABA the *Silver Queen*—which left Brooklands on 4th February, 1920, *en route* for Cape Town. On 11th February the machine was wrecked in a forced landing at Korosko. A replacement Vimy, christened *Silver Queen II*, was obtained, and the aircraft left Heliopolis on 22nd February, only to crash a week afterwards while leaving Bulawayo for Pretoria. Undaunted, van Ryneveld and Quintin Brand obtained a D.H.9—H5648—to enable them to continue to Cape Town, which they reached eventually on 20th March.

The post-war recession in the aircraft industry ultimately had its effect on the Sopwith Aviation Company, resulting in the closure of the firm during 1920. Well-nigh immediately, however, the company was in business again in November, 1920, as the H. G. Hawker Engineering Co. Ltd., and by the following month had drawn up its first design—the Hawker Humpback three-seat, fleet spotter reconnaissance and general-purpose biplane. A two-bay, equal-span machine with folding, unstaggered wings, the Humpback was based on a liquid-cooled engine and was designed with a broad-track under-carriage, the main wheels of which were mounted beneath the inner interplane struts. A pair of smaller nosewheels installed below the nose were an unusual feature of the layout, which progressed no further than the project stage.

One of four Fairey IIIDs supplied to the Netherlands. (*Fairey Photo.*)

116

Under F. Duncanson as the head of its design section, Fairey had produced in 1917 the Type III N10 seaplane and followed it with the IIIA, IIIB and IIIC until the end of the 1914–18 War. During 1920 a new derivative—the three-seat IIID prototype N9450—appeared, making its first flight in August of that year as a seaplane from Hamble in the hands of Lt.-Col. Vincent Nicholl. The IIID was fitted with the 375 h.p. Eagle VIII engine and equipped as a general-purpose type for the Fleet Air Arm, its duties to include

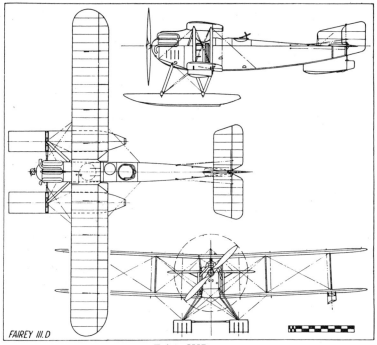

FAIREY III.D

Fairey IIID

bombing with the missiles carried externally. The IIID carried on the standard wood and fabric type of construction and was armed with a single forwards-firing Vickers gun accompanied by a Lewis in the rear cockpit. Tests were successful, the type was accepted and production was carried out to Specification 38/22. Over a period of some five years several batches of IIIDs were built, in some of which the Eagle was supplanted by the 450 h.p. Lion IIB, V or VA. Overall performance was enhanced by the incorporation of the Fairey variable-camber gear in the trailing edges. The total of IIIDs constructed reached about two hundred and seven eventually, including a number of landplanes—equipped with oleo undercarriages—with which R.A.F. crews conducted several long-distance flights during the mid-1920s.

In common with most of the other firms making up the British aircraft manufacturing industry, the Blackburn Aeroplane and Motor Company soon found that its hopes of a bright post-war future were far from reaching

Blackburn Swift incorporating sweptback wings. (*Blackburn Photo.*)

fulfilment. The slump in aircraft orders was weathered fortuitously in the Olympia, Leeds, factory by production of various items, including car and motor-coach bodies. Robert Blackburn was determined, however, that the firm should continue in business as manufacturers of aircraft, and accordingly decided to press ahead with a new Private Venture prototype in conjunction with Napier as supplier of the engine. A predilection for tackling the problems involved in producing successful naval aircraft had already made itself manifest, so that it was hardly surprising that the new project was a torpedo-carrying biplane.

Named the Swift, the machine adhered to the single-seat formula set by the same firm's earlier Blackburd and was designed and constructed in the short period of five months, only just in time to be displayed at the Aero Show held

N9806, one of a batch of Blackburn Darts for the Fleet Air Arm. (*Blackburn Photo.*)

Blackburn Dart for Japan. (*Blackburn Photo.*)

in July, 1920, at Olympia, at which it had to appear without its controls and with a dummy radiator. The design was the work of Maj. F. A. Bumpus, and the engine selected as a basis for it was the reliable 450 h.p. Lion IB. The prototype Swift was later given the civil registration G-EAVN for

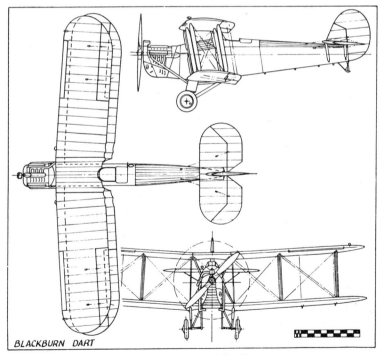

BLACKBURN DART

Blackburn Dart Mk. II

119

demonstration purposes before being bought by the Air Ministry six months afterwards in January, 1921, for testing at Martlesham as N139.

Although its fuselage lines were still fairly austere, the Swift was a far handsomer aeroplane than its predecessor, the Blackburd. The two-bay, folding, equal-span wings were without sweepback, and the pilot was located in line with the trailing edge at a fairly high level, with the coaming before him sloping downwards—for maximum visibility during deck-landing—towards the low-set Lion which was installed with pronounced upthrust. As a matter of course, the undercarriage was divided into two units to incorporate the 18 in. torpedo. Composite construction was used in the Swift with steel tubing forming the fuselage, the central portion of which was specially designed as one particularly strong unit embodying the upper centre-section, the lower wing roots and the undercarriage; the wings' structure was of normal wooden, two-spar type. Fabric constituted the Swift's covering medium. One tricky technical hurdle which the Swift's design team had taken in its stride was that of providing a system of folding for staggered wings. The fitting of the Lion in the nose was hardly among the tidiest of installations, a lengthy exhaust pipe from each side bank of cylinders stretching downwards at an angle to pass under the lower wings, accompanied by a third long exhaust—from the central bank of cylinders—which was led along the starboard side of the fuselage. About the neatest part of the entire engine arrangement lay in the clean mounting of the radiator and its shutters in the nose beneath the Lion. Various modifications made to the basic Swift design included the incorporation of sweepback in the main wing panels outboard of the centre-section, and a revised tail unit and engine installation.

Success attended the Blackburn initiative and, although not ordered for the Fleet Air Arm, about twenty-five Swifts were built for overseas customers, two of which were bought by the U.S. Navy for evaluation of the single-seat torpedo-carrier concept. Such an idea, however, did not appeal to the Americans, who continued to adhere for another twenty years to torpedo aircraft with two or three crew members. Elsewhere, including Great Britain, the Swift had made its mark, and the gamble of proceeding with it as a Private Venture had paid off in finally setting the Blackburn concern on its feet as specialist designers and constructors of naval aircraft for the next forty-five years.

In the course of 1920, while the Swift was being evolved, three prototypes of a companion single-seat torpedo-carrier—the Dart—were under construction by Blackburn under Maj. Bumpus's direction. Developed from the Swift, N140, N141 and N142 were completed during the year, retaining the divided undercarriage to enable the 18 in. 1,100 lb. Mk. IX torpedo to be slung between the wheels. Alternatively, the Dart could carry beneath its wings an equivalent load of bombs, the largest acceptable single missile being of 520 lb. The 450 h.p. Napier Lion IIB or Lion V was used to power the Dart, giving it a top speed at sea level of 110 m.p.h. Specification 9/21 for a torpedo landplane was cancelled later and superseded by Specification 32/22, to which the Dart was produced for the F.A.A. as the Mk. II. The Dart was eminently well suited for its purpose and was of particular use in providing the Fleet Air

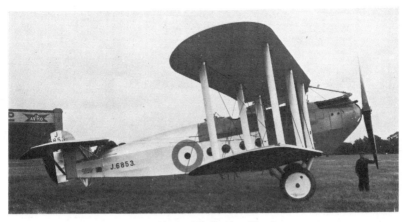

Avro Aldershot Mk. I. (*Avro Photo.*)

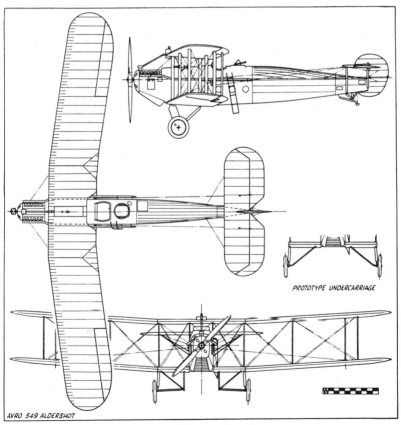

AVRO 549 ALDERSHOT

Avro Aldershot Mk. III

121

Arm with a reliable torpedo-carrier with which to gain plenty of basic experience in the art of launching. The first production Darts were delivered in 1923, the type subsequently remaining in service for the ensuing ten years.

At the beginning of the 1920s the incumbent Director of Research at the Air Ministry issued at an increasing rate details of various types of aircraft for which tenders were invited from the industry. In a number of instances these early requirements resulted only in projects, without prototypes being built. Among them were D. of R. Type 9 of 1921 for a three-seat, coastal defence torpedo-bomber for which de Havilland prepared a layout for the D.H.36, a large single-engine biplane of 86 ft. span. The machine was to have resembled the D.H.27 Derby with the central pylon support for the upper wings replaced by conventional struts. The divided unit style of undercarriage used on the Derby would have proved ideal for the housing of the torpedo.

Also to D. of R. Type 9, Bristol tendered the unbuilt three-seat Type 71 triplane, which was designed around the very powerful sixteen-cylinder, water-cooled 1,000 h.p. Napier Cub.

Specification 2/20 called for D. of R. Type 4B, a heavy, long-range, single-engine day bomber. The Bristol contribution consisted of a proposal only for the Type 55 biplane with a Condor engine.

Both Avro and de Havilland, however, constructed prototypes. The Avro entry for 2/20 was the 549 Aldershot Mk. I designed by Roy Chadwick, two examples—J6852 and J6853—being ordered on 2nd December, 1920. The 650 h.p. Condor III was selected to power the massive 68 ft. span biplane fitted with folding, three-bay wings which were unstaggered but swept back outboard of the centre-section. The Aldershot's deep fuselage embodied a lower deck cabin containing the bomb-aimer and radio operator. Just aft of the trailing edge a broad cockpit housed a pair of pilots side-by-side, while immediately to their rear a gunner was located with a single Scarff-mounted defensive Lewis gun.

Both prototypes were built at the Avro Hamble works, their initial testing taking place in the early part of 1922 in H. J. L. Hinkler's hands. Modifications found necessary after testing of J6852 included revision of the fin and rudder and an increase of about 6 ft. in the fuselage length. Later in 1922 J6852's Condor was replaced by a 1,000 h.p. Cub, a modification which brought in its train a new main undercarriage with four wheels. As the 549A Aldershot Mk. II, J6852, made its first flight with the Cub on 15th December, 1922, at Hamble, again with Hinkler at the controls.

Eventually, the Aldershot was ordered for a single squadron of the R.A.F. when a contract was placed in 1923 for fifteen Mk. IIIs powered by the 650 h.p. Condor III to equip No. 99 Squadron upon its resuscitation in April, 1924, after four years disbandment since April, 1920. From being the sole unit to use the Aldershot, No. 99 went on to be the squadron selected as the first unit over a period of years to introduce several different types of new bomber to the R.A.F. The Aldershot was able to accommodate internally a bomb load of 2,000 lb., but was replaced in 1926 after only two years with No. 99.

J6894, the D.H.27 Derby. (*de Havilland Photo.*)

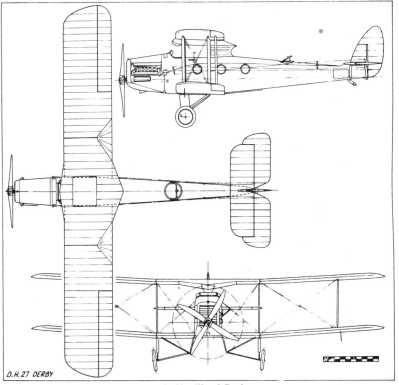

D.H.27 DERBY

de Havilland Derby

123

The first prototype Handley Page Hanley Mk. I N143. (*Handley Page Photo.*)

The first prototype J6852 was re-engined again in 1926 to become the Type 549C Aldershot Mk. IV with the six-cylinder 850 h.p. Beardmore Typhoon, making its first take-off on 10th January, 1927, at Hamble.

The Aldershot's unsuccessful rival to Specification 2/20 was the D.H.27 Derby, a slightly smaller machine of which two examples—J6894 and J6895—were built. The Derby's folding wings of 64 ft. 6 in. span were braced in two-bay cellules with the centre-section attached to the fuselage by a pylon incorporating the fuel tanks. A central cabin was provided for the navigator and bomb-aimer, the pilot being located in a high-set cockpit under the upper leading edge. The Derby was protected by a single Lewis gun manned from a Scarff ring position mid-way in the top of the rear fuselage. The divided undercarriage permitted the housing of a single large bomb beneath the fuse-lage as an alternative load. The engine used was the 650 h.p. Condor III in place of the lower-power 525 h.p. Condor IA, around which the Derby was at first schemed. The initial flight of J6894 was made in September, 1922, from Stag Lane Aerodrome at Edgware; subsequently, the unsuccessful de Havilland contenders to 2/20 were employed on experimental flying.

Specification 3/20 for a deck-landing torpedo-carrier brought forth tenders from Blackburn for an experimental version of the Dart and from Handley Page for the H.P.19 Type T Hanley. Three prototypes of the Hanley—the Mk. I N143, Mk. II N144 and Mk. III N145—were ordered, the first of which was completed in 1922, N143 making its initial flight from Cricklewood on 3rd March of the same year. A single-seat, two-bay biplane designed by George Volkert, the machine was notable as the first Handley Page aircraft evolved specifically to embody slots. In the case of the Hanley this feature was particularly desirable to confer the best possible low-speed characteristics for deck-landing at sea, attained by incorporating fixed slots in the entire span of both upper and lower leading edges; slotted ailerons were also embodied in the folding wings. The Hanley was powered by the 450 h.p. Napier Lion driving a two-blade propeller. No production was ordered for the type, as Specification 3/20 was cancelled by Specification 32/22, which supplanted also Specification 9/21.

During 1922 a new general-purpose prototype biplane from R. K. Pierson, the Vickers Type 71 Vixen Mk. I G-EBEC, made its appearance at Weybridge. The Vixen was a two-seater of rather squat aspect—engendered by a particularly deep fuselage—and fitted with a 450 h.p. Lion enclosed in a cowling of full depth which housed also the frontal radiator. The machine's single-bay wings were unequal in span and carried cable-connected ailerons on all four tips. A very generous cut-out in the upper centre-section aided the pilot's view; the observer's cockpit was surmounted by a Scarff ring-mounting.

In 1924 G-EBEC was modified in several respects to become the Type 87 Vixen Mk. II; further alterations to G-EBEC in 1928, including the replacement of the Lion by the 650 h.p. Condor IIIA, produced the Type 124 Vixen Mk. VI.

Steps were taken by the Air Ministry during 1921 to prepare for a replacement long-range, twin-engine night bomber, to take over from the Vimy, by issuing Specification 1/21, around which R. K. Pierson designed the Vickers Type 57 Virginia Mk. I prototype J6856.

Almost automatically for the period a biplane layout was selected, the span being 86 ft. The engines were two 450 h.p. Lions mounted on the lower wings as tractors in rectangular-section nacelles. The lengthy slab-sided fuselage was attached to the lower pair of the parallel-chord, equal-span, unstaggered mainplanes and terminated at the rear in a biplane tail. The

H.P. Hanley Mk. III N145 with modified undercarriage. (*Handley Page Photo.*)

G-EBEC, the Vickers Type 71 Vixen Mk. I. (*Vickers Photo.*)

Virginia carried cable-connected ailerons on all four surfaces; the machine's size made twin pairs of main wheels mandatory.

The all-silver J6856 was completed in 1922 and went for its Service Trials at the end of the year in December. The R.A.F. decided to adopt it with minor modifications, a decision which was to result in the Virginia serving eventually until 1937. The early production examples to Specification 28/23 followed the prototype in possessing straight leading edges to the wings and dihedral on the lower planes only. The first of the new heavy bombers joined the R.A.F. late in 1924, with No. 7 Squadron at Bircham Newton introducing them into service. The Virginia carried a crew of four and was armed with a single Lewis gun in the nose and, in the later Mk. IX and Mk. X versions, two similar weapons in the extreme tail end aft of the empennage.

Over the next few years revised versions were successively produced and included the Type 76 Mk. II; the Type 79 Mk. III; the Type 99 Mk. IV; the Type 112 Mk. VII with wooden airframe, 86 ft. span wings with dihedral on upper and lower surfaces, sweptback outer wing panels, a lengthened new style of nose and a pair of Lion Vs; the Type 128 Mk. IX, which received an airframe mainly of wood and was fitted with fixed fins, rudders of rhomboidal shape and a gun position in the tail; and the Type 139 Mk. X with the 570 h.p. Lion V. The Types 140 and 167 with the Lion XI were also designated Mk. X. The Mk. X introduced the all-metal airframe for the Virginia as well as Handley Page slots and a tailwheel; fixed fins, however, were deleted. In a number of instances the Virginia Mk. IXs and Mk. Xs were earlier marks brought up to date, the span of the Mk. X being increased to 87 ft. 8 in. and its bomb load to 3,000 lb. Final Virginia production was to Specification 5/31.

The prototype J6856 underwent tests with an unparalleled additional armament which took the form of a pair of experimental 'fighting tops'— nacelles mounted on the upper wings to house a Lewis gunner each. In its first version as the prototype Mk. I, J6856's nacelles were fitted flush with the wings' under surfaces mid-way in the bay outboard of the engines—to extend fore and aft with the gun rings at the nose end. In its later form as a Mk. VII

126

with the engines raised above the lower wings, the gunners' nacelles on J6856 were much shorter, being inset a short distance into the trailing edge to project to the rear. In this later position the upper pair of gunners were thus able to cover the rear far more effectively, leaving the nose gunner responsible for dealing with frontal attacks.

Until the advent of the Virginia in squadron service, the Vimy heavy bombers of the R.A.F. had—in the main—been finished overall in silver. 1923 saw the introduction of the new Nivo matt green finish for night bombers which was applied to the Virginias coming into the squadrons; some early examples, however, appeared in the obsolescent silver. At the same time, the night style red and blue roundel was adopted and the rudder stripes were discarded.

1923 witnessed the appearance from Fairey of a landplane development of the Pintail. Named the Fawn and designed to meet the needs of Specification 5/21 based on D. of R. Type 3, which called for a two-seat army reconnaissance aircraft but with a top speed of about 6 m.p.h. lower than that of the D.H.9A, the Mk. I prototype J6907 made its first flight in March, 1923. In

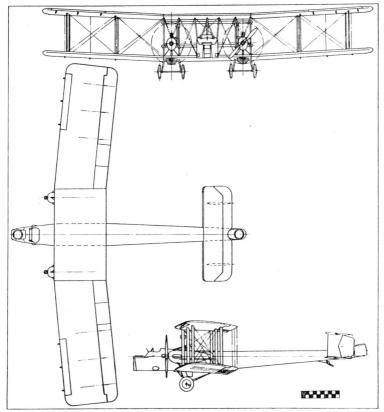

Vickers Virginia Mk. IX

127

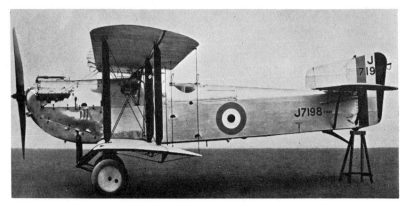

Fairey Fawn Mk. II. (*Fairey Photo.*)

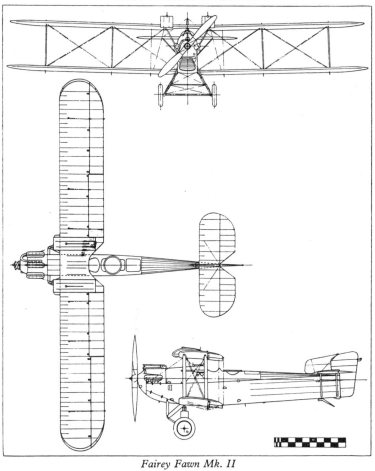

Fairey Fawn Mk. II

128

evolving the Fawn, F. Duncanson had retained the basic two-bay biplane layout of the Pintail, but had deleted the stagger embodied in the wings and had increased their span to 49 ft. 11 in. The Lion II, delivering 470 h.p., was installed in the Fawn's nose; the machine's airframe, Fairey F403, was constructed of wood and given a fabric covering.

In September, 1923, two further prototypes—F404 J6908 and F405 J6909 —made their début as Mk. IIs with longer fuselages; this version was adopted as the Service model and passed into production during 1923 to Specification 20/23, which was for a single-engine day bomber and reconnaissance landplane. After trials with a dual side-mounted installation a nose radiator became the standard type and large fuel tanks were installed on the top surfaces of the upper wings. Despite the heavy drag penalty engendered through this exterior location of the tanks, it was adopted to comply with the Air Ministry's wish that they should not be carried inside the fuselage.

Two further Fawn Mk. Is, J7182 and J7183, preceded J7184—the first production Fawn Mk. II—which made its initial flight on 29th January, 1924, from the Fairey test aerodrome at Northolt, Middlesex. Specification 1/25 was issued to cover the 1925 batch of twelve Fawn Mk. IIIs—from J7768 to J7779—which were fitted with the supercharged Lion. A final order placed in March, 1926, for a further eight Mk. IIIs from J7978 to J7985 brought to seventy the production total for the R.A.F. of its first new post-war, two-seat light bomber, a type of machine of which it had been greatly in need. The Fawn's bomb load was 460 lb. and its armament a Vickers gun for the pilot and a Lewis for the observer. An experimental installation was made in one Fawn of the 470 h.p. Napier Lioness, an unsupercharged version of the Lion which was adapted for inverted mounting to improve the view over the nose.

Two de Havilland projects of 1922 which came to naught were those of the D.H.38 and the D.H.39, both of which were proposed as bomber and reconnaissance developments of the D.H.14A. The 450 h.p. Lion V would have powered the D.H.38, and the D.H.39 was planned to use the 360 h.p. Eagle VIII.

Avro prepared a design study, the 550, for a three-seat triplane for fleet reconnaissance to Specification 37/22 during the same period.

An offspring of the Boulton and Paul Bourges was constructed and flown in 1922. The machine was the P.15 Bolton, J6584, a single all-metal version of its progenitor with an increased span and using high-tensile steel construction. A pair of 450 h.p. Lions were installed on the lower wings, but were not fully cowled, so that smaller radiators could be used. Other unusual ideas embodied by John North in his design were the use of a nosewheel, to forestall nose-overs, and the splitting of the fin into a small vertical surface hinged to act as a trimmer controlled by a wheel provided for the pilot. The main undercarriage utilized specially developed Boulton and Paul oleo-pneumatic legs. The Bolton retained the three-seat arrangement of the Bourges, with a gun ring in the nose and another aft of the wings.

Orders from the Air Ministry for prototype aircraft continued to be received by Boulton and Paul and were instrumental in a direct way for the continued development in the 1920s of the firm's concept of the highly manoeuvrable

J6584, the Boulton and Paul P.15 Bolton. (*Boulton Paul Photo.*)

twin-engine bomber. The Bolton was followed in 1923 by the Bugle to Specification 30/22 for a medium-range day bomber landplane with two engines. J6984 and J6985, the first two P.25 Bugle Mk. Is, were three-seaters evolved around a pair of 400 h.p. Bristol Jupiter II/III air-cooled radial engines mounted at mid-gap between the three-bay, equal-span 65 ft. 0·5 in. wings. Fuel was contained in two large semi-circular tanks fitted flush with the undersides of the upper centre-section. In place of the wire connections used between the ailerons of the Bolton and the Bourges, struts were fitted to those of the Bugle. Construction of the Bugle was mainly steel, and the engine mountings of circular-section tube were hinged. The Bugle Mk. I's bomb load was stored externally, and the machine's pair of Scarff-mounted Lewis guns were disposed one in the nose, with the other in a dorsal position aft of the wings. Oleo-pneumatic shock absorbers were applied to the divided main wheels and to the tailskid also.

During 1924 a modified Bugle Mk. I—J7235—was completed as a four-seater. The span had been reduced to 62 ft. 6 in., the engines changed to a pair of 400 h.p. Jupiter IVs and the fuel tankage increased. J7235 joined No. 58 Squadron in 1925 for a period of Service Trials and assessment alongside the current Virginia, and spectators at the 1925 Hendon Air Display were treated to a remarkable exhibition of the Bugle's aerobatic prowess, even to the inclusion of a loop. J7259 and J7260 were two additional Bugles ordered in January, 1924. 1925 produced another version of the square-cut Bugle—the

The Boulton and Paul P.25 Bugle Mk. I J6984. (*Boulton Paul Photo.*)

Vickers Victoria Mk. V K2340 which served as the prototype for the Victoria Mk. VI. (*Vickers Photo.*)

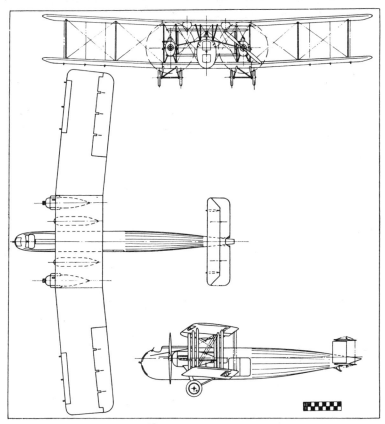

Vickers Victoria Mk. V

131

P.25a Bugle Mk. II—with a change of engines to a pair of water-cooled 450 h.p. Lions mounted on the lower wings. The previously exposed ventral bomb-racks were given a streamlined fairing, and the tanks were transferred from their original exposed position under the upper centre-section to a new location inside the fuselage. Maximum weight rose to 8,914 lb. Two Mk. IIs, both four-seaters, were built—J7266 and J7267.

The Bugle was an excellent design displaying good performance and superb powers of manoeuvre, but its advent at a time of crippling financial stringency reduced its chances of adoption as R.A.F. equipment. Even so, the experience gained by Boulton and Paul with the Bourges, Bolton and Bugle was to stand the company in good stead in the near future.

The adoption—in the face of much opposition—of the policy of air control by the Royal Air Force in the Middle East introduced the need for troop transports in support of any operations which might be undertaken. The first troop-carrier for the R.A.F. entered service in 1922, and was the Vernon produced by Vickers as an adaptation of the Vimy.

The Vernon was followed quickly by the Vickers Victoria designed to Specification 5/20 and derived from the Virginia. Napier Lion V engines were fitted to the Mk. III, the initial production version. A pair of 570 h.p. Lion XIs powered the Mk. V which followed to Specification 6/31; the Mk. VI to Specification 25/33 utilized two air-cooled radial 622 h.p. Bristol Pegasus IM3s. In its rôle as a bomber-transport the Victoria's bombs were released by sighting through an opening beneath the pilot's cockpit.

Two layouts for a coastal defence torpedo biplane were prepared during 1923. One project was the Bristol Type 82 with a pair of Lion engines, and the other was the three-seat de Havilland D.H.45 of 86 ft. span powered by two 450 h.p. Lions.

Blackburn progress in the development of the torpedo-carrier under Maj. Bumpus was exemplified in the summer of 1924 when N166—the first of the pair of gargantuan Cubaroo prototype biplanes—took-off from Brough on its maiden flight. Together with its companion, N167, N166 was powered by the powerful water-cooled, sixteen-cylinder Napier Cub, which delivered 1,000 h.p. at 1,800 r.p.m., making it the most powerful aero-engine then conceived installed in the largest single-engine aircraft by then constructed. The Cub's cylinders were arranged in four banks of four each, set with the upper banks in a narrower vee than was formed by the lower cylinders of broader angle.

The Cub had been designed by Montague Napier following his insistence during 1919 that Napier should prepare in good time a successor to the very successful Lion. The outcome of his determination was that the Air Ministry placed a contract with the firm in September, 1919, for six prototypes of the Cub at a cost of £10,000 each. The Cub—far more powerful than any competitors from Armstrong Siddeley, Bristol or Rolls-Royce—was ready for use in 1922.

The installation in the Cubaroo was made in the nose of an exceptionally deep fuselage, the pilot's open cockpit being situated high up above the engine

The first Blackburn Cubaroo N166. (*Blackburn Photo.*)

and just ahead of the leading edge. The 88 ft. equal-span, two-bay wings were unstaggered and arranged to fold. The upper wings were carried over the fuselage on centre-section struts, resulting in an unusually large gap between the planes. The biplane tail incorporated upper and lower elevators, and the wings employed cable-connected ailerons on each tip. Just aft of the upper wings was the cockpit for the gunner, armed with a Scarff-mounted Lewis. The rear portion of the Cubaroo's fuselage was of trapezoidal cross-section, a factor which improved in some measure the gunner's field of fire. The machine's undercarriage was necessarily of proportions in keeping with the massiveness of the Cubaroo, being composed of a pair of divided units consisting of two wheels each; the 1·5 ton 21 in. torpedo was carried on a crutch between the two sets of wheels. The equivalent weight of bombs could be carried as an alternative load to the torpedo, and an endurance of ten hours was possible. The Cubaroo was tested with a two-blade wooden propeller and a metal type with three blades. An alternative engine, the 1,000 h.p. Beardmore Simoon with compression ignition, was tested in one of the Cubaroos. Circumstances dashed the high hopes which Napier entertained regarding large-scale production of the powerful Cub. After initial encouragement and practical backing, the Air Ministry withdrew its support in September, 1925, at the end of six years. The time had not yet arrived for the demand for a 1,000 h.p. engine for Service aircraft, and another decade had still to pass before such a power rating was accepted as the norm.

To specification 31/22 for a twin-engine, medium-range, landplane night bomber, Handley Page produced the H.P.24 W.8d Hyderabad, an adaptation by S. T. A. Richards of the firm's W.8 civil airliner which had appeared just a year after the Armistice. Named after the Indian city, the four-seat

Handley Page Hyderabad Mk. I with early form of fin and rudder. (*Handley Page Photo.*)

Hyderabad retained its civil ancestor's basic airframe, the main structural alterations made being the revision of the nose portion of the fuselage. The pilot's cockpit was higher and taken a little to the rear, while the nose gunner occupied a low-set position in the extreme nose and well below the pilot's line

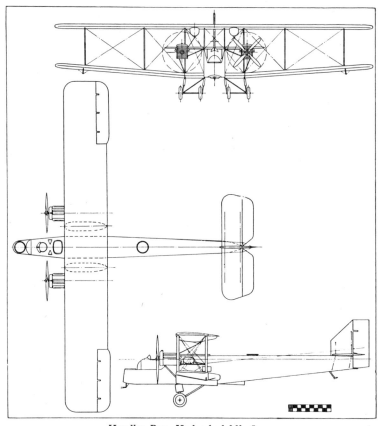

Handley Page Hyderabad Mk. I

J7006, the D.H.42A Dingo Mk. I. (*de Havilland Photo.*)

of sight. A second Lewis gun position mid-way along the upper fuselage was supplemented by a third ventral station immediately beneath. Twin 450 h.p. Lions, complete with frontal radiators, were mounted at mid-gap between the equal-span wings, and the Hyderabad was supported on a divided under-

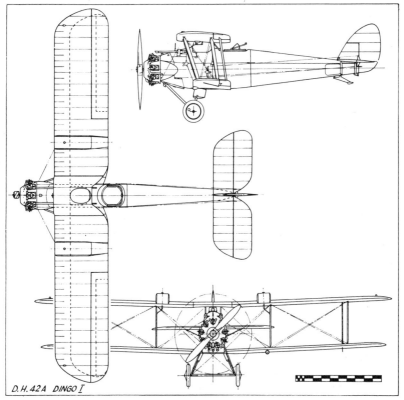

D.H. 42A DINGO I

de Havilland Dingo Mk. I

135

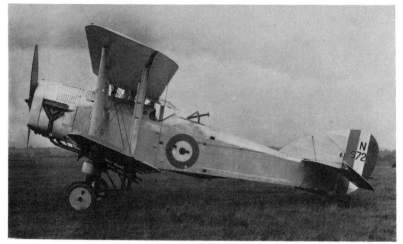

The fourth Handley Page Hendon. (*Handley Page Photo.*)

carriage with four wheels. Bomb load was 1,100 lb.; of note was the fact that Handley Page slots were fitted for the first time to so large an aircraft.

J6994, the prototype, made its maiden flight in October, 1923, from Cricklewood and went into production to Specification 15/24 as the R.A.F.'s last biplane bomber of wooden construction. No. 99 Squadron, equipped for the brief span of only two years with Aldershots, in December, 1925, became the first recipient of the Hyderabad Mk. I. No. 99's early examples had rudders with rounded upper outline and embodied a horn balance of substantial area; the balance was subsequently discarded in favour of a plain rudder of the same angular profile as that employed on the civil W.8e and W.10. Forty-five Hyderabads were produced for use by four R.A.F. squadrons.

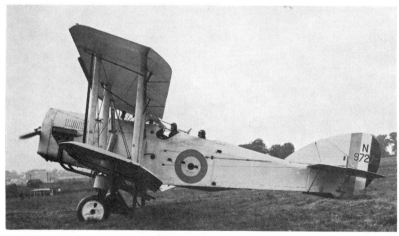

Handley Page Hendon N9727 with inter-connected slots and ailerons. (*Handley Page Photo.*)

136

12th March, 1924, was the date of the first flight of J7006, the de Havilland D.H.42A Dingo Mk. I prototype two-seat, army co-operation biplane to Specification 8/24. The machine's engine was the 410 h.p. Jupiter III, and its flying surfaces followed the well-established de Havilland outline. A pair of Vickers guns fired forwards, and the rear cockpit carried a Lewis on the usual Scarff ring. A wooden airframe was used for the Mk. I, but J7007, the D.H.42B Dingo Mk. II, was constructed with a steel tubing fuselage and powered by the 436 h.p. Jupiter IV. Both Dingoes' two-bay wings were of unequal-span and possessed lower surfaces having a narrower chord than that of the upper planes. Each Dingo was used purely for experimental flying.

Although by the mid-1920s the Blackburn company was firmly established as the primary supplier of torpedo-bombers, Handley Page—in spite of its recognized position as constructors of bombers and civil transports—continued to endeavour to enter the market for the torpedo-carrier, so that, in 1924, there appeared from Cricklewood the H.P.25 Hendon Type Ta two-seat biplane designed by G. R. Volkert for use from aircraft carriers. Named after the adjacent borough with its famous pioneer airfield, the Hendon was a revision of the single-seat Hanley and used, too, the 450 h.p. Lion. Six Hendons—N9724 to N9729—were produced to Specification 25/23; the first of the batch—N9724—was completed in June, 1924, making its initial flight the next month on 7th July at the Cricklewood Aerodrome. The observer's cockpit in the Hendon was immediately to the rear of the pilot, and the Handley Page automatic wingtip slots on both upper and lower wings were coupled by rods to the slotted ailerons.

Six examples—J7277 to J7282—also constituted the number in the batch of prototype Vickers Type 94 Venture general-purpose two-seat biplanes, the first of which appeared at Brooklands in the course of 1924. The Venture was a revised version of the Vixen and retained the ubiquitous Lion as its power plant.

The 486 h.p. Lion was used also in the Vickers Valparaiso two-seat general-purpose biplane of 1923, another of R. K. Pierson's derivatives from his earlier Vixen. The Rolls-Royce Eagle IX was specified as an alternative engine for the Valparaiso. Both the Venture and the Valparaiso were conventional machines with single-bay wings, the lower surfaces of which were smaller than those of the upper set.

Several firms submitted designs to the Air Ministry in response to Specification 26/23 issued in August, 1923, laying down the requirement for a two-seat, long-range day bomber landplane to employ a single 650 h.p. Condor III engine. Three prototypes were to be supplied, and Bristol tendered the Type 90 Berkeley, the original design being the result of collaboration between W. T. Reid and C. W. Tinson. On Reid's resignation F. S. Barnwell assisted in putting the final touches to the design. J7403, the first Berkeley, made its initial flight on 5th March, 1925, from Filton with Capt. C. F. Uwins at the controls.

The machine was a conventional three-bay biplane with unstaggered, equal-span wings attached to a fairly deep fuselage. The pilot was seated high in the nose, the upper centre-section leading edge being cut back to accommodate his head, and he was provided with a single fixed Vickers; the observer used a Scarff-mounted Lewis from the dorsal cockpit. The specification demanded a top speed of 120 m.p.h., a range of 1,200 miles and the ability to transport a bomb load of a quarter of a ton. The Berkeley recorded a maximum speed of the required 120 m.p.h. with the Condor III and was able to accommodate a single 520 lb. bomb or an equivalent load. Both J7403 and J7404, the second prototype completed in December, 1925, utilized wooden wings and tailplane, but J7405—the third Berkeley—had an all-metal airframe.

The Handley Page approach to 26/23 resolved itself into three H.P.28 Type C/7 Handcross prototypes—J7498 to J7500—J7498's maiden flight being made by Sqn. Ldr. T. H. England from Radlett on 18th December, 1924. Designed by George Volkert, the Handcross was an imposing three-bay

J7405, third of the Bristol Berkeley prototypes. (*Bristol Photo.*)

biplane with upper wings of greater span and chord than the lower pair. The 60 ft. span top planes were supported on the fuselage by two pairs of struts set as inverted Vs. The pilot's location was beneath the upper centre-section, and the observer, with a Lewis gun on a Scarff ring, was a short distance aft of the trailing edge. The undercarriage was in two split units, and the under-wing racks supplemented the main bomb-bay, which was in a fairing beneath the fuselage. A two-blade metal propeller was driven by the 650 h.p. Condor III, the fuel for which was carried in a pair of prominent full-chord tanks housed flush below the upper mainplanes. Armament for the pilot consisted of the usual single Vickers gun.

Westland also accepted the 26/23 challenge with three prototype Yeovil biplanes; two were Mk. Is—J7508 and J7509—completed in 1925, and one was the Mk. II J7510 ready in 1926. Arthur Davenport's design was evolved around the specified 650 h.p. Condor III, which was borne in the nose of a relatively deep fuselage. The crew of two were seated in tandem close to each other, and the 59 ft. 6 in. wings were equal in span but were of narrower chord on the lower surfaces. The pilot's Vickers gun was installed in the nose and the observer's Lewis carried on the conventional Scarff mounting.

J7508's maiden flight was conducted by Capt. F. T. Courtney at Andover during June, 1925. Both this machine and J7509 were of composite construc-

J7498, the first Handley Page Handcross. (*Handley Page Photo.*)

tion, but J7510 was of metal throughout. External differences between the first prototype and the other two were evident in the undercarriage struts, the fin and rudder profile and in the shape of the fairings covering the exposed fuel tanks on top of the upper wings. The Yeovil was capable of accommodating a 520 lb. bomb load and reached the stipulated speed of 120 m.p.h. Following Courtney's initial testing of the Yeovil, Maj. L. P. Openshaw subsequently took over the work of development flying on the three prototypes.

Ultimately, the Hawker contender to Specification 26/23 was determined to be the most suitable for adoption by the R.A.F. W. G. Carter's design was

J7508, the Westland Yeovil Mk. I, first of three prototypes. (*Westland Photo.*)

139

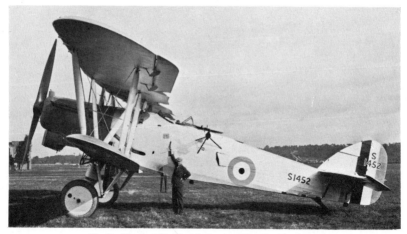

Hawker Horsley Mk. II with Condor III. (*Hawker Photo.*)

centred, like its rivals, on the 650 h.p. Condor III. The two-seat, two-bay biplane Horsley was originally to be called the Kingston after its birthplace, but eventually took its name from T. O. M. Sopwith's home of 'Horsley Towers'.

The Mk. I prototype J7511 featured all-wood construction and was destined to be the last Hawker aircraft type so built. The Horsley's upper wings were greater both in span and chord than the lower pair, and the inner interplane struts were of N type. The pair of cockpits were set adjacent to each other, the pilot being armed with a synchronized Vickers while his observer used a Lewis gun. Initially, J7511 carried side-mounted radiators, but these were soon replaced by a single block installed beneath the Condor. The upper wings were also without the sweepback which was incorporated later.

J7511's first take-off was at Brooklands in 1925 with F. P. Raynham flying, accompanied by Sydney Camm in the rear cockpit. Specification 22/25 was

Hawker Horsley Mk. II J8620 fitted with Leopard I. (*Bristol Siddeley Photo.*)

140

drawn up and issued to Hawker to cover the development of the Horsley as a single-engine, day bomber landplane; this development by Camm of the basic design also took into account the bomb load demands of Specification 23/25 and the torpedo-carrying requirements of Specification 24/25. The second Horsley prototype was J7721.

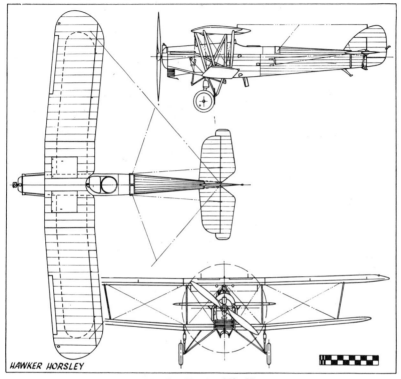

Hawker Horsley Mk. II

The first production order was placed during March, 1926, for thirty-eight machines, of which about the first ten were the wooden airframe Mk. Is, the rest being Mk. IIs of composite construction. Further R.A.F. orders were placed for the production Horsley to Specification 2/27 and M.17/27 for the Armstrong Siddeley Leopard torpedo landplane conversion. The Mk. II Horsley was equipped with the 665 h.p. Condor IIIA and was capable of accommodating either a bomb load of 600 lb. or a 2,150 lb. torpedo. Specification 17/29 was issued to cover the development of the all-metal torpedo-carrying Horsley, followed by Specification 2/31 for production of the all-metal Horsley Mk. II torpedo bomber.

A further development by Maj. Bumpus of the Blackburn Swift and Dart series was that of the two-seat Velos torpedo-carrier mounted on twin floats which was demonstrated by Capt. N. H. Woodhead at Brough, Yorkshire, on 28th October, 1925, to a party composed of the Press and foreign air attachés.

141

Blackburn Velos. (*Blackburn Photo.*)

The Velos's long single-step pontoon floats were strongly attached without cross-braces so that the torpedo could be stowed between them beneath the fuselage and launched cleanly. The Velos was powered by the 500 h.p. Lion V and incorporated a gun-ring and dual controls in the rear cockpit. Production of the Velos was handled by the Blackburn-operated Greek National Aircraft Factory set up at Old Phaleron, near Athens, the machines being supplied to the Royal Hellenic Naval Air Service and to Spain.

Vickers were responsible in 1924 for a new general-purpose and army co-operation biplane from R. K. Pierson, the two-seat Type 113 Vespa. The

G-ABIL, Vickers Type 210 Vespa in two-seat form. (*Vickers Photo.*)

142

machine was of fairly broad span—50 ft.—and carried its fuselage supported on struts between the upper and lower planes. The lower wings were shorter in span and chord than the top pair. The Vespa's pilot sat with his head in a generous aperture between the main spars of the upper wings, which were separated from the fuselage decking by a very small gap. The two-bay wings were staggered fairly sharply to provide a good view.

The all-wood Mk. I of 1925 used the 515 h.p. Jupiter VI. In its Mk. IV form supplied to the Irish Army Air Corps, the Vespa was fitted with the geared 492 h.p. Armstrong Siddeley Jaguar. The Vespa's main claim to fame was its flight on 16th September, 1932, when G-ABIL 0-5, the Type 210 Vespa Mk. IV single-seater powered with a 550 h.p. Pegasus IS3, was taken to 43,976 ft. by Capt. C. F. Uwins to set a new world's height record for Great Britain.

Vickers Type 210 Vespa Mk. IV supplied to the Irish Army Air Corps. (*Irish Air Corps Photo.*)

Three prototypes of the fleet reconnaissance Ferret biplane were constructed by Fairey to Specification 37/22 in the mid-1920s. Designed by F. Duncanson, the first—the Mk. I three-seater F538 N190—appeared during 1925 and was powered by the 400 h.p. Jaguar IV. The span of the slightly staggered, two-bay wings was 39 ft. 9·5 in., and the Ferret was notable as the first Fairey aircraft with an all-metal frame. Interchangeability of parts was a feature of the design, which was developed from the Fairey III range, and the IIIE designation is believed to have been applied to it. A Scarff ring carried the rear Lewis gun, and the Ferret Mk. I was fitted with a larger fin than its two successors which were completed in 1926.

The Ferret Mk. II F539 N191 received increased power with the 425 h.p. Jupiter VI. Larger wings of 40 ft. 6·75 in. span were fitted to both the Mk. II and the Mk. III. Deck arrester gear on N191 consisted of hooks on the under-carriage's transverse axle; the machine also underwent trials on twin floats. The Ferret Mk. III F540 N192 also received the 425 h.p. Jupiter VI, but in place of the rear Lewis Scarff ring used on N190 and N191 the Mk. III employed the Fairey high-speed mounting. N192 was constructed as a two-seater, whereas both the Mk. I and Mk. II had accommodated three. In each

143

Fairey Ferret Mk. III. (*Fairey Photo.*)

model the pilot had been equipped with a Vickers gun on the fore-decking, but N192, in its rôle as a general-purpose machine, was fitted with bomb-racks beneath the lower wings.

No production ensued for the Ferret, but a new Fairey bomber of 1925, the Fox Mk. I, was ordered for a single squadron of the R.A.F.—No. 12. The newcomer was the result of the firm's acquisition of the British rights for several American features, including the water-cooled Curtiss D-12 engine and its allied wing-surface radiator, the Curtiss-Reed metal propeller and wing aerofoils of high efficiency. The Fox prototype, which made its first flight at Hendon on 3rd January, 1925, with Capt. Norman Macmillan flying it, represented an unprecedentedly great technical advance in the field of the two-seat day bomber and demonstrated a startling increase in top speed of more than 40 m.p.h. over that of the Fawn, the current two-seat R.A.F. day bomber.

The general concept of the Fox was that of C. R. Fairey, and the design was evolved under his direction by Marcel Lobelle and P. A. Ralli, whose talents resulted in a machine with a performance which enabled it to outpace con-temporary R.A.F. fighters. The key to the success of the elegant Fox lay in creating a light and an exceptionally clean airframe for the single-bay biplane layout, and this was achieved, among other means, by mounting the two radia-tors for the Felix—the name bestowed upon the D-12 by Fairey—flush with the underside of the upper centre-section. The unequal-span wings were of fine outline and well staggered, with ailerons on all four planes. The fin and rudder of the Mk. I were in profile typical of their antecedents from Fairey. Airframe construction consisted of wooden wings and tailplane, allied to a composite fuselage formed from ash and spruce with the exception of the steel tubing centre portion, which carried the engine bearers, undercarriage and the wing attachment points. Every advantage was taken of the opportunity offered of accomplishing an outstandingly clean installation of the engine, the

144

cowling of which set a new standard for British Service aircraft. The pilot's Vickers Mk. II gun was submerged in a channel on the port side of the nose, and a further contribution to the process of eliminating excrescences was the use of the Fairey high-speed mounting for the rear cockpit's Lewis Mk. III gun. The compactness of the Fox—its span was only 38 ft.—assisted in achieving the excellent top speed of 156·5 m.p.h. at 6,500 ft. The machine's offensive load consisted of two 230 lb. or four 112 lb. bombs.

The cost of developing the Fox as a Private Venture had eaten drastically into the financial reserves of the company by the time that a demonstration had been arranged to take place before Air Ministry officials. The remarkably high performance of the Fox constituted something of an embarrassment for those responsible for the drawing up and issue of specifications to the industry, as the Fox had appeared out of the blue to confound their theories of performance required of current R.A.F. bombers. The fact had to be faced by Fairey that it was not going to be an easy task to persuade the Air Ministry to buy a bomber of advanced performance—superior, in fact, to the R.A.F.'s single-seat fighters then in service—which had outstripped by far official

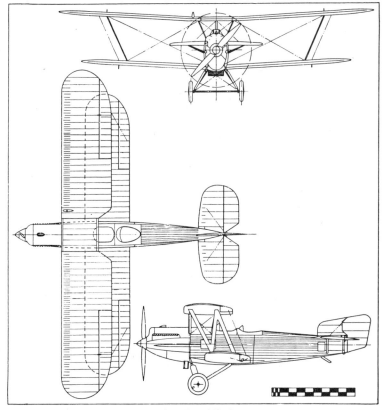

Fairey Fox Mk. I

145

requirements. Nevertheless, in October, 1925, the Chief of Air Staff, Air Chief Marshal Sir Hugh M. Trenchard, in the company of other members of the Air Council and the Air Ministry, arrived at Northolt to see Capt. Macmillan put the historic Fox through its paces. Fairey won the day, and Trenchard ordered one squadron of Foxes on the spot.

Two months later, on 10th December, the first production Fox Mk. I J7941—produced to Specification 21/25—made its maiden flight and No. 12 Squadron received its first 430 h.p. Felix-engined Mk. I in June, 1926, at Andover. Seriously inadequate cooling by the surface radiators of the prototype resulted in the production version being fitted with an additional retractable honeycomb radiator block under the fuselage.

During this period a new engine, the F.XI, appeared from Rolls-Royce, and Capt. Macmillan and C. R. McMullin, Fairey assistant test pilot, carried out extensive tests with the prototype F.XI in a Fox. Once teething troubles were settled, the new engine was adopted as the unsupercharged F.XIB or Kestrel IB in the Fox Mk. IA as the re-engined Mk. Is were redesignated. J9026, the first Fox Mk. IA with the Kestrel, made its initial flight on 29th August, 1927. The conversion to the Kestrel increased the Fox's top speed to 160 m.p.h. The reconditioning was carried out to Specifications 1/27 and 17/30; Specification 11/27 superseded 21/25 in covering production of the Fox, the total number constructed being twenty-eight in addition to the original 33 ft. 6 in. span prototype. Fox J9027 was eventually returned to Fairey in 1929 for trials with evaporation cooling of the Kestrel IB by means of condensers in the wings, and J9515 was used for the same purpose.

Although it served with but one R.A.F. squadron, the Fox was undoubtedly one of the most important and significant British aircraft of the mid-1920s, being a magnificent example of private enterprise and courage unhampered by prejudice and ineptitude inherent in official attitudes. In addition, the advent of the Fox was responsible for the belated stimulus so badly needed at the time to encourage continued development of the high-speed bomber with its many attributes.

The Fox itself was evolved in 1929 into an extensively revised all-metal version as the Mk. II for export, in which form it reached a maximum speed of 190 m.p.h. The prototype Mk. II J9834 was designed in accordance with Specification 12/26 following representations made to the Air Ministry by C. R. Fairey when it was found that his company had not been asked to submit a tender for the requirement. In the resulting competitive trials for 12/26 both the Avro Antelope and the Fox Mk. II were beaten by the Hawker Hart, the defeat of the Fox Mk. II being attributable to the late start in its design and also to the more acceptable form of metal construction of the Hart to R.A.F. maintenance needs.

The Fairey Fox, in all its technological brilliance, had demonstrated just what could be achieved in one step by designers within an aircraft company working with encouragement and inspiration from the right level and with a relatively free hand to put into practice the dictates of their brains in the light of their skill and experience. The result—in the Fox—was a product of profound importance, a fact recognized by Trenchard immediately upon impact with his searching and independent mind.

The birth of the Fox brought repercussions in the airframe and engine industry of the United Kingdom, acting particularly as a spur to the development of the liquid-cooled, inline engine—with its natural advantage of clean installation—and to aircraft designers generally by demonstrating the possibilities ahead.

Great Britain was indeed fortunate beyond comprehension in possessing during the 1920s a Chief of Air Staff of the calibre of Trenchard. Immediately after the Armistice the war-weary victors had started to sow the seeds of the next World War by flinging their protective armour to the winds in indulging in the most dangerous and suicidal policy that can be thrust unwanted upon the country—that of disarmament. Within a short span the R.A.F. had been decimated beyond recognition, but, to Trenchard's everlasting credit, he had recognized the unlimited destructive potential in air power and the fact that, in any future war, it would undoubtedly be employed to the fullest extent. His sagacity and indomitable spirit were brought fully into his fight not only to preserve the remnants of his once mighty air force but also to re-create it as a force worthy of the nation and one which would serve it well and without shame during the periods of danger which any appreciative survey of history discloses as inevitably to be faced repetitively as one decade succeeds another. In his laudable endeavours Trenchard was faced with opposition from politicians intent upon promoting their personal ideals of pacifism at the expense of the country and whose shameful policies were ultimately to be responsible for the Second World War later and on whose heads would lie the blood of many helpless thousands of Britons as a result of the scandalously low level to which the defences of the nation were allowed to sink.

The basic precept behind Trenchard's proposed structure for the Royal Air Force was that of the inclusion of a strong bomber force, capable of being wielded to attack and destroy not only an enemy's air bases but also the factories creating all kinds of war material and the transport system used to move men and supplies. Trenchard's cardinal argument was that an enemy's homeland should be attacked immediately, thereby taking the conflict away from British shores and keeping the foe constantly on the defensive. Defending fighters would naturally be needed to safeguard the British Isles, but the main duty of the R.A.F. would be to attack the enemy relentlessly. This policy would naturally mean the constitution and the maintenance of a large, well-trained force of bombing aircraft. Trenchard's integrity and his forceful personality won him the promise of expansion for the R.A.F. to a total of fifty-two squadrons, with the proposed ratio of two-thirds bombers to one-third fighters. Despite the promises made, expansion proceeded at a slow rate, with the ever-present problem of shortage of funds for the purchase of suitable aircraft. Another factor which was to have a disastrous effect on the rate of progress made towards establishing a force of acceptable size was that of the incredibly unrealistic 'Ten Year Rule' which supposed that, from 1924, a major war was unlikely to break out within ten years. Any supposition more

N192, the Fairey Ferret Mk. III. (*Fairey Photo.*)

The Vickers Vespa Mk. VI G-ABIL as a single-seater. (*Bristol Siddeley Photo.*)

inane would be difficult to imagine; yet such an assumption was made by the elected guardians of the nation's welfare to the detriment of the Royal Air Force, which, to the few with sufficient intelligence and foresight, was the Service upon which the safety of the United Kingdom was to depend to a steadily increasing degree.

A.W. Atlas Mk. I J9537 demonstrating message collection technique. (*Armstrong Whitworth Photo.*)

CHAPTER FOUR

SINGLES AND TWINS

By the time that the mid-point of the 1920s had been reached, the basic requirements of the Royal Air Force and the Fleet Air Arm in bomber and torpedo-carrying aircraft had become fairly stable and rationalized. Under Trenchard's providential and strenuous guidance the R.A.F. had managed to retain its separate identity, and his forthright insistence that, as a force, it should possess the power to meet its commitments and any contingencies which might arise had finally prevailed, so that, during 1925, agreement was reached in the Air Ministry for expansion to reach a total of fifty-two squadrons, with a ratio of two to one in favour of bomber units. This proposed increase was based on the recommendations of the Interim Report of the Salisbury Committee which had been announced in June, 1923. The requirements had been assessed and discussed at a lamentable and depressing period when Great Britain was suffering from political uncertainty and changes of government, which included eventually the dreary régime of its first Socialist administration for a relatively brief spell from the beginning of 1924 until October, 1924.

The proposals came at a time when an unrealistic belief in the lasting goodwill of other nations led the United Kingdom along the most dangerous of all the paths which it can take at any time—that of disarmament. This utter folly and its consequent failure to provide an air force of adequate size to undertake its current duties and to deter any potential attacker was encouraged and fermented by the fallacious hopes raised by the proposal to hold a disarmament conference under the auspices of the ineffectual and hamstrung League of Nations.

It was in the midst of this indefensible and demoralizing atmosphere that Trenchard had to fight for the development of new aircraft for the bomber squadrons of the Royal Air Force and for the torpedo-bearing units of the Fleet Air Arm. Progress in re-equipment of existing units and in the formation of new squadrons continued slowly and sporadically, the entire programme lagging behind the agreed schedule.

While production was initiated of the small number of already-approved bomber and torpedo-bomber designs—either entirely new or later marks of existing types—an interesting variety of fresh prototypes appeared to take their places in the gradually expanding development history of British aircraft in those classes. A Bristol design, the Type 93 Boarhound Mk. I two-seat biplane of 1924, was built as a Private Venture, registered G-EBLG, to Specification 8/24 as an aspirant for the Bristol F.2B Fighter replacement. A 425 h.p. Jupiter IV provided the power for a machine which was typical in style for its period. In the course of its genesis Frank Barnwell revised the design on more than one occasion; at the same time the system of steel construction was altered. C. F. Uwins conducted the first flight on 28th May, 1925; modification of the Boarhound design as a general-purpose type to compete as a D.H.9A replacement followed later.

After competitive trials against the Bristol Boarhound, D.H. Hyena and Vickers Vespa, the Atlas—an Armstrong Whitworth design—was eventually selected to succeed the Bristol F.2B, production being to Specification 33/26. Designed by J. Lloyd, the Atlas turned out to be a very reliable and versatile aircraft which remained in production until 1933, the total constructed—in addition to the pair of prototypes J8675 and J8777—reaching four hundred and forty-nine, including one hundred and forty-six of the trainer derivative. Within its scope came artillery observation, supply dropping, message picking-up, photographic reconnaissance and ground attack by bombing and machine-gunning. The Atlas was a completely fresh metal and fabric biplane design, the first prototype J8675 being taken into the air for its initial flight on 10th May, 1925. The Atlas's wings differed in span and were swept back from the centre line. Picking up of messages from the ground was accomplished by lowering the hook hinged to the undercarriage axle and flying low so that it engaged with the object slung by line between a pair of upright posts. Two guns were carried, a fixed Vickers for the pilot and a Scarff-mounted Lewis for the observer. The Atlas's 450 h.p. Jaguar IVC was mounted uncowled in the nose, and its bomb load consisted of four of 112 lb., each suspended beneath the wings. No. 26 Squadron at Catterick became in October, 1927, the first unit to be equipped with the new two-seater for army co-operation duties, and the Atlas Mk. I was subsequently established as a common sight both in Britain and overseas.

The de Havilland contender to Specification 33/26 was a two-bay, unequal-span biplane—the D.H.56 Hyena. Two prototypes—J7780 and J7781—were

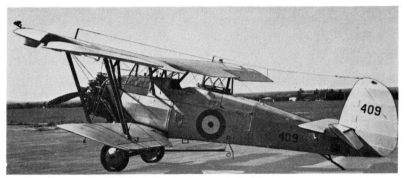

A.W. Atlas of the R.C.A.F. (*R.C.A.F. Photo.*)

completed in 1926, the first using the 385 h.p. Jaguar III and the second the 422 h.p. Jaguar IV. Equipment was carried for a range of duties, the Hyena's bomb-rack being situated beneath the port lower wing. The usual armament

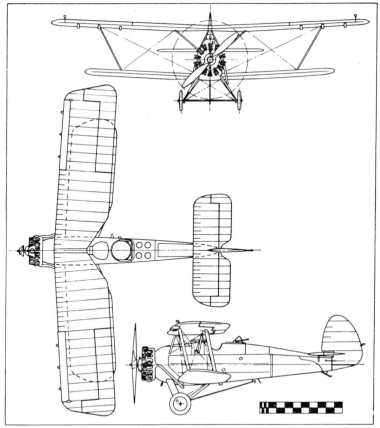

Armstrong Whitworth Atlas Mk. I

151

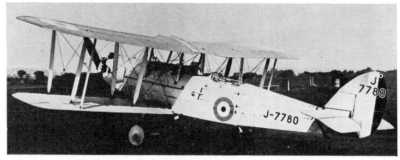

J7780, the first prototype D.H.56 Hyena. (*de Havilland Photo.*)

—a fixed Vickers for the pilot and a Scarff-mounted Lewis for the observer—
was applied to the design. After preliminary testing, J7780 exchanged its
Jaguar III for the more powerful Jaguar IV.

Among the small group of outstandingly large prototype military biplanes
designed and constructed in Great Britain a few years after the 1914–18 War
were N171 and N172, respectively the Mk. I and Mk. II versions of the Avro
557 Ava. Chadwick's 1924 design embraced the rôles of night bomber,

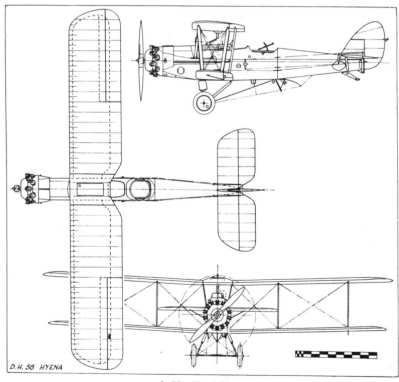

D.H. 56 HYENA

de Havilland Hyena

152

coastal defence and torpedo-carrier. A pair of 650 h.p. Condors, driving four-blade propellers, were chosen to power the 96 ft. 10 in. span Ava N171 and were installed at mid-gap between the three-bay folding wings. Dual controls were provided for the pilots seated side by side in a fuselage of considerable depth. The rear of the machine terminated in a biplane tail incorporating twin fins and rudders. Three gun positions defended the Ava—nose, dorsal and ventral—that in the last location being lowered for action. As a coastal defence type, N171 was able to accommodate a bomb load of 2,000 lb. in its

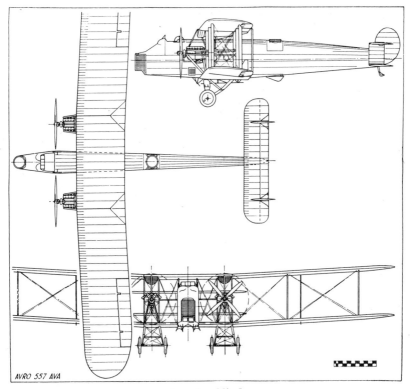

AVRO 557 AVA

Avro Ava Mk. I

capacious fuselage or alternatively could transport one 21 in. Whitehead torpedo slung between the split main wheel units. First flown at Hamble on 22nd April, 1927, N172 was slightly smaller in span with 95 ft. 4 in. square-cut wings. Although the Avas were twin-engine machines, they had their origin in an earlier single-engine project by Chadwick, the 1,000 h.p. Cub-powered Avro 556 designed to Specification 16/22 for D. of R. Type 9.

Issued to provide a two-seat, ship-borne torpedo-carrier for the Fleet Air Arm, Specification 21/23 was tackled by Handley Page with the H.P.31 Harrow and Blackburn with the Ripon. G. R. Volkert was again responsible for the Handley Page design, two of which—N205 and N206—were built;

N206 was tested on twin floats. N205's maiden flight was carried out by Sqn. Ldr. T. H. England at Radlett on 24th April, 1926. As a matter of course for a carrier torpedo-bomber, the equal-span wings were made to fold. A distinctive feature, however, was that normal centre-section struts were omitted, the wide-span upper centre-section being supported on the lower wings by a pair of interplane struts. Handley Page slots had become a standard fitting to the firm's aircraft by the mid-1920s, and two sets were incorporated in the Harrow—one for better lateral stability and the other for use as usual at slow speeds. The slots were inter-connected with slotted ailerons. The Harrow Mk. I's 470 h.p. Lion VA, cooled by a frontal radiator, was set low in the nose so that the upper decking sloped down from the pilot's cockpit to the spinner at a fairly steep angle, a feature calculated to assist the view

Handley Page Harrow Mk. II N205. (*Handley Page Photo.*)

from the cockpit for landing. The machine's torpedo was slung in the accepted location between the widely-spaced undercarriage units; a prone bomb-aiming position was provided beneath the pilot's seat. Forwards-firing armament consisted of a single fixed Vickers to starboard, and the rear cockpit received the normal Lewis. The 530 h.p. Lion XIA powered the Harrow Mk. II, the nose being flanked by a radiator on each side.

The Harrow was a completely new design and a very clean machine aerodynamically for its period, but the 21/23 requirement was met by its competitor from Brough, the Ripon, which—in its Mk. I version—appeared also in 1926. In the Ripon Maj. Bumpus perpetuated the general lines of the Dart, but the increased range demanded by the requirement meant the incorporation of an observer's cockpit immediately to the rear of the pilot. A rather angular nose accommodated the Lion V, which carried two of its short exhausts to starboard and the third pipe to port; the upright radiator block was mounted just behind the two-blade propeller. Single-bay wings were used in place of the two-bay cellules of the Dart, but embodied a greater degree of sweepback than was employed on the single-seater. The wings folded outboard of the centre-section, both upper and lower parts of which were braced to the fuselage by short, sturdy struts. The Ripon's structure was mainly of wood, covered with fabric. The first Ripon Mk. I prototype

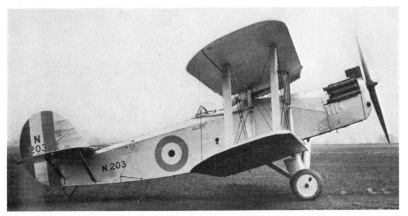

N203, the prototype Blackburn Ripon Mk. I. (*Blackburn Photo.*)

was N203, and N204 was the Mk. I second prototype, which was tested on floats.

Before being ordered into production to Specification 2/29, as a replacement for the Dart, the Ripon underwent considerable revision and was tested in its Mk. II form as N231. The modified machine exhibited a fin and rudder of high aspect ratio in place of the earlier well-rounded profile, and its considerably

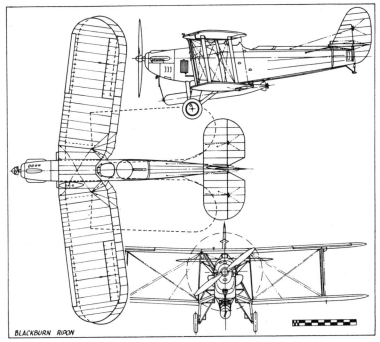

BLACKBURN RIPON

Blackburn Ripon Mk. IIA

N231, the prototype Blackburn Ripon Mk. II, fitted with revised fin and rudder. (*Blackburn Photo.*)

more powerful Lion XI was graced with a far cleaner cowling. Twin retractable lateral radiators replaced the previous arrangement, and additional stringers faired the underside of the fuselage. With still further alteration to a composite structure and the 570 h.p. Lion XIA, the Ripon passed into production for the Fleet Air Arm as the Mk. IIA to Specification 2/29 with an offensive load of 1,500 lb. constituted either as a Mk. VIII or Mk. X torpedo or bombs. The pilot's Vickers gun and the observer's Lewis served as offensive weapons. Overall performance of this class of aircraft was gradually increasing, the Ripon Mk. IIA possessing a top speed of 126 m.p.h. at sea level. Additional refinements to the Mk. IIA after some service had accumulated were the Handley Page slots installed on the upper wings and an exhaust collector manifold for the Lion, discharging beneath the nose.

Overseas interest in acquiring the Ripon came with an order from Finland

Blackburn Pegasus-Ripon B-5, employed as prototype Baffin. (*Blackburn Photo.*)

for the Mk. IIF, which flew with an air-cooled radial, either the Armstrong Siddeley Panther or the Gnome Rhône-built Bristol Jupiter.

An experimental version of the Ripon—the Mk. III S1272—was built using an all-metal airframe incorporating, among other alterations, redesigned wingtips and a Lion XI. Official tests of the Mk. III were conducted at A. & A. E. E. Martlesham and two of the Mk. IIAs—S1268 and S1468—were tested on floats. The relatively deep fuselage of the Ripon allowed room for a prone bomb-aiming position in the underside of the fuselage. Specification 13/31 covered production of another batch of Ripon Mk. IIAs.

Avro 571 Buffalo Mk. I with rounded wingtips and ailerons on lower wings. (*Avro Photo.*)

Two derivatives of the Ripon, both fitted with air-cooled radials, underwent tests in 1932. These were the Armstrong Siddeley Tiger version, which carried the marking B-4, and B-5 equipped with the Bristol Pegasus and under development to Specification 4/33 as the Baffin—the Ripon's successor.

A. V. Roe and Co. designed a Private Venture two-seat, multi-purpose biplane, the 571 Buffalo, to Specification 21/23. Completed in 1926 and test-flown at Hamble in the same year, it utilized portions of the wings and the tail of the Bison and was but little pleasanter to the eye. About the shapeliest aspect of the Buffalo lay in the clean cowling of the 450 h.p. Lion VA. The single-bay, equal-span wings folded conventionally to the rear and embodied ailerons on the lower surfaces only. The Buffalo's airframe was composite in construction, and the fuselage was of considerable depth, in common with those of its contemporaries designed for the same duties as carrier-borne torpedo bombers. The observer was thus able to lie prone in the bomb-aiming position and also to navigate from inside in reasonable comfort. A fuselage trough housed the pilot's Vickers, while a Scarff ring took care of the pair of Lewis guns in the rear. The Buffalo Mk. I was registered G-EBNW and executed its maiden flight from Hamble in 1926. Its original fin and rudder—of Bison type—were soon supplanted by large, angular surfaces, and in 1927

157

Avro 572 Buffalo Mk. II with revised wingtips and four ailerons. (*Avro Photo.*)

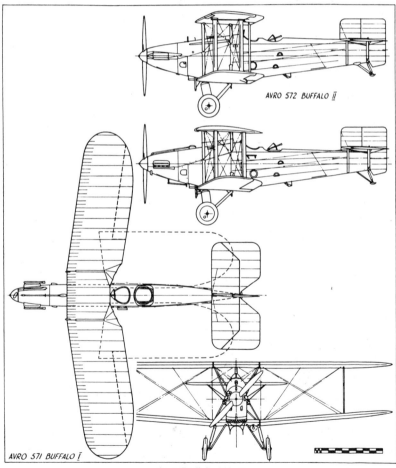

AVRO 572 BUFFALO II

AVRO 571 BUFFALO I

Avro Buffalo Mk. I
158

completely new wings of metal were fabricated embodying four strut-connected ailerons and Handley Page slots. A 530 h.p. Lion XIA took the place of the Lion VA, and G-EBNW was redesignated the 572 Buffalo Mk. II. During the summer of 1928 the Air Ministry bought the machine, numbered it N239 and tested it at M.A.E.E. Felixstowe on twin floats which had been fitted by Avro at Hamble.

No attempt was made to construct the Avro 597, a projected straightforward adaptation of the Buffalo.

An interesting group of prototypes resulted from the release of Specification 23/25 in respect of a two-seat, single-engine, high-altitude, landplane day bomber with possible use of the 495 h.p. Bristol Jupiter VII radial with a geared supercharger. Four companies produced prototypes to 23/25; three of them—Gloster, Handley Page and Hawker—adhered to the biplane formula, but Westland branched out with a monoplane.

In his design for Gloster—still officially the Gloucestershire Aircraft Company until 11th November, 1926—H. P. Folland, already held in the highest esteem over a number of years for his brilliant capabilities as a fighter designer, laid out the Private Venture G.25 Goring around the Jupiter VII with its gear-drive supercharger. However, development trials being carried out concurrently with this engine installation were accompanied by a lack of general reliability in the engine and recurrent trouble with the supercharger, leading to eventual abandonment of the entire power plant for use in the Goring.

To continue the project Folland was obliged to revise the Goring to use an alternative engine and selected the direct-drive 425 h.p. Jupiter VI for the purpose. The single prototype J8674 appeared in 1927 with this engine and displayed the unmistakable Folland touch in its compact, trim outline. With its unequal-span, single-bay wings the general appearance of the Goring approached that of a scaled-up Grouse Mk. II. The machine was designed to be able to transport a bomb load of 700 lb. or a torpedo in compliance with the alternative task of coastal defence torpedo-bomber contained in the specification. To take the torpedo an alternative split-axle undercarriage was designed.

Gloster Goring J8674 with early style of fin and rudder. (*Gloster Photo.*)

Gloster Goring fitted with revised vertical tail surfaces. (*Gloster Photo.*)

One of the Goring's pair of machine-guns was arranged to fire downwards through the floor of the fuselage; the observer's Lewis was mounted on the usual rotating ring.

Following tests by Flt. Lt. R. H. Stocken in 1931 as a twin-float seaplane using Gloster floats and the geared 460 h.p. Jupiter VIII, which gave it a top speed of 123 m.p.h., the Goring reverted to testing as a landplane powered by the 575 h.p. Jupiter XF and fitted with a revised tail unit. J8674 was subsequently employed as a Bristol engine test-bed, receiving in turn the 745 h.p. Mercury VIIA, 570 h.p. Pegasus II and the sleeve-valve 670 h.p. Perseus IIL.

From the Claremont Road, Cricklewood, works of Handley Page there emerged in 1928 George Volkert's H.P.34 Hare design for the 23/25 requirement. J8622 differed from Volkert's previous designs in the same category by virtue of the size of its lower wings, which possessed considerably less area than that of the upper surfaces, and in the omission of wire interplane

Handley Page Hare. (*Handley Page Photo.*)

160

Hawker Harrier Mk. I J8325 fitted with Hydra. (*Hawker Photo.*)

bracing which was displaced by a single heavy diagonal strut to take the landing loads in each of the single-bay wing cellules. Ailerons of very generous area occupied the trailing edge of the upper wings, and Handley Page movable slots stretched along the entire leading edge of the outer panels of the top

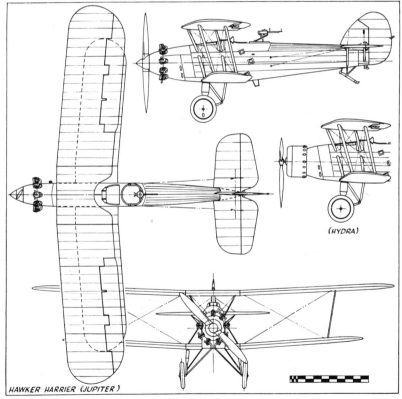

HAWKER HARRIER (JUPITER)

(HYDRA)

Hawker Harrier Mk. I

161

mainplanes. Power for the Hare came from the 485 h.p. Jupiter VIII installed uncowled in the nose to drive a four-blade propeller. The pilot's Vickers gun fired from a channel in the port coaming, and his observer operated his Lewis on a Scarff ring rotating in a recessed portion of the rear decking. In place of its under-wing load of bombs the Hare was able to take a torpedo between the divided undercarriage units.

The Hare flew from Radlett to make its maiden flight on 24th February, 1928, with Sqn. Ldr. T. H. England at the controls. In the course of subsequent testing a cowled Armstrong Siddeley Panther was fitted, but, finally, the Hare was sold in 1932 for registration as G-ACEL to J. N. Addinsell, who intended to use it on a long-distance flight which did not materialize.

The Hawker offering to Specification 23/25 was Sydney Camm's Harrier Mk. I J8325, which was completed during 1927. The planform of the wings differed but little from the surfaces used by the Horsley. The Harrier, however, was somewhat smaller and had single-bay cellules. The design, using a fabric-covered steel tubing and duralumin airframe, was evolved around the geared Jupiter VIII and received a twin-unit undercarriage so that a torpedo could be accommodated should the need arise later. The Harrier's armament consisted of the usual Vickers for the pilot and a Lewis for the observer, and the machine's bomb load was made up of either eight 112 lb. or four 250 lb. bombs. Flt. Lt. P. W. S. Bulman conducted the Harrier's first take-off at Brooklands in 1927 but, from the start, the machine was found to lack sufficient power owing to losses engendered by the gearing of the Jupiter.

Subsequently, the Harrier was modified during 1928 to meet the torpedo-carrying requirements of Specification 24/25 by equipping it to carry the Mk. VIII torpedo. Boosting of the geared Jupiter VIII to deliver 583 h.p. still failed to overcome the lack of power, and late in 1929 the Harrier passed to Bristol for the testing at Filton of diverse radials, among them the sixteen-cylinder Bristol Hydra and the Orion, otherwise the Jupiter VII.

Arthur Davenport's design, the Witch, as the Westland contribution to the field for Specification 23/25 was undoubtedly the most advanced of the quartet. As an enthusiastic devotee of the monoplane, Davenport was without qualms in adopting the formula at a time when the biplane was firmly entrenched and without a sign that its long-lived supremacy might be ending. J8596 inherited the parasol layout following the experience gained with the Widgeon and the Wizard and was designed in the first instance around the abortive 495 h.p. Orion. The non-availability of this engine led to the substitution of the 420 h.p. Jupiter VI with which the machine appeared in 1928.

Far from being characterized by the lack of beauty which its name suggested, the Witch was an exceedingly handsome product as a practical bomber design. An all-metal fuselage supported by struts the 61 ft. span moderately sweptback wings of composite construction. The indisputable aerodynamic advantages gained by adopting the monoplane layout were not compromised by exposing the 520 lb. bomb load to the airstream as it was carried inside the fore-fuselage in a bay, the floor of which was covered by four doors which

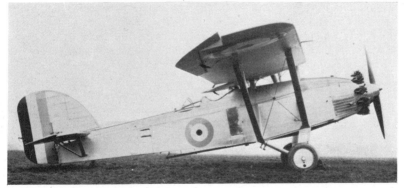

Westland Witch Mk. I J8596 with revised fin and rudder. (*Westland Photo.*)

were arranged to spring open under the weight of the missiles in the event of an emergency release being necessary. As well as permitting unimpeded passage for the bombs, the wide-track, twin-unit undercarriage automatically made possible the employment of the Witch as a torpedo launcher. The standard pilot's synchronized Vickers and observer's Scarff-mounted Lewis constituted the machine's defensive armament.

Flt. Lt. L. G. Paget undertook J8596's first flight at Yeovil in 1928. Subsequently, an alteration was effected in the leading edge of the fin and rudder with the removal of the indentation adjacent to the horn balance and the substitution of a continuous curved outline. In the course of 1929 the 480 h.p. Jupiter VIIIF replaced the earlier engine in J8596, and the aircraft was redesignated Witch Mk. II. After a period of experimental work the machine served with the Parachute Training Unit at Henlow for several years.

Specification 23/25 was unsuccessful in procuring a new bomber with the qualities required, one of the factors contributing to the disappointment being the delay in arrival of the Jupiter VII and X with gear-driven superchargers.

Evaluated also to the high-altitude day bomber requirements of Specification 23/25, although ordered in December, 1926, as a prototype naval torpedo-bomber to Specification 24/25, was the two-seat Blackburn Beagle N236. In

Blackburn Beagle N236 with auxiliary fuel tank beneath fuselage. (*Blackburn Photo.*)

163

his design Maj. Bumpus retained the general single-bay biplane layout of the Ripon allied to composite construction, but adopted blunt tips for each of the flying and control surfaces in conjunction with a fuselage faired by stringers to an oval shape. The solitary Beagle was completed in 1928 with a Jupiter VIII, which was exchanged later for a Jupiter VIIIF. Two guns were carried— a Vickers for the pilot and a Lewis for the observer. Although in appearance a competent enough design, the Beagle was not adopted to either specification but led a useful life at Gosport engaged in torpedo development.

Once in a while the date of a first flight is of note when it marks the flying début of what transpires to be a particularly significant aeroplane. 19th March, 1926, the day on which Capt. Norman Macmillan conducted the maiden flight at Northolt of a new Fairey biplane—the prototype IIIF N198 to Specification 19/24—was no exception and signified the entry of one of the most prominent and effective of British aircraft of the years between the two Great Wars.

The IIIF represented the final development in the successful Fairey III series which had been initiated some nine years earlier in 1917 with the N.10. Although it was not a particularly large machine, Lobelle and Ralli contrived with the IIIF's elegant fuselage lines, matched to fairly high aspect ratio wings, to produce a two-bay biplane of handsome and stately aspect.

N198's Fairey airframe F574 embodied a steel tubing fuselage and wooden wings covered overall with fabric. Its clean nose contours housed a 450 h.p. Napier Lion with a retractable radiator on the underside just ahead of the undercarriage. Full advantage was taken of the benefits conferred by the Fairey Patent Camber Gear, which was installed on upper and lower trailing edges. The rather inelegant undercarriage of the IIID had been discarded in favour of a simpler form which was also able to absorb the required vertical descent rate of 12 ft./sec. N198 sported the early style of arrester gear hooks on the main axle and a revised form of the IIID's vertical tail surfaces embodying a rudder which was taller than the fin.

A second IIIF prototype—N225—followed the first and was fitted out as a three-seater for the Fleet Air Arm as opposed to N198, which was a general-purpose two-seater. The R.A.F. adopted the two-seat IIIF as the Mk. IVC retaining composite construction, the Mk. IVM, which was metal throughout with the exception of wooden ribs for the fin and rudder, and the Mk. IVM/A, which received an airframe entirely of metal. These all-metal versions were produced to Specification 36/26, and Specification 37/26 covered IIIF development. Another all-metal version, produced to Specification 3/31, was the Mk. IVB. The Mk. IVB was powered by the 570 h.p. Lion XIA.

The F.A.A.'s Mk. I three-seater received the 450 h.p. Lion VA and its Mk. IIIM the more powerful 570 h.p. Lion XIA. The early design of vertical tail surfaces was replaced towards the end of 1927 by a far shapelier style with a gently curved leading edge. In both R.A.F. and F.A.A. versions the IIIF carried a single ·303 Vickers gun for the pilot and a ·303 Lewis for the observer and was able to accommodate a bomb load of 500 lb. Specification 10/31 was issued to cover IIIF production for the Fleet Air Arm.

Fairey IIIF Mk. IVM with Jupiter VIII. (*Bristol Siddeley Photo.*)

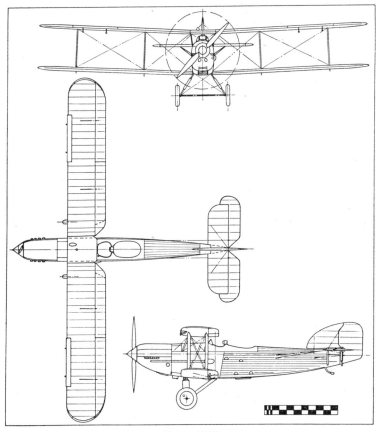

Fairey IIIF

165

Complete type trials of IIIF Mk. IVM W.P. J9150 were carried out at M.A.E.E. Felixstowe and summarized in Report F/38B of December, 1929. The machine was covered by Specification 27/27 under Contracts 809923/27 and 8050101/28 and was fitted with a Jupiter VIII J8010/104114 developing 520 h.p. at 2,000 r.p.m. and driving a four-blade Fairey-Reed L.H.T. propeller 11 ft. 11·5 in. in diameter. J9150 was fitted with quickly-detachable twin metal floats 23 ft. 9 in. long, 3 ft. 2·5 in. in beam and 2 ft. 9 in. deep. The weight empty was 3,941·5 lb., and at the loaded weight of 6,090 lb. a depth of water of 1 ft. 10·5 in. was required to float the aircraft.

Measurements recorded by the report gave the span as 45 ft. 9 in., length 36 ft. 1·5 in., height 13 ft. 2 in., width folded 15 ft. 7 in., wing area 438·52 sq. ft. and wing loading 13·88 lb./sq. ft. The machine under test was equipped with a naval T.21A W/T set and a P.18 camera. Full throttle was not allowed below a height of 4,000 ft. Performance trials yielded a maximum speed of 111 kt. at 5,000 ft., a climb rate of 740 ft./min. at sea level, a service ceiling of 14,850 ft. and an estimated absolute ceiling of 16,600 ft. J9150 required a take-off run with 12° flaps of 383 yds. which took 20·8 sec. in a 3 m.p.h. headwind. Also with flaps set at 12° the landing run of 204 yds. occupied 11·7 sec., the landing speed being 56 kt. I.A.S. The general assessment of the controls was that they were good but heavy, with controllability stable in each plane. The windscreen and view were considered good, the cockpit being free from draughts. Both front and rear cockpits were found to be reasonably free from exhaust fumes, but were particularly uncomfortable when excessive oil temperatures during tests exceeded 90° C. and oil fumes entered. The cockpits were roomy and comfortable, and the layout of controls and instruments assessed as good. The compass was thought to be too low for the pilot to read it easily, and the throw-out lever for the water rudders was badly placed.

Early in the trials one of the gear star wheels seized on its shaft, necessitating return of the Jupiter to Bristol for repair. The engine was satisfactory when sent back to Felixstowe, but registered unusually high oil temperatures of 100° C. and vibrated heavily. Despite these faults, it gave full power and r.p.m. and a steady performance. In the course of the type trials no defects were discovered calling for modifications either in design or construction. The layout of the water rudder control was considered unnecessarily complex and to possess excessive friction in its system. Engine installation and maintenance were easy, but maintenance of the aircraft was not easy enough for seaplane work. The underside of the fuselage was not sufficiently closed against entry of sea water during take-off and landing, thereby being open to constant corrosion. J9150's controls were heavy but reasonably responsive; this heaviness constituted a definite handicap on manoeuvrability, which was otherwise good. The ailerons and elevators were sluggish at slow speeds, and the ailerons became ineffective before the elevators. Effectiveness of the rudder remained down to stalling speed, but lateral control became heavier and more sluggish with increase in angle of the flaps. If stalled at anything approaching full flap angle the machine became vicious, but was found to be stable about all axes and easy to fly for long periods in calm or bumpy air.

The single Fairey IIIF supplied to the Irish Army Air Corps. (*Irish Air Corps Photo.*)

However, constant rudder correction was needed to keep straight against a tendency all the time to turn to starboard. This turning habit was found to be less than that demonstrated by the IIIF with the Lion XI. The take-off with the Jupiter VIII, none the less, was not as clean as that possessed by the version with the Lion XI, even with the same floats, and a slight porpoising was evident while taking-off. Water handling was satisfactory, but the machine was dirty when taxying at slow speeds. Performance with the Jupiter VIII compared very favourably with that demonstrated by the Lion XI model, and altitude performance with the air-cooled radial was distinctly better, but was so handicapped by heavy controls that the variant could not be considered satisfactory as a Fleet Air Arm type. Considerable improvement in detail design was thought essential to reduce rapid deterioration of the whole aircraft owing to corrosion.

During September, 1933, S1779—a Fairey IIIF Mk. III seaplane completed in September, 1931—was delivered to M.A.E.E. Felixstowe for performance tests to be conducted on a IIIF which was two years old. The object was to check any loss of performance compared with a new seaplane of the same type and to determine the reasons for any such deterioration.

The results were summarized in Report F/121 dated February, 1934. S1779 was a standard IIIF prepared for catapulting which underwent its handling flight by Fairey on 11th September, 1931. Just over a month later, on 16th October, it was flown to Lee-on-Solent for delivery as a seaplane, and some three weeks afterwards, on 12th November, the machine underwent catapult trials on the seaplane carrier H.M.S. *Ark Royal*, during which it sustained damage to the undercarriage and port lower wingtip. From November, 1931, until August, 1932, forty-nine catapult launchings were made with S1779 from H.M.S. *Norfolk*. On 1st February, 1933, the aircraft entered the workshops at Lee-on-Solent for a complete airframe overhaul, which was followed in April, 1933, by nine catapult launchings from H.M.S. *Leander* and in May, 1933, by ten similar launchings from H.M.S. *Ark Royal*. On 15th May, 1933, S1779 was reported to be sluggish on the controls and to have deteriorated in performance; subsequent re-rigging on 2nd June, 1933, was without benefit, as the controls remained sluggish.

On 19th September, 1933, S1779 arrived at Felixstowe for testing and was inspected and checked. The survey disclosed departures from standard rigging of the wings and that the port flap had an obsolete shock absorber cord instead of spring-loaded tubes. The weight empty was 4,623 lb. and loaded 6,300 lb. A 12 ft. diameter two-blade duralumin propeller was driven by a Lion XI. Flight trials with S1779 disclosed a loss of speed of about 4 kt. at all heights and a climb rate about 60 ft./min. less than that of the original IIIF. Tests were made for climb rates and for level speeds at various heights and for take-off time. A leak in the static portion of the A.S.I., combined with incorrect rigging, gave an under estimation of 3·5 kt. in level speed. A difference in the port wing flaps from those to starboard resulted in making the machine fly with one wing down. This was resolved by replacing

Vickers Type 146 Vivid G-EBPY. *(Vickers Photo.)*

those on the port planes. Compared with the original IIIF type trials figures a loss of 3·5% full throttle level speed was registered, together with 6% less climb and a take-off time which was 4 sec. longer. General manoeuvrability equalled that attained by other IIIFs, but S1779 was a little tail heavier than other average examples of the type. It was concluded that the decrease in the performance of S1779 was consistent with the aircraft's age and history.

Apart from its lengthy and honourable service with the R.A.F. and the F.A.A., the ubiquitous IIIF was supplied to the air services of several overseas countries, including the Argentine, Chile, China, Greece, India, the Irish Free State, Latvia, New Zealand and Russia. As well as flying experimentally with the Jupiter VIII, alternative engine installations were made with the 460 h.p. Armstrong Siddeley Jaguar VI and 525 h.p. Panther IIA, 720 h.p. Napier Culverin, 480 h.p. Rolls-Royce Kestrel II and 450 h.p. Lorraine 12 Ed.

Among the miscellany of Vickers two-seat general-purpose biplanes to make their appearance at Brooklands during this period was the solitary Type 146 Vivid of 1926, which was allotted the civil registration G-EBPY. The machine—with its upper span of 45 ft. 1 in.—was fairly large for a single-bay type and was powered by a 590 h.p. Lion XIA. In his Vivid design Pierson evolved an amalgam of various features displayed in the Vespa and Vixen series. No progress was made with the machine in its intended rôle and, after trials at Southampton as a seaplane, it was sold for use as a private aircraft.

Since constructing their five Bugles Boulton and Paul interest in the high-performance medium bomber had not abated and intensive research continued in an endeavour to extract the maximum qualities from the formula. Specification 9/24 for a twin-engine, medium-range, day bomber landplane with Napier Lions provided the company with the opportunity to embody in a new design the results of their comprehensive experiments to improve the aerodynamic qualities accruing from improved shapes of fuselage, wings and engine nacelles and to reduce to the minimum the interference which arose at the junctions of such bodies and surfaces.

The outcome from John North was the P.29 Sidestrand Mk. I, a new three-seat bomber with outstanding attributes for its time, which were achieved by endowing it with a degree of efficiency which was exceptionally high compared with its contemporaries. Named after a village near Cromer, Norfolk, the prototype Sidestrand Mk. I J7938 displayed a shapely fuselage composed of curved profiles married to flying and control surfaces of the angular style adopted for its bomber predecessors from Norwich. Boulton and Paul engineering expertise was applied in full measure in evolving an original and eminently practical and successful system of fuselage construction, consisting of locked joint steel tubing fabricated from strip drawn to the required tubular section with one edge being wrapped around a bead formed along the opposite edge. This process enabled tubing to be made from stainless steel, an operation which could not, at that period, be managed using the solid-drawn procedure. A useful adjunct, incidentally, was an always-welcome saving in weight. An ingenious matching system of attachment fittings was evolved simultaneously to facilitate the construction of airframes using the new components.

The Sidestrand was provided with three Lewis-gun positions—one in the nose, another amidships in the upper decking and a third in a ventral tunnel pointing towards the tail. J7938's pair of engines were 425 h.p. Jupiter VIs, installed in swivelling mounts on the lower of the three-bay wings. Sqn. Ldr. C. A. Rea was responsible in 1926 for the machine's maiden flight at Mouse-hold Aerodrome, a mile or so from the Norwich works, at the conclusion of which one of the lower wings hit a hockey goal-post on the field. Martlesham Heath trials followed and drew praise for the Sidestrand's performance, but lightening of lateral control was considered necessary. This was effected with complete satisfaction by fitting Frise ailerons, and a further improvement in control was gained by mounting a separate servo rudder some distance aft of the main surface. Handley Page slots were finally added to endow the Sidestrand with its superb powers of manoeuvre so that it was capable of aerobatics which included looping, spinning and rolling. A second Sidestrand prototype, J7939, was completed also in 1926 with minor alterations—which included new vertical tail surfaces—and was equipped later with Jupiter VIIFs.

The Sidestrand was ordered as equipment for a single unit, No. 101 Squadron, and entered service in March, 1929, in its P.29a Mk. II version with the direct-drive 425 h.p. Jupiter VI. Once No. 101 had settled down to flying its new aircraft it quickly established a far higher degree of bombing

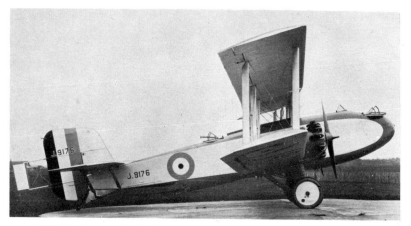

J9176, the first production Boulton and Paul Sidestrand Mk. III. (*Boulton Paul Photo.*)

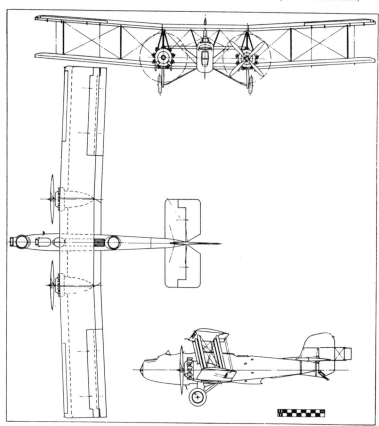

Boulton and Paul Sidestrand Mk. II

170

accuracy than had been attained hitherto. No. 101's Sidestrands were eventually re-engined with the geared Jupiter VIII and 460 h.p. Jupiter VIIIF engines with which the top speed rose to 140 m.p.h. at 10,000 ft. At the same time they were redesignated Sidestrand Mk. III. The offensive load accommodated amounted to two 230 lb. or 250 lb. bombs in addition to a single one of 520 lb. or 550 lb., two of 230 lb. or 250 lb., or four 112 lb. bombs. Aiming from the nose position was by the Mk. 2H high-speed course-setting sight, and other equipment included either a P.7 or an F.8 camera, oxygen and two-way radio.

Although only eighteen Sidestrands constituted the production run and but one squadron was equipped with the type, the advent of the masterly Sidestrand was significant, as it marked the return—after a gap since the retirement of the D.H.10—of the twin-engine, high-performance bomber to R.A.F. service, a type which has not since been absent from its equipment. The development potential inherent in such a successful design was obvious, but, before the major step was taken by producing a new model, trials were conducted with the Sidestrand acting as a test-bed. J7939, redesignated P.29a Mk. IIIS, was employed to evaluate a pair of supercharged, geared Jupiter XFB engines, undertaking trials also with circular Townend ring cowlings installed around the power plants.

Boulton and Paul were particularly concerned with the increased efficiency accruing from the cowling rings, as, in conjunction with the originator Dr. H. C. H. Townend and the Department of Scientific and Industrial Research, the company had undertaken the development, manufacture and marketing of this advanced form of engine cowling in its many variations. The Mk. IIIS bore undoubted testimony to the effectiveness of the modifications, demonstrating a top speed of 167 m.p.h. at 11,000 ft., a service ceiling of 30,000 ft. and a climb to 11,000 ft. in 8·5 min.

Sidestrand development was covered by Specification 25/27, which in turn was superseded by Specification 10/29 for preparation of the Mk. III version.

Although de Havilland design effort in the 1920s was being devoted increasingly to the temptingly unlimited—and ultimately very rewarding—field of commercial aircraft, the firm still found time and capacity to indulge occasionally in a military project. One such essay was the D.H.65 Hound, a Private Venture two-seat general-purpose biplane constructed at Stag Lane during 1926 which made its first flight at the same venue with Capt. H. S. Broad on 17th November, 1926, as G-EBNJ. With 45 ft. equal-span wings set with slight stagger, two-bay bracing was employed and a direct-drive 530 h.p. Lion VIII delivered the power.

The Hound was designed to give the best possible performance and embodied the latest ideas from de Havilland. The combination of the Lion, streamlining and an all-wood airframe contrived to endow it with a top speed of 160 m.p.h. G-EBNJ was subsequently modified to take the geared 540 h.p. Lion XA and was redesignated D.H.65A. The decision was taken to allow it to compete in the trials for Specification 12/26, although it did not meet the Air Ministry's expectation of an all-metal airframe nor did it match the requirement in other respects.

D.H.65A Hound as prepared for speed-with-load record attempts in 1928 equipped with Lion XI. *(de Havilland Photo.)*

In the spring of 1928 the D.H.65A was modified and fitted with a 540 h.p. Lion XI for successful attempts on speed-with-load records which were made by Broad on 26th and 27th April, 1928. Further Service evaluation was made in the following autumn with the Lion XA again in place, but an official order for the Hound eluded de Havilland.

A second considerably modified machine was built in 1928 as the D.H.65J Hound Mk. II using the air-cooled radial 520 h.p. Jupiter VIIIF and a split-unit undercarriage. The Hound Mk. II was designed to meet Australian conditions with accommodation for a 450 lb. load of bombs under the wings or a torpedo beneath the fuselage. Once again, no progress was made beyond the prototype.

At about the same time as the Hound was conceived, de Havilland prepared the D.H.69, an unbuilt project for a fast day bomber of 36 ft. span derived from the D.H.65A and based on the supercharged Rolls-Royce F engine.

Unbuilt projects from Avro during the same period included the 577 general-purpose landplane discussed early in 1926, its 578 derivative on floats and the 580 bomber with four Jupiters which was also mooted at the beginning of 1926.

D.H.65J Hound Mk. II fitted with 520 h.p. Jupiter VIIIF. *(Bristol Siddeley Photo.)*

172

At Rochester, in their works alongside the Medway, Short Brothers were mainly involved with the many facets of their work as constructors of floatplanes and flying-boats, but they, too, occasionally diverted a portion of their resources to other fields. An instance of this was provided by the appearance in 1927 of the S.3b Chamois two-seat, army co-operation biplane J7295, which had been designed by Oswald Short and converted from the first S.3a Springbok Mk. II. The main difference immediately noticeable was the use of smaller lower wings and the alterations to single-bay bracing. The 450 h.p. Jupiter IV was installed as the Chamois's engine, and the bomb load was borne in under-wing racks. The Chamois was undoubtedly at the time the shapeliest of the machines in its class, but no production order materialized. John Lankester Parker flew J7295 on its first flight at Lympne on 14th March, 1927.

J7295, Short Chamois S.3b. (*Short Photo.*)

In all likelihood the far-reaching consequences which resulted from the issue of Specification 12/26 in May, 1926, were entirely unanticipated at the time at which the requirement for a replacement two-seat, high-performance, day bomber landplane were discussed and decided. Proposals by Avro and Hawker were met with agreement for each firm to design and construct a prototype, and the omission of Fairey from the competition was rectified later following the company's representations.

The Fairey entry was a drastically revised model of the Fox designated Fox Mk. IIM. Lobelle and Ralli devised an all-metal structure and altered the lines considerably so that the upper wings were much larger than the lower. Dihedral was retained in the upper planes but eliminated from the lower set. The nose entry was greatly improved by the use of the unsupercharged 480 h.p. Rolls-Royce F.XIB—otherwise known as the Kestrel IB—and the single prototype Mk. IIM J9834—Fairey airframe F1138—was able to record a maximum speed of 190 m.p.h. upon completion in 1929.

Avro 604 Antelope J9183. (*Avro Photo.*)

The Avro entry to Specification 12/26 was another biplane, the 604 Antelope, ready to make its first flight at Hamble in November, 1938. J9183 was representative of the biplanes which Roy Chadwick designed at the time, and it exhibited the typical Avro style of fin and rudder profile then in use. The machine's single-bay wings were staggered and of the relatively small span of 36 ft. for the upper surfaces. The Antelope also was fitted with the 480 h.p. Rolls-Royce F.XIB, the radiator being installed in a forward position below the sump. Lateral control of the Antelope was provided by Frise ailerons on the upper wings; the centre-section struts took the form of an inverted-V cabane. Standard armament of one Vickers and one Lewis was carried, the Lewis in the rear cockpit being installed on a ring mounting of Avro design. The Antelope's bomb load was stored in under-wing racks for release by the observer aiming from a position in the fuselage floor. Although the Antelope failed to win the 12/26 contest, J9183 spent a while with No. 100 Squadron on Service Trials, subsequently becoming a test-bed at Farnborough for Gloster–Hele–Shaw–Beacham variable-pitch propellers matched to the 525 h.p. Rolls-Royce Kestrel IB and also the 477 h.p. Kestrel IIS.

In designing the Hawker contender for Specification 12/26 Sydney Camm succeeded in conceiving a machine which was unwittingly destined to become a classic creation in its class and to be the progenitor of an extensive range of variants from Kingston stretching ahead for the next decade.

The use of the Kestrel in the Hart presented Camm with the opportunity to blend it with exemplary cowling lines into a slim, elegant fuselage to which were attached staggered, single-bay wings of unequal span, the upper planes of which were swept rearwards outboard of the centre-section. The tail unit was of matchingly refined shape and the undercarriage consisted of a clean, oleo-pneumatic unit. The Hart's Vickers gun fired from a trough in the port side, and the observer's Lewis swung from the usual ring in the rear cockpit; the bomb load of 500 lb. was borne externally beneath the wings and fuselage. Construction of J9052, the prototype Hart, was started in 1927 following acceptance of the tender to 12/26, and the machine eventually emerged at

Hawker Hart J9938 of the first production batch. (*Gloster Photo.*)

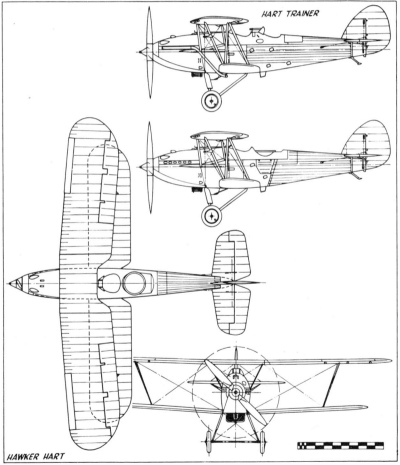

HART TRAINER

HAWKER HART

Hawker Hart Mk. I

175

Brooklands to display its shapely beauty as a thoroughbred before being taken on its maiden flight by Flt. Lt. P. W. S. Bulman in June, 1928. The Hart was an unqualified success from the start and was able to oust its rivals—the Antelope and the Fox Mk. IIM—without difficulty.

And so the R.A.F. gained its new light day bomber, Specification 9/29 being drawn up for issue to Hawker in June, 1929, to cover the first production batch. No. 33 Squadron was selected to introduce the new fast two-seater into service, relinquishing its Horsleys in favour of the Hart Mk. I in January, 1930. The elegant and compact Hart justifiably and swiftly became the most celebrated of high-performance bombers of its era, and the fame engendered by its outstanding qualities was soon instrumental in bringing orders from abroad.

Further development and production of the Hart was by way of Specifications 20/30 for the R.A.F., 9/31 for India, 25/31 with Kestrel IIS, 8/33 for the R.A.F. succeeding 20/30, 12/33 for India succeeding 9/31, 18/34 for Hart Mk. IB and 31/34 for armoured Hart development. Variants for foreign air services included the Kestrel versions for Estonia and Yugoslavia and that with the air-cooled radial Pegasus for Sweden.

The consolidation of the R.A.F. during the decade following the 1914–18 War and its accompanying assumption of a growing quota of commitments served to emphasize the approaching obsolescence of various classes of its equipment. The concept of a type of aircraft capable of performing as many duties as practicable was, in an era of unrealistic impecuniosity, indisputably an attractive proposition. By 1927, therefore, the decision had to be taken to prepare to replace ageing, outmoded aircraft, so Specification 26/27 was circulated to create a new two-seat, general-purpose landplane to take the place of the D.H.9A. Increased performance and load-carrying capacity were stipulated, but, for reasons of economy, the successor to the de Havilland machine was to incorporate as many D.H.9A components as possible. In addition, an all-metal airframe was preferred but not compulsory; the same

1301, first Hawker Swedish Hart. (*Hawker Photo.*)

Gloster Goral J8673. (*Bristol Siddeley Photo.*)

conditions related to the Lion engine to encourage the use of large existing stocks of the Napier engine.

Orders for military and naval aircraft were—at the time—far from plentiful, and the requirement brought a sizeable response from the industry, several of the machines being Private Ventures.

In conjunction with Henry Folland, Capt. S. J. Waters was responsible for the G.22 Goral J8673, the Gloster aspirant to 26/27. The Goral was built in 1926 and was among the first of the 26/27 contenders to be ready. Its designers complied with the Air Ministry's suggestion that D.H.9A components should form part of the airframe and incorporated its two-bay wings as well as other parts from the de Havilland machine. Although the major portion of the Goral's airframe was of metal, a special feature of the design was that metal components could be replaced by wood, in the event of repairs being necessary in some remote area which was without facilities for fabricating in metal.

A 425 h.p. Jupiter VIA engine was prominent in the nose of a refined fuselage faired to oval section, and a pair of long exhaust pipes extended beneath the fuselage as far as the rear cockpit. Had the Goral been ordered into production, it was proposed to fit the geared Jupiter VIII in place of the direct-drive Jupiter VI. The use of the D.H.9A mainplane gave the Goral the appearance of a cleaned-up D.H.9A, but, in general, the machine was still not appealing aesthetically. A Vickers gun was provided for the pilot, and the observer's Lewis was fired from a gun-ring which was set high in the rear decking. Flight trials at A. & A. E. E. Martlesham were made with the Goral during March, 1928.

Two designs were prepared by R. K. Pierson as Vickers entries for the 26/27 trials at A. & A. E. E. Martlesham. One was the Vixen Mk. VI, a development of 1926 fitted with Condor power; the other was the Valiant, an imposing single-bay biplane with staggered wings of unequal span and with strut-connected ailerons on both upper and lower surfaces. The Type 131 Valiant was completed at Brooklands in 1927 and carried an uncowled 515 h.p. Jupiter VI in its nose. The pilot's cockpit was installed at a high level in the deep fore-fuselage; the observer immediately to his rear occupied a position in which the gun-ring was set low in a recessed portion of the coaming. A generous cut-out was made in the upper centre-section. Construction of the Valiant was of metal covered with fabric, and the single example built received

G-EBVM, the Vickers Valiant. (*Vickers Photo.*)

the civil registration G-EBVM at the end of 1927 as a demonstration aircraft, subsequently to be sold abroad a year later in December, 1928.

15th June, 1926, had witnessed at Stag Lane the first flight of J7028, the D.H.9AJ Stag. The machine was the last of the D.H.9A line and was based originally on the Lion for its power. J7028 eventually emerged at Edgware with an air-cooled radial, the direct-drive Jupiter VI, and was among the entries for Specification 26/27.

Armstrong Whitworth also submitted a tender to 26/27 in the form of J9129, a single general-purpose version of the army co-operation Atlas.

The Bristol entrant to 26/27 materialized as the Type 93A Beaver G-EBQF, a general-purpose adaptation by F. S. Barnwell of the Type 93 Boarhound. The Beaver was basically the same as its precursor, but incorporated refinements to upper and lower ailerons, a new fin and rudder with more elegant lines, an improved tailskid and cleaner cowling of the Jupiter assisted by the addition of a spinner. C. F. Uwins was the Beaver's pilot on the machine's maiden flight on 23rd February, 1927, and it went to Martlesham a few weeks later to take its place alongside the other 26/27 competitors.

In mid-1927 Bristol prepared the Type 106 project with a Jupiter to a revised requirement for the general-purpose specification, but the proposed aircraft was not built.

Fairey also entered the 26/27 trials, submitting a version of the IIIF.

The ultimate winner of the tests at Martlesham for the 26/27 requirement was provided by Westland. As the firm which developed the D.H.9A, the

Bristol Type 93A Beaver G-EBQF. (*Bristol Photo.*)

178

Wapiti Mk. IA A5-12 of the R.A.A.F. (*R.A.A.F. Photo.*)

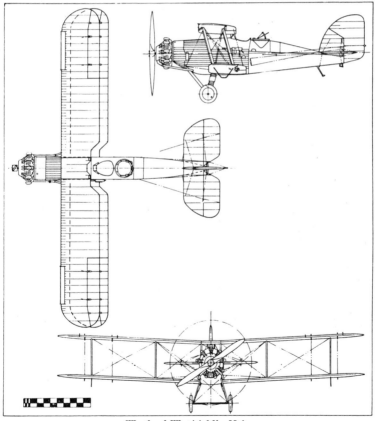

Westland Wapiti Mk. IIA

179

machine due for retirement, the Yeovil company was in a particularly strong position to meet the need to incorporate as many as possible of the D.H.9A's components. In evolving the Wapiti, as the Westland entry was named, Arthur Davenport succeeded in utilizing a high proportion of the D.H.9A's parts, including the wings, tail unit, ailerons and interplane struts. The undercarriage was a unit which Westland had devised for possible use on the D.H.9A. To meet the stipulations of Specification 26/27 it was necessary to devise a completely new fuselage for the Wapiti made 1 ft. deeper and 5·5 in. wider than that of the D.H.9A and provided with a front section of duralumin tubing, covered by metal panels, allied to a rear section of wire-braced, wooden girder form. In an attempt to extract the greatest aerodynamic efficiency from the wings, the cut-out in the upper centre-section was kept to the minimum; in consequence, to maintain an adequate view for the pilot, his cockpit was located fairly well aft with the observer adjacent to the rear. J8495, the prototype Wapiti, was designed around the direct-drive 420 h.p. Jupiter VI and was armed with the pilot's Vickers gun installed on an external bracket on the port side of the fuselage and with the observer's Lewis on the normal Scarff ring. The bomb load of 580 lb. was borne in racks beneath the fuselage and lower wings.

Maj. L. P. Openshaw conducted the initial flight of J8495 in March, 1927, and soon uncovered an unaccountable deficiency in directional control. The D.H.9A rudder was found to be ineffective, and the trouble was traced to the omission—in the course of preparing detail design drawings—of an entire fuselage bay of some 1 ft. 6 in. in length. An increase was made in the area of J8495's vertical tail surfaces, the new rudder being tall and angular. A second revision took place with the installation of an even larger but shapelier fin and rudder, complete during mid-1927 with a curved fillet—later discarded upon production—extending from the fin to the rear decking.

After protracted trials at Martlesham the Westland design was proclaimed the winner and was ordered in December, 1927, as the Wapiti Mk. I, the first batch of twenty-five being built in 1928 embodying minor alterations from the prototype. During the same year No. 84 Squadron at Shaibah in Iraq became the first to receive the new general-purpose two-seater. Specification 26/27 was superseded by Specification 1/29, and Specification 12/30 was drawn up to cover the version for India. The geared Jupiter VIII was used in the Wapiti Mk. IA, which was given also an increase in stagger. A divided undercarriage was fitted to the Wapiti Mk. IB, and the machine was supplied to South Africa equipped with the Jupiter VIIIF; during service the Jupiter was supplanted by the Panther.

The Wapiti Mk. II, to general-purpose and army co-operation Specification 16/31, was equipped with the Jupiter VIII mounted in a modernized all-metal airframe consisting of square-section duralumin tubing for the fuselage and wings designed—and fabricated initially—by the Steel Wing Company; later Westland undertook manufacture of these wings. The relatively short production run of ten Mk. IIs was succeeded in 1931 by the Mk. IIA powered by the Jupiter VIII, VIIIF, IXF or XFA. In addition to the prototype J9247, four hundred and twenty-nine Mk. IIAs were constructed. To endow the Mk. IIA with the greatest possible versatility it was designed to utilize several alternative types of landing gear, including the split-axle type, twin floats or skis. Among other general-purpose models of the Wapiti were the Mk. III for South Africa equipped with either the Jupiter IXF or the Jaguar VI; the Mk. V, which regained the missing bay by extending the fuselage length and at the same time received an improved stronger undercarriage complete with brakes, a tailwheel and a rudder of increased area—thirty-five were produced; and the Mk. VIII, four of which were supplied to China powered by the Panther IIA. Twenty-five R.A.F. Wapitis were transferred to the R.C.A.F. and, to cope with the severe cold of the Canadian winter, a canopy was devised and installed to enclose the pilot's cockpit. The Wapiti proved an extremely adaptable test-bed for various engines, and a number were used for this purpose for several years.

R.C.A.F. Wapiti 509 equipped with cockpit canopy. (*R.C.A.F. Photo.*)

Trials with Wapiti Mk. I J9084, to Specification 26/27 on Contract No. 802348/27 and fitted with twin metal floats made by Short Brothers, were described in M.A.E.E. Felixstowe Report F/32A of May, 1929. The machine, equipped with a Jupiter VIF.T. engine No. J6256/103870 developing 472 h.p. at 1,700 r.p.m., weighed 3,357 lb. empty and 5,400 lb. loaded. Its floats were of dural, fitted with water rudders and were 23 ft. 6·75 in. long, 2 ft. 4·9 in. deep and 2 ft. 11 in. in beam. Steel tube undercarriage struts and booms, faired with wood, attached the floats to the fuselage. J9084's mainplane area of 490·94 sq. ft. gave a wing loading of 11 lb./sq. ft.; span was 46 ft. 5 in., length 33 ft. 7 in. and height 14 ft. 5 in. The maximum speed attained was 98 kt. at 5,000 ft. and 97 kt. at sea level, climb rate 725 ft./min., at sea level, service ceiling 13,100 ft., estimated absolute ceiling 15,050 ft., take-off run 300 yd. in 18·6 sec. in an 8 kt. wind, landing speed 46 kt. and landing run 158 yd. in 10 sec. in an 8 kt. wind.

J9084 possessed a three-section, composite wood and tubular metal fuselage allied to equal-span, staggered, wire-braced wooden wings attached with wooden interplane and centre-section struts. The aircraft carried two guns—one Vickers and one Lewis, four 112 lb. bombs beneath the wings, a G.3 camera, desert equipment and a T.21B carrier-wave radio receiver operated from the rear cockpit.

Assessment of the pilot's view was that it was very good for its type and that the cockpit was roomy and comfortable. The rudder bar, however, was too near to the pilot, thereby cramping his legs. The windscreen was not bad but not as effective as it could be, as it was probably too far from the pilot. Layout of instruments and controls was very good, the tail trim wheel being well placed and exceptionally convenient to use. It was found that, if the pilot's safety belt were left unfastened, there was the chance that it might foul the rudder bar. This contingency occurred during the tests. Installation of the Jupiter was good and all parts were easily accessible. First handling trials revealed certain structural weaknesses causing unusual flexing while on the water; modifications were therefore made to the undercarriage structure and the centre-section bracing, and these eliminated the trouble.

Handling with the gear provided with the Wapiti was considered quite impracticable, so, after tests with it, J9084 was handled on a beach trolley throughout its type trials. Such a system was regarded as obsolete for seaplanes, and the Blackburn pattern of handling device was therefore recommended for standardization. It was considered that all seaplanes should have slinging gear, as this would save a considerable amount of time when fitting float undercarriages. Maintenance was generally good, but that of the floats was handicapped by inspection covers retained by a large number of screws. It was recommended that quickly detachable covers should consequently be fitted. The drain holes in the float boom wells needed enlarging.

J9084's flying qualities as a two-seat floatplane were assessed as outstanding, and the controls, with the exception of the rudder, were good and light with rapid response. The rudder control was heavier, and if made lighter it would be to the great advantage of the flying qualities of the aircraft. Low-speed control was very good, and the impression gained was that involuntary entry into a spin—even with considerable misuse of the controls—was extremely unlikely. The tail trim wheel was sensitive and easy to use over the whole speed range. The machine was particularly easy to fly at a steady airspeed either on the level or in a climb, it was stable longitudinally and laterally, could be flown comfortably hands-off and was easy to fly for long distances in calm or bumpy weather. Take-off and landing on floats was easy, but in choppy water the Wapiti tended to porpoise on take-off and then to be thrown into the air in a stalled attitude. This was not thought to be a serious defect, and deepening of the V shape in the floats' underside near the step should effect a cure.

The most fundamental change to take place in the later 1920s in the design of British military and naval operational aircraft was the abandonment of wood in favour of metal for airframes. Investigation into advanced metal structures for large aeroplanes was being conducted, particularly by the firm of Röhrbach in Germany. The Scottish engineering company of William Beardmore

The enormous Beardmore Inflexible J7557. (*Beardmore Photo.*)

showed considerable interest in the new processes being devised, and arranged for W. S. Shackleton to design a new bomber around the German Röhrbach patents.

There was no evidence of half-measures in the eventual product, which, after three years in construction at Dalmuir from 1925 until 1927, emerged early in 1928 as the behemoth Inflexible. At a time when bomber designers were committed almost entirely to the biplane formula, Shackleton had struck out into a virtually unexplored field in British bomber endeavour by adopting the high-wing monoplane layout. The awe-inspiring Inflexible was fabricated throughout from duralumin—except for steel fittings—and was duralumin-covered overall. All flying and control surfaces were of parallel chord and were cantilever. The 157 ft. 6 in. span wings exhibited the high aspect ratio of 12·5 and were attached at shoulder level to the slab-sided fuselage. In elevation the fuselage possessed a reasonably elegant line in marked contrast with the sharply angular aspect of the rest of the machine. Total length was 75 ft. 6 in. or 82 ft. including the servo rudder. Three 650 h.p. Condor II engines, driving two-blade propellers, were selected to power the massive monoplane; one, cooled by an underslung radiator, was installed in the nose, and the remaining two were disposed flush with the undersides of the wings. In view of the great size and 37,000 lb.—or over 16·5 tons—weight of the Inflexible, it might have been expected that the landing gear would have utilized multiple wheels to spread the load. Nevertheless, two immense main wheels only were provided of 7 ft. 4 in. diameter, equipped with Dunlop high-pressure tyres and hydraulic brakes. A single heavy flying wire extended from the front horizontal undercarriage strut on each side to a point about one-third of the distance from the wingtips. The pilot's cockpit was just behind the central Condor and a short distance ahead of the wings. Ailerons, elevators and rudder were each fitted with a rectangular balancing surface which projected prominently. In addition, a servo rudder was carried on struts to the rear of the main rudder to assist the pilot in moving the large surface.

While under construction the giant was allotted the civil registration G-EBNG, but when completed it was painted in the standard R.A.F. dark green night bomber finish and carried the serial J7557 in white on the fuselage. Assembly took place at A. & A.E.E. Martlesham Heath, Sqn. Ldr. J. Noakes carrying out the first flight there on 5th March, 1928. Later trials were in the hands of Sqn. Ldr. R. A. de Haga Haig, and the machine made a majestic public appearance at the 1928 Hendon Air Display. Subsequently, various modifications took place in an endeavour to improve the performance, but the Inflexible's strong structure was so heavy that it was unable to transport

A.W. Ajax G-EBLM/J9128. (*Armstrong Whitworth Photo.*)

any worthwhile load. Eventually, after two years, the airframe was broken down at Martlesham to be utilized for structural research and corrosion tests. By the beginning of January, 1930, the three Condors had been removed, and the machine was standing without its engines inside the hangar of B Flight of No. 22 Squadron. Some twelve months later, in January, 1931, the wings were taken off, to be left outside in the open air to assess their resistance to the effects of the elements. Although the mighty Inflexible represented an essay in advanced design and structural practice, it remains just an outsize curiosity in the annals of bomber development of its period, the sole relic of it extant being a single wheel in the National Aeronautical Collection at South Kensington.

Steady sponsorship of the torpedo-carrier had brought the evolution of this

A.W.17 Aries prototype J9037. (*Armstrong Whitworth Photo.*)

184

class of aeroplane to a point where, by the approach of the 1930s, Great Britain was pre-eminent in its design and manufacture. This development was intended to be fostered by the preparation and issue of Specification M.5/28 for a two-seat, shipborne torpedo landplane. At Cricklewood George Volkert prepared the H.P.41 for Handley Page, and Sydney Camm designed the Hawker M.5/28 at Kingston. In neither case was a prototype built, as the requirement was subsequently cancelled in favour of a revised Specification M.1/30.

Considerable attention was paid at this time to the evolution of suitably versatile army co-operation two-seaters, two of which were constructed by Armstrong Whitworth in response to Specification 20/25 for an army co-operation type which could be maintained easily. Designed by J. Lloyd and built at Coventry, both the A.W. Ajax and the A.W.17 Aries were biplanes retaining the general lines of the established Atlas.

The Ajax prototype was built during 1925 and appeared first as a trainer adaptation of the Atlas Mk. I with the civil registration G-EBLM. Its engine was the 385 h.p. Jaguar III. An order was placed by the Air Ministry in 1927 for two examples of the Ajax—J8802 and J8803. In its 20/25 form as Ajax J9128, the 550 h.p. Panther was fitted and the wing span reduced to 36 ft. 4 in. The machine's first flight in this guise took place on 26th January, 1928.

The Aries J9037 performed its maiden flight on 3rd May, 1930, displaying a definite attempt at complying with Specification 20/25's edict that it should be easy to maintain by dispensing with normal interplane flying and landing wires, their place being taken on each side by a pair of sturdy diagonal struts. The upper span of the Aries was increased to 37 ft. 7 in., wide-span upper ailerons were fitted and were inter-connected with the movable Handley Page slots on the leading edge. The Ajax's engine was a special geared Jaguar developing 460 h.p. The machine was armed with a Vickers gun carried to port in the fore-decking and a Lewis on a Scarff ring in the rear cockpit; a message pick-up hook was hinged to the undercarriage axle, and the bomb load was stowed beneath the lower wings. Neither the Ajax nor the Aries progressed beyond assessment as prototypes.

Among the many projects investigated was one by A. V. Roe and Co. for the Avro 609, a three-seat general-purpose seaplane which was proposed during December, 1927. Chadwick's design would have been a development of the 608 Hawk biplane with the same type of engine—the Jupiter.

Japanese interest in torpedo-bombers, a decade or so later to be applied with dramatic effect, had been increasing steadily after the 1914–18 War, and in 1929 Blackburn completed the single prototype of the 3.M.R.4 or Reconnaissance J three-seat torpedo biplane for dispatch to Japan. G. E. Petty had been responsible for the major part of the design in conjunction with Maj. Bumpus and had evolved a very sturdy and aggressively businesslike two-bay biplane with staggered, equal-span, square-cut wings. The 3.M.R.4 was somewhat larger than the Fleet Air Arm's current Ripon and was powered by a liquid-cooled 625 h.p. Hispano-Suiza engine installed in a clean cowling and driving a two-blade propeller. Four cable-connected ailerons were fitted, and

185

Handley Page movable slots occupied the upper outer leading edge of the wings. A broad-track, divided undercarriage facilitated accommodation of the torpedo or alternative stores in the same location. The 3.M.R.4 was duly delivered to Japan, where it received the designation Type 92.

The development of the basic Hyderabad continued at Cricklewood resulting on 26th March, 1927, in the first flight at Radlett of the prototype Handley Page H.P.33 Hinaidi Mk. I J7745 flown by Sqn. Ldr. T. H. England. The design, by George Volkert, was a four-seat heavy night bomber powered by a pair of 440 h.p. Jupiter VIII air-cooled radials in place of its predecessor's water-cooled Lions. J7745 was not a new aircraft but a modified Hyderabad retaining, therefore, the earlier machine's wooden airframe. The Hinaidi's wings were swept back outboard of the centre-section. Specification 13/29 covered production of thirty-three H.P.36 Hinaidi Mk. IIs which were revised to have metal airframes. Another six Hinaidis were produced by conversions from Hyderabads. Sqn. Ldr. England flew the first Hinaidi Mk. II from Radlett initially on 25th November, 1931.

As with the Hyderabad, No. 99 Squadron was the first to be supplied with the Hinaidi, the new equipment starting to arrive on 2nd October, 1929. The three Lewis-gun positions were the same as those of the Hyderabad, but the Hinaidi offered an increase in bomb load of some 350 lb. A small improvement in general performance was evident also. The H.P.44 Hinaidi Mk. III was designed in 1930 to use a pair of 480 h.p. Jaguars.

Since flying had become a reality the natural trend had been for the aeroplane to become larger and correspondingly heavier and, as in any sphere of engineering, the pursuit of increased performance had manifested itself as a matter of course. The heavy bomber was no exception, and the need to replace eventually the R.A.F.'s Hinaidis and Virginias was responsible for the setting out of the requirements of Specification B.19/27 for a landplane night bomber. The request brought responses from a considerable proportion of the industry, interest being shown by Avro, Bristol, Fairey, Handley Page, Hawker and Vickers. In several instances this stopped short at unnamed projects.

Blackburn 3.M.R.4 for Japan. (*Blackburn Photo.*)

Handley Page Hinaidi Mk. II J9033. (*Bristol Siddeley Photo.*)

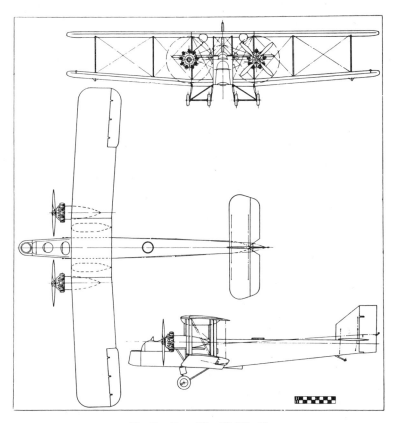

Handley Page Hinaidi Mk. II

Vickers Type 195 B.19/27 Mk. II J9131 with two-bay wings. (*Vickers Photo.*)

In the case of the Avro 613 B.19/27, a general layout of which was prepared in May, 1928, to use a pair of Jaguar IVs, the serial J9249 was allotted to the unrealized project.

At Bristol the Type 108 using two Jupiter engines was proposed in 1927, but no order was received for a prototype.

The Hawker B.19/27 project was likewise unsuccessful. A four-seat biplane using a pair of tractor Jupiter Xs mounted on the lower planes of the two-bay, unequal-span, staggered wings was proposed. Twin fins and rudders would have been installed between the biplane horizontal tail surfaces, and a sturdy divided undercarriage of broad track formed part of the layout. Gun-rings were to occupy the extreme nose and tail, while the pilot would have been seated ahead of the wings in a cockpit set to starboard. Although a promising design on paper, the machine was not built.

A determined effort to meet B.19/27 was made at Weybridge by Vickers. Two designs—the Types 150 and 195—were constructed, but the Type 225, prepared in 1933 to B.19/27 requirements, was still-born.

Designed by R. K. Pierson, the B.19/27 Mk. I Type 150 appeared in 1930 as a four-seat biplane with two-bay bracing and unequal-span wings swept back outboard of the centre-section. All-metal construction with fabric covering was used, and the machine had for power a pair of F.XIVS Kestrels

Vickers Type 255 B.19/27 Mk. III Vannock J9131 with revised three-bay wings. (*Vickers Photo.*)

installed as tractors at mid-gap. Lewis-gun positions were at the extremes of the fuselage, in nose and tail. In common with several large Vickers civil aircraft of the same period—notably the Vellore Mks. I, II and III, Viastra Mks. II, III, VI, VIII and X and the Vellox—the Type 150 featured biplane tail surfaces of high aspect ratio, at the two extremities of which were attached tall rudders of narrow parallel chord. The lower tailplane was fixed across the bottom longerons, while the upper surface passed across the fuselage supported by four short struts splayed outwards in pyramid form. The fuselage's deep central section housed a cabin, access being through a door in the port

J9130, the H.P.38 Heyford prototype. (*Handley Page Photo.*)

side below the inverted-V centre-section struts. Cable-connected ailerons occupied all four wingtips, and Handley Page movable slots were mounted on the upper wings. Twin main wheels and a tailwheel constituted the landing gear. The Vickers Type 150's lineal descent from the Virginia was evident to a high degree from its general aspect, although the later machine was notably cleaner in every respect.

In its second version as the B.19/27 Mk. II J9131, the Vickers Type 195 emerged at Brooklands during 1932 with two air-cooled radial 622 h.p. Pegasus IM3 engines replacing the Kestrels. Spats had been added to the pair of main wheels, but otherwise the design was substantially the same. In a still further modified version, the Type 195 J9131 existed in 1932 as the B.19/27 Mk. III with an exhaust collector ring incorporated in the engine cowling and with an extra pair of inner interplane struts added on each side transforming the wings into three-bay cellules. In this form it became the Type 255 Vannock.

To Handley Page eventually went the order for the R.A.F.'s new heavy night bomber to B.19/27. The machine was a four-seat biplane conceived by G. R. Volkert and endowed with a singular but exceedingly purposeful appearance. The prototype H.P.38 J9130 was completed in the summer of 1930, making its maiden flight in June of that year at Radlett piloted by Sqn. Ldr. T. H. England. The Heyford's main claim to originality lay in the high-set position of its fuselage, which was attached flush to the underside of the upper wings. As the bomb load was stowed in the lower centre-section of

K3489, the first production H.P.50 Heyford Mk. I. (*Handley Page Photo.*)

specially increased depth, the gap of the staggered wings combined to bring the bomb-bay unusually near to ground level, thereby contributing greatly to ease of bombing-up. At the same time the location of the pilot's cockpit bestowed a superb view from the nose, and the front and mid-upper gunners'

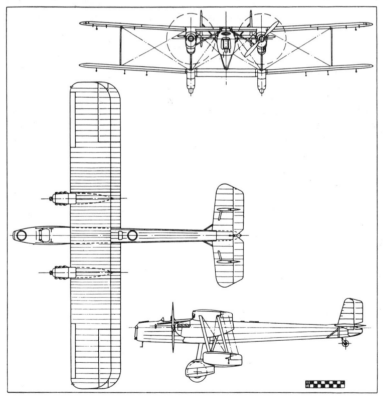

Handley Page Heyford Mk. IA

190

positions in the same plane were in a similar position, with first-rate fields of fire containing little obstruction to their aim. The Heyford's wings at 75 ft. were the same in span as those of its immediate lineal precursors, the Hyderabad and Hinaidi, and were of identical area at 1,470 sq. ft. The H.P.38 prototype received a fabric-covered, all-metal airframe and a pair of 550 h.p. Kestrel II engines installed beneath the upper mainplanes. A third Lewis gun was provided in the ventral position in an ingenious retractable rotating turret which could be lowered to defend the underside against attacking aircraft. Twin fins and rudders formed a prominent part of the rear of the machine, and lateral control was provided by four cable-connected ailerons. The undercarriage's main wheels were housed in large spats, the units being attached direct to the lower wings in line with the engines. As was natural with each product from Handley Page, slots were installed on the top mainplanes.

Upon acceptance by the R.A.F., the H.P.38 went into production to Specification B.23/32 as the H.P.50 Heyford Mk. I to achieve distinction as the Service's final biplane type of heavy bomber. Various improvements were made in the production Mk. I, the fuselage consisting of an aluminium-covered, duralumin-braced monocoque fore portion joined to a rear part of wire-braced, steel tubing structure, covered with fabric. A smoother cowling installation covered the pair of 525 h.p. Kestrel IIIS engines in the Mk. I, short ram's-horn exhaust manifolds replaced the long exhausts of the H.P.38 prototype and the underslung radiator beneath each engine was enclosed in a tunnel housing. The spats were deepened to cover the lower portion of the wheels. K3489, the first production Mk. I, made its maiden flight on 21st June, 1933, at Radlett piloted by Maj. J. L. B. H. Cordes, and No. 99 Squadron, by now used to being the first to receive new Handley Page heavy bombers, took its first Heyfords on strength in July, 1933, at Upper Heyford.

The Mk. IA was the next version of the Heyford—with the 525 h.p. Kestrel IIIS, followed by the Mk. II and Mk. III, each using the 640 h.p. Kestrel VI. The prototype Mk. II, K3503 from the initial batch of Mk. Is, was fitted with an enclosed canopy for the pilot but production Mk. IIs retained the open form of cockpit. Overall performance of the Mk. II had been improved over that of the Mk. I by various means, including reduction of weight and drag, greater propeller efficiency and reduced consumption of fuel. New engine nacelles of better form and smaller cross-section had contributed to lower drag. Heyford Mk. II production was to Specification 28/34 and that of the Mk. III to Specification 27/35. The Heyford's normal bomb load was 2,800 lb., but this could be increased to 3,500 lb. maximum.

The inherent development potential of the Fairey IIIF line was exploited once again when the IIIF Mk. V was produced from the IIIF Mk. IVB as the R.A.F.'s day bomber and general-purpose Gordon Mk. I. The IIIF's normal water-cooled Lion was supplanted in the Gordon by the air-cooled 525 h.p. Armstrong Siddeley Panther IIA installed uncowled. Minor alterations included a revised nose to take the new style of engine, removal of the pilot's

Vickers gun from the cowling trough to an external position on the port side of the fuselage and changes in the electrical and fuel systems. The modifications had little effect on the character of the IIIF design, and the Gordon was just as stately and handsome an aeroplane as its immediate antecedent.

The prototype Gordon Mk. I J9154 was derived in 1930 from a IIIF Mk. IVM/A F1020 and production of the Mk. I was undertaken to Specification 18/30. A second Gordon prototype, K1697, was built in 1931 using the fuselage of a IIIF Mk. IVB. The R.A.F.'s Gordon carried a crew of two and a load consisting of two 230 lb. or 250 lb. or four 112 lb. bombs, together with four smaller bombs of 20 lb. each. The first production Gordons were taken on to the strength of No. 40 Squadron in April, 1931, when the unit reformed at Upper Heyford on the first day of the month. A revised Gordon, the Mk. II, made its appearance later as the result of Specification 14/33, embodying a new rear fuselage, Frise-type ailerons on each wing and a taller fin and rudder of more rounded and less elongated outline—as used by the Seal which followed—to promote better harmony between the control surfaces. Gordon production reached a total of one hundred and sixty plus about thirty converted from serving IIIF airframes.

In some instances Gordons were flown as seaplanes on twin floats, and M.A.E.E. Felixstowe Report F/112 of March, 1933, described the handling tests undertaken with K1740, a Gordon Mk. I of No. 40 Squadron which had been equipped with a IIIF's pair of metal floats. To fit the Gordon the IIIF floats had to be slightly modified and were then unable to accommodate the IIIF water rudders. Special rudders on order were not ready in time so that the trials were made with experimental rudders which had been sent with the floats. To reduce the possibility of damage to the floats' sterns in the course of handling on the slipway, their sternposts had been shortened so that the posts did not project so far beneath the keel. The new inspection openings fitted to the floats were considered to be an improvement, but could be damaged easily if the tops of the floats were walked upon.

Fairey Gordon floatplane of the Brazilian Naval Air Service. (*Fairey Photo.*)

Fairey Gordon Mk. I. (*Bristol Siddeley Photo.*)

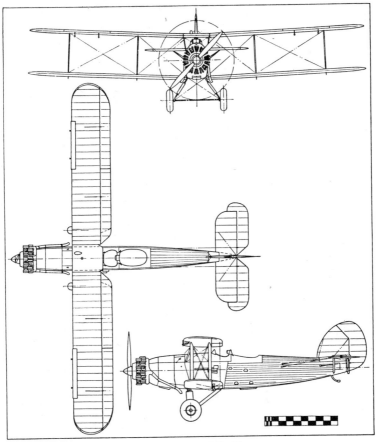

Fairey Gordon Mk. II

193

K1740, tested at a loaded weight of 6,300 lb., took off in 20·5 sec. with 5° of flap into a wind of 10–12 m.p.h.; using 12° of flap into a wind of the same speed the take-off time was reduced slightly to 19 sec. Water behaviour was assessed as little different from that exhibited by the Panther-engine IIIF, although the weight was 300 lb. greater. Easier water handling of the Gordon resulted from a better pilot's view than that of the standard IIIF. Both take-off and landing were easy with less tendency to turn than with the IIIF. The take-off was reasonably clean without porpoising, and in a flat calm there was no tendency to stick on the water as with the IIIF. In the air the Gordon handled in the same way as the Panther IIIF. The controls were found to be too heavy, constituting a handicap to manoeuvrability. Behaviour was satisfactory on diving the Gordon to 165 m.p.h. General assessment of the floats for the Gordon was that they were satisfactory but that the inspection covers needed strengthening.

M.A.E.E. Felixstowe Report F/112B of December, 1933, dealt with performance tests on K1740 as a general-purpose floatplane with an empty weight of 4,144 lb. and loaded to 6,393 lb., including crew of two, guns, four 112 lb. bombs and radio equipment. Service ceiling was recorded as 9,180 ft., climb rate 385 ft./min. at 3,000 ft., top speed 103·5 kt. at 3,000 ft., take-off without wind and with 5° flap 44 sec., and without wind and with 12° flap 39 sec. Estimated absolute ceiling was 11,300 ft.

K1740 was received at Felixstowe as a standard Gordon landplane fitted with Panther IIA A.S.7715/107297, which, geared and with modified supercharger, developed 535 b.h.p. at 2,000 r.p.m. at 3,000 ft. turning a Fairey-Reed two-blade propeller 11 ft. 9 in. in diameter. Air and water handling were satisfactory up to 7,000 lb. A.U.W. for taking-off in calm water.

By the end of the 1920s, the passing of but some fifteen years since the British bomber had first been evolved—albeit at the beginning in a primitive and extemporized form—had found it established in numerous guises, both as a landplane and as a seaplane. The bomber's development in several distinct categories—light, medium, heavy and general purpose for use either by day or by night—was maintained at a fairly steady rate by the issue of specifications intended to result not only in entirely new aircraft to replace obsolescent machines but also to assist and encourage manufacturers to design and construct intermediate and advanced prototypes with the object of stimulating new lines of technical advance. The same process applied also to the Fleet Air Arm with its specialized requirements for torpedo-bombers and for aircraft operating as landplanes from shore bases and afloat and in the form of seaplanes.

The difficult post-war period of some eleven years had witnessed the birth of a collection of diverse designs in many categories, few—if any—of which could be classed as impractical or bizarre. In fact, the evolution of British bomber and torpedo-carrying aircraft had been established on sound, rational lines—a process which was to continue into the ensuing decade with increasingly creditable results.

J9950, the Boulton and Paul P.32. (*Boulton Paul Photo.*)

CHAPTER FIVE

MURMURINGS OF MONOPLANES

As the first hesitant and confused decade to follow the 1914–18 War slipped swiftly into the past, its successor took its place overnight as the 1930s advanced to assume their increasingly troubled and finally tragic and catastrophic place in history. The era began in the midst of a steadily worsening depression which spread its unsought influence eastwards across the Atlantic to engulf Great Britain and Europe.

By the time that 1930 had arrived the meagre programme, started five years earlier to expand the Air Defence of Great Britain to fifty-two squadrons —consisting of thirty-five bomber and seventeen fighter—in five years, had progressed only partly towards completion. Theoretically, at least, the seventeen fighter squadrons were available, but only twelve of the bomber units had been formed. Four of these were equipped with twin-engine night bombers, while eight had single-engine day bombers. The rate at which the bomber force was supposed to have been built up had suffered, in addition to the scarcity of money for the purpose, from the machinations of the advocates of disarmament.

In spite of the grandiose speeches and the farcical delusion that the example of disarmament set by Britain would be followed by the rest of the world, the development of the bomber aircraft by the industry and its designers progressed steadily in several directions. All-metal construction for Service aircraft was *de rigueur*, and the bomber and torpedo-bomber—in company with the fighter and other types—were, especially in their engines, receiving direct advantages from the money and the effort which had been invested and expended over the years in the endeavours to win the Schneider Trophy contests. The considerably smaller frontal area inherent in the inline engine ensured that, in spite of the disadvantages imposed by its liquid cooling system, it was the subject of unending investigation for racing purposes. Both Napier and Rolls-Royce concentrated their resources to great effect on its evolution, with consequent incalculable benefit a few years hence. It was evident also that certain aircraft manufacturing companies had established a particular class of aeroplane as their *forte*, although, when a competitive R.A.F. or F.A.A. requirement was announced, the practice had arisen of several firms submitting tenders for prototypes outside their normally accepted type of production aircraft. None the less, designers were able to display considerable versatility and ingenuity in conceiving machines for widely divergent rôles.

In general, the companies constituting the British aircraft construction industry had, so far, continued to concentrate their resources and activities on the same class of aeroplane as that with which their reputations had been established during the late war. Both Handley Page and Vickers had assumed their places as the principal suppliers of the heavier class of bomber, Hawker and Westland were well attuned to the light bomber and general-purpose types, Blackburn had progressed steadily with naval torpedo-bombers and the name of Fairey was synonymous with general-purpose landplanes and seaplanes. After a start—dictated by circumstances—in the province of military and naval aircraft, other firms had veered strongly towards the civil market with significant success but returned spasmodically to produce a prototype or two in answer to Air Ministry specifications for new Service aircraft.

Two large biplanes of unusual layout—as far as British techniques in power arrangement were concerned—emanated in 1931 from Boulton and Paul and de Havilland as a result of the companies' tenders to Specification B.22/27, which was drawn up to produce a four-seat, long-range, heavy night bomber.

The 100 ft. span P.32 J9950, which John North designed for Boulton and Paul, left no doubt in the mind as to its ancestry, as, in the refined line of its fuselage and the square-cut planform of the three-bay, staggered, folding wings, it was obviously a near descendant of the Sidestrand. The most significant and unusual feature—possessed in common by both the P.32 and its rival, the D.H.72—was the use of three tractor engines, the location of the third being in the centre of the upper mainplanes. The P.32's structure in the main followed that adopted for the Sidestrand using a metal airframe covered with fabric, the broad span dictating folding of the wings to 47 ft. 6 in. The upper centre-section was straight, but that of the lower wings was given anhedral. The use of very long diagonal axles in each of the twin, divided undercarriage units resulted in an unusually wide gap between the two wheels on each side. The P.32 was protected by three machine-gun positions in the fuselage—nose, dorsal and rear—Scarff rings carrying those in the front and middle.

The three engines were of the same type—the Jupiter XF—but were subsequently exchanged for medium-supercharged 575 h.p. Jupiter XFBMs surrounded by Townend rings which incorporated exhaust collectors. The pair of Jupiters flanking the fuselage were installed direct on the lower wings, and all three drove four-blade propellers. Each of the twin rudders was equipped with a smaller servo surface outrigged on struts to its rear. J9950 eventually made its first take-off in January, 1931, from Mousehold piloted by Sqn. Ldr. C. A. Rea. At this period in bomber evolution it was still

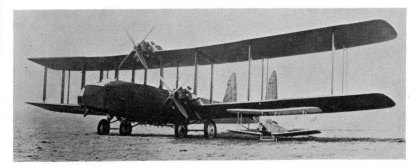

The D.H.72 J9184 completed by Gloster. (*de Havilland Photo.*)

possible—and often the custom—for a prototype to be constructed in a relatively short time, but, in the case of the P.32, the gestation was considerably longer than had been intended, owing to continued uncertainty over the power plant to be used. The choice had fallen on a Bristol air-cooled type with the Jupiter VIII, Mercury V—later to be developed into the Pegasus—and the Jupiter X investigated in turn.

Often, when more than one prototype was built to a specific requirement,

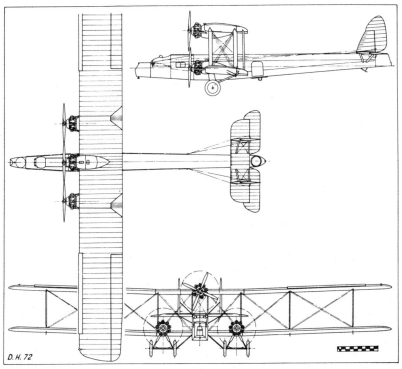

de Havilland D.H. 72

197

the resulting aircraft from different concerns were of totally dissimilar concept to perform the same tasks. At other times designers would arrive at the same conclusions for the optimum layout, and their creations would be strikingly alike in size and appearance. The two B.22/27 prototypes demonstrated this similarity, and the P.32's competitor from de Havilland resembled closely the Boulton and Paul product but lacked the elegance of fuselage line possessed by the P.32. Work on the D.H.72 J9184 was started at Stag Lane in 1928, and the machine was designed to have an all-metal airframe. So far the firm's experience had been mainly with wooden structures, and the new venture proceeded at a very slow rate at the Edgware works until, finally, the partly constructed biplane was transferred to the Gloster factory at Brockworth for completion.

At the time when the D.H.72 was conceived Jupiter VI power plants were decided upon, but, as the months passed, improved versions of the Jupiter were scheduled until, upon completion for its maiden flight in 1931, three uncowled Jupiter XFS engines, driving four-blade propellers, were installed. In common with the P.32, the 95 ft. equal-span, three-bay wings folded outboard of the straight centre-section. Gunners' cockpits occupied each end of the fuselage, on the underside of which bombs could be stowed in external racks. The D.H.72's upper and lower ailerons were connected by a pair of struts on each side, and the machine's main undercarriage consisted of twin wheels beneath each of the wing-mounted engines.

Despite the application of several years of design and construction effort to produce the massive P.32 and D.H.72, the Air Ministry's plans changed, and the requirement was abandoned; the P.32 ended its days at Martlesham following a public appearance at the 1932 Hendon Air Display.

The fascination which the very large biplane still held at this time for those planning future equipment needs for the R.A.F.'s heavy bomber squadrons manifested itself again in 1931 with the emergence of the five-seat Vickers Type 163 O-2. Four 480 h.p. Kestrel III engines were disposed at mid-gap in tandem pairs on each side between the 90 ft. span wings. Pierson's design followed the lines of the Type 150 very closely, retaining unequal-span, square-cut wings rigged with considerable gap, sweepback outboard of the centre-section and with the upper planes carried across the top of the fuselage. Design of the biplane tail unit was virtually identical with that of the Type

Vickers Type 163 O-2 in its original form with radiators in upper centre-section and without spats.
(*Vickers Photo.*)

Bristol Type 118 R-3/K2873. (*Bristol Photo.*)

150, and the wide-track, divided, single-wheel undercarriage units later received the currently popular refinement of large spats. The Type 163 was defended in the nose and at the tail by Lewis guns. Increasing consideration for the comfort of the crew—a factor which was of direct benefit in improving their efficiency and that of the aircraft—was evident in the provision of a fully glazed canopy for the cockpit. The height of the fuselage resulted in a roomy cabin for navigation and operation of the radio equipment, access being through a door on the starboard side. The tractor engines drove two-blade propellers, but four blades were used on each of the rear pair of Kestrels. In its original unspatted form, the Type 163's radiators were installed in the upper centre-section above the engines, but when O-2 appeared with spats over its wheels the radiators had been altered to consist of a pair of surfaces mounted vertically on the flanks of the Kestrels and arched to meet above the cowlings. In common with several of its contemporaries in the same category, the wings of the Type 163 were arranged to fold, thereby reducing its width to 44 ft. 6 in. for hangar parking. Handley Page movable slots were prominent on the upper leading edges of O-2's wings.

Disappointingly little progress was made at this period by Bristol with designs prepared by Frank Barnwell for general-purpose duties. Among the West Country firm's prototypes constructed at the close of the 1920s was the Type 118 of 1929, a two-seat biplane carrying in its nose a 590 h.p. Jupiter XFA and able to fulfil a broad range of duties. The machine was of conventional design with a fabric-covered metal airframe. The single-bay, unequal-span wing cellules dispensed with wire bracing between the planes, using as a substitute a single diagonal strut on each side. The broad-track undercarriage was divided into two separate units. The bomb load was carried externally and aimed from a prone position beneath the pilot's relatively elevated position in the fuselage. The standard armament was fitted, consisting of a Vickers gun for the pilot firing from a groove in the port decking and a Scarff-mounted Lewis at the rear.

199

Bristol Type 120 R-6/K3587. (*Bristol Photo.*)

Given the civil registration G-ABEZ, the Type 118 made its first flight on 22nd January, 1931, with C. F. Uwins at the controls and continued its development flying during the year as R-3. Following satisfactory tests at A. & A.E.E. Martlesham, the Type 118 was fitted in February, 1932, with a 600 h.p. Mercury V driving a four-blade propeller and passed to the Air Ministry as the Type 118A K2873 for trials with its new engine.

The second prototype to be constructed became the Type 120, which differed mainly in having a lightweight cupola recessed into the rear decking as protection against the elements for the gunner. 29th January, 1932, was the date of the Type 120's initial flight at Filton as R-6 fitted with the 600 h.p. Mercury V and a two-blade propeller. During the following April a 650 h.p. Pegasus IM3 replaced the earlier engine, and in March, 1933, the Type 120 was acquired by the Air Ministry for testing at Martlesham as K3587. Comparative trials were made there with and without the cupola in place.

The successful evolution of the Fairey IIIF into the Gordon and its adaptation to use a radial engine in place of the liquid-cooled Lion was pursued to its logical conclusion in the three-seat Seal which Marcel Lobelle prepared as the IIIF's successor for the Fleet Air Arm. The prototype Seal S1325 first flew on 11th September, 1930, and was produced by taking the airframe of a IIIF Mk. IIIB, modifying it and, initially, giving it the designation IIIF Mk. VI.

The prototype Seal was constructed to Specification 12/29 and was fitted with the 525 h.p. Panther IIA and the Gordon's style of fin and rudder. Fleet Air Arm acceptance was swift, and the Seal Mk. I passed into production in 1932 to Specification 17/32 with new vertical tail surfaces of more rounded outline and a tailwheel in place of the earlier skid. K3477—Fairey airframe F1843—was the first production Seal, the total constructed—excluding the prototype—reaching ninety-one. Specification 11/34 was issued to cover the subsequent production batch.

The stately Seal proved just as successful as its counterpart Gordon of the R.A.F. and was similarly flown on floats as well as in its landplane form.

Fairey Seal K3481. *(Fairey Photo.)*

S1325 was utilized again as the prototype Seal seaplane, taking-off from water for the first time at Hamble on 29th September, 1932. In its landplane form the Seal was notable in becoming the first machine in F.A.A. service to use wheel brakes and was also fitted with the frame style of carrier arrester hook

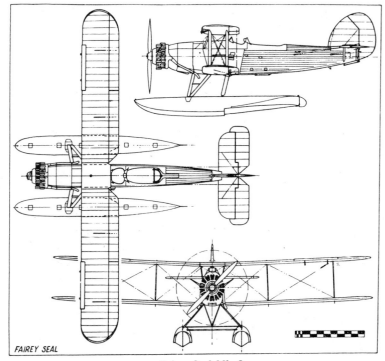

FAIREY SEAL

Fairey Seal Mk. I

Fairey Fox Mk. IVM. (*Fairey Photo.*)

hinged for lowering at the rear of the fuselage, constituting the first time that a Fairey design had entered the Fleet Air Arm with this type of gear. The Seal was able to carry a 500 lb. bomb load beneath its wings; defensive armament consisted of a Vickers gun on the port side of the fuselage for the pilot and a Lewis on a Fairey high-speed mounting in the rear cockpit.

During 1933 another Fairey twin-float biplane made its appearance as the Fox Mk. IVM. The machine was a two-seater and basically the same as the Fox Mk. IIIM. The engine installed was the 480 h.p. Kestrel II, and the machine carried, in addition to its rear Fairey-mounted Lewis gun, a Vickers in a trough on each side of the nose.

The success of the Hinaidi brought forth a medium-range bomber transport variant to Specification C.20/27. The H.P.35 design, by George Volkert, was at first called the Chitral, but was renamed Clive Mk. I in its wooden prototype form as J9126, which made its maiden flight in February, 1928. The production version was revised with a metal airframe and designated Clive Mk. II, joining the R.A.F. during 1931. It was powered by two 460 h.p. Jupiter VIIIF engines and, as a day bomber, accommodated a bomb load of 1,300 lb. With the exception of the fore-fuselage and engine mountings, the Clive's structure was interchangeable with that of the Hinaidi Mk. II. Bomb-aiming was carried out with a course-setting sight from a prone position on

J9126, the prototype Handley Page Clive Mk. I. (*Handley Page Photo.*)

202

the starboard side of the fuselage a little to the rear of the pilot, the missiles being slung on racks beneath the lower wings. Two defensive Lewis guns were provided—one in the nose and the other in the mid-upper position. The Clive was able to transport seventeen fully-armed troops.

Although the demands of Specification B.19/27 had been satisfied by Handley Page with the Heyford, which went into service with eight R.A.F. night bomber squadrons, the requirement was also of extreme significance in that it was responsible in addition for the introduction to the Service of its first monoplane heavy bomber—the Fairey Hendon. The designer charged with evolving the prototype to the stipulations of B.19/27 was D. L. Hollis Williams, who had created as handsome an aircraft design in the pair of elegant Fairey Long-range Monoplanes of the same period.

With the advent of the Hendon and its somewhat timorous and tardy acceptance to equip fully only one R.A.F. squadron—No. 38—the event constituted one of the most important milestones in the history of the Service's aircraft, bringing to an end the long-standing domination of the biplane as its heavy bomber type. Until November, 1934, when the name Hendon was officially bestowed on it, the machine was known as the Fairey Night Bomber. Stress and performance calculations were carried out by P. A. Ralli as head of the Fairey technical department, and the prototype K1695 was completed in 1931. The multitude of considerations involved in the advanced conception of such a radical new bomber finally resulted in the adoption of the cantilever low-wing layout with its many attendant advantages. Throughout the entire period of the 1920s, aeronautical design had proceeded apace, with investigation and experiment taking place without respite in every conceivable aspect of the science. Acceptance of commercial flying and its associated growth in the course of the first post-war decade had not matched the expectations of its protagonists and had been disappointingly slow. On the other hand, military and naval aircraft were fortunate in benefiting from steady development promoted by the needs of the Services for replacement aeroplanes for various duties. The Air Ministry's insistence on all-metal construction, linked with increased power from existing engines and the promise of higher output to be derived from new power plants, the intensive attention being paid to the important subject of improved propeller design, the evolution of more efficient wing sections, control surfaces and superchargers and better armament installation—together with research applied to the myriad other items which made up the increasingly complex bomber aircraft—all combined to make it possible at last to take a lengthy and stimulating step forward in heavy bomber development and to embark upon the logical next stage in its evolution.

The prototype K1695's primary structure was fabricated from steel tubing and high-tensile steel drawn to section, the secondary components—including the ribs and fairings—being made from duralumin and other light alloys. The fuselage was unusual in side elevation in possessing almost constant depth from nose to tail and was matched to a rectangular centre-section of such great thickness that it occupied half the height of the fuselage. The

K1695, the prototype Fairey Hendon Mk. I modified as the prototype Hendon Mk. II. (*Fairey Photo.*)

outer wing panels were also correspondingly very deep and were tapered equally on leading and trailing edges. Apart from their lifting power, these unusually thick wings were claimed to be relatively insensitive to changes in load. The enormous mainplanes—101 ft. 9 in. in span and 1,446 sq. ft. in area—were built up around two main spars, each consisting of four sections of high-tensile, corrugated steel riveted together as a square tube; the bracing of the outer panels was carried out internally with steel tubing formed into

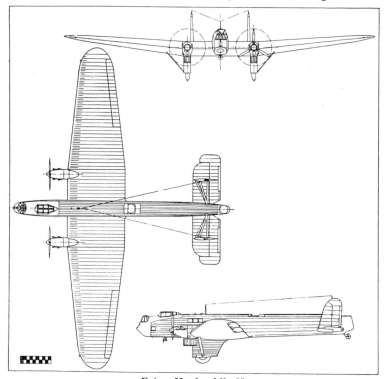

Fairey Hendon Mk. II

pyramid structures, complemented by wire bracing of streamline section to oppose torsion. The entire airframe was covered with fabric. The provision of a corrugated duralumin sheet catwalk for the crew—five of whom were carried—from the nose gunner's cockpit to that in the tail resulted from offsetting the pilot's enclosed cockpit to port. Besides acting as the bearer of the engines, the centre-section housed the fuel tanks and provided internal stowage for the 1,660 lb. load of bombs. Aiming of the missiles was from a position in the nose, where the bomb-aimer was able to sit at his sight. Nose, dorsal and tail cockpits for the gunners each carried a single Lewis gun on a Fairey ring-mounting with internal stowage for the weapons. The under-carriage's main pair of wheels were mounted beneath the engine nacelles and fully faired with trousers of deep chord. Twin fins and rudders were installed on a low-set tailplane, and the layout of the flying and control surfaces in relation to the gun positions ensured that a blind spot did not exist more than 22 ft. from the machine. In the first instance the Fairey Night Bomber proto-type was designed around the Mercury V engine—later renamed the Pegasus—but, finally, K1695 in its Mk. I version received a pair of 525 h.p. Jupiter XF cowled radials Nos. 10013J and 10015J driving two-blade wooden propellers.

Since the days of the 1914–18 War Fairey had been allowed by the Air Ministry to use Northolt Aerodrome as a testing ground for its landplanes, but in 1929 the firm received notice that this facility would no longer be available. The company thereupon bought the ground at Harmondsworth in Middlesex which became in 1930 its Great West Aerodrome. It was at this excellent all-grass airfield that Capt. Norman Macmillan seated himself in the cockpit of K1695 on 17th November, 1930, to start the massive new bomber's taxying tests at 12.45 p.m. for 19 min. with six passengers on board. At 12.48 p.m. the next day, on 18th November, he carried out the second series of runs on the ground for 33 min., accompanied by three passengers. Two days later, on 20th November, the machine was made ready again for its third set of trials. These lasted for 38 min. from 15.46 p.m.; Capt. Macmillan had four others aboard and conducted taxying tests and straight hops just off the ground at an altitude of 1 ft. As a result of these initial trials, various minor details received attention during the ensuing few days. Finally, with the machine's designer—D. L. Hollis Williams—as his sole passenger, Capt. Macmillan eased K1695 from the surface of the Great West Aerodrome at 10.51 a.m. on 25th November, 1930, to make a successful initial flight lasting 17 min. reaching a maximum height of 1,500 ft. in the process. The second flight took place the next day at 15.17 on 26th November, Capt. Macmillan having with him Maj. T. M. Barlow, the Fairey chief engineer, and Mr. Roberts, the senior airfield charge hand engineer. The trip lasted for 21 min. with 1,200 ft. as the highest altitude attained. The pilot found the machine easy to fly and possessing a flattish glide and a relatively slow landing speed. Although easy to handle in the air, it was a little sluggish on the controls, which needed some attention. This was Capt. Macmillan's last flight for Fairey, as he had previously resigned from the firm and left almost immediately to become in 1931 chief consultant test pilot to the Armstrong

Blackburn M.1/30 S1640. (*Blackburn Photo.*)

Siddeley Development Company. At the beginning of 1931 C. R. McMullin took over as Fairey chief test pilot and consequently became responsible for development flying of K1695. The aircraft was subsequently damaged when he was making a landing at the Great West Aerodrome and caught some telegraph wires during the approach to the field.

In the course of reconstruction several revisions were made to K1695, resulting in its redesignation as the Mk. II. With the Jupiters early stalling of the wings had induced a degree of longitudinal instability, trouble which it was decided was caused by buffeting set up by the engines. The Jupiters were discarded and replaced by two closely-cowled 480 h.p. Kestrel IIIS engines with their attendant radiators set underneath to blend into the undercarriage fairings. Wash-out of the wingtips was incorporated to delay their stall so that it occurred after that of the remainder of the wing surface. In its new form in 1932 K1695's pilot's cockpit was without its canopy; a second cockpit was installed immediately behind.

Following trials the Fairey Night Bomber was accepted by the Air Ministry and ordered to equip No. 38 Squadron as the Hendon Mk. II, the first of a total of fourteen arriving on 20th November, 1936. In its production version to Specification 20/34 further modifications were evident. Two 600 h.p. Kestrel VI engines were fitted, driving three-blade Fairey-Reed metal propellers, and the pilot's cockpit canopy had been reinstated, appearing on No. 38's aircraft both in a single-seat form with a tapered rear fairing and a tandem-seat version which had a stepped-up rear portion. The higher speeds of which the striking new monoplane was capable made it imperative to give the front gunner—at least—some protection against the slipstream to enable him to use his machine-gun to advantage, and his cockpit was consequently equipped with a simple type of rotating domed cupola. The production Hendon Mk. II received also new rudders of parallel chord with horn balances set at an angle. At the end of 1936, therefore, the Royal Air Force took delivery of its first modern cantilever monoplane bomber and thus passed

206

into an important new era in the life of one of its most vital Commands. As an alternative to operating as a bomber, the Hendon was able to perform as a troop-carrier, taking between fifteen and twenty fully-armed soldiers in its cabin. A contract was raised for the production of a further sixty Hendons, but was subsequently cancelled in the face of the development by then of several new and even more advanced types.

Carrier-borne torpedo-bomber development received further impetus with the issue of Specification M.1/30, which succeeded the earlier M.5/28 requirement. Interest in the proposal resulted in prototypes from Blackburn, Handley Page and Vickers and the unbuilt Avro M.1/30 project.

The Blackburn M.1/30 prototype S1640 made its appearance at Brough in 1932 as a two-seat, single-bay, equal-span biplane in which Maj. Bumpus extended a stage further the general appearance of Blackburn biplanes established already in the Beagle and the Nautilus. His more recent designs were incorporating square-cut flying surfaces and fairly prominent horn balances on the tail controls. With a span of 49 ft. 4 in. S1640 was a fairly large—and imposing—aircraft. The output from engines was increasing steadily, so that the performance of the new machine was able to benefit accordingly from the use of the 825 h.p. Rolls-Royce Buzzard IIIMS, a twelve-cylinder vee liquid-cooled unit which was installed with very clean cowling lines in the nose of the fabric-covered, steel-tubing fuselage. Metal with fabric covering was employed for the rest of the airframe, and the equal-chord, folding wings incorporated cable-connected ailerons on each surface. The M.1/30's strut-braced tailplane was mounted on the fin a short distance above the fuselage. Torpedo accommodation was afforded by employing the usual divided-axle undercarriage. S1640's port upper decking housed the pilot's Vickers gun, and his observer operated a single Lewis gun from the rear cockpit.

The H.P.46 S1642, George Volkert's design to M.1/30 for Handley Page, was ready likewise in 1932 and was a two-seat biplane with folding wings, at 50 ft. slightly greater in span than the Blackburn M.1/30 and fitted also with the powerful 825 h.p. Buzzard IIIMS. S1642's initial take-off was made at Radlett on 25th October, 1932, with Sqn. Ldr. T. H. England at the controls as the firm's chief test pilot. Subsequent testing to Air Ministry requirements was in the hands of Maj. Cordes. The H.P.46 was an exceedingly clean design with single-bay, equal-span wings set with slight positive stagger of 9 in. The entire machine was fighter-like in aspect, with several design points indicative of sound original thought aimed at extracting maximum performance from the machine. The engine, driving a two-blade 14 ft. diameter propeller, was housed in the nose of a very slim, deep fuselage, and the upper wings' unusually thin centre-section rested at a tangent on the curved coaming in line with the pilot's eyes, thereby interfering as little as possible with the view from the cockpit. The positioning of the observer on the same level gave him an excellent field of fire for his Lewis gun; the pilot's Vickers fired along a groove in the port side of the cowling. Perhaps the most prominent feature of the design was the very sharp anhedral angle embodied in the thick centre-section of the lower mainplanes, at the apices of which were attached the mainwheel units. These consisted of two pairs of small 31·2 in. diameter wheels, each pair being mounted one on each side of a short central shock-absorbing strut, the whole unit being faired into the underside of the wing root by a broad, shallow spat. The tailwheel also was housed in a spat. The Buzzard's radiator block extended the full width of the fuselage and projected prominently beneath the nose; long exhaust pipes reached as far as the rear cockpit. The angle of the lower wing roots enabled a torpedo or a single large bomb to be housed comfortably beneath the fuselage and resulted in a sharp dihedral angle to the lower outer panels. N interplane struts braced the mainplanes, four broad-span ailerons were embodied in the trailing edges, and Handley Page slots extended along the upper outer panels' entire leading edge.

The Vickers prototype to M.1/30 consisted of the Type 207 S1641 designed by R. K. Pierson around the 825 h.p. Buzzard IIIMS. The machine followed the typical single-bay biplane formula, but was notable in accommodating its pilot in a cockpit in line with the leading edge of the wings, a location which was exceedingly advantageous for torpedo aiming but which militated against ease of communication with the rear cockpit, from which it was separated by several feet, as the gunner was situated aft of the wings. The folding, unequal-span wings possessed a substantial gap, the upper surfaces being without

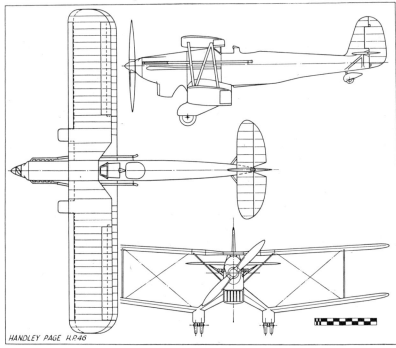

Handley Page H.P. 46

208

dihedral and bearing the pair of ailerons; dihedral was, however, incorporated in the lower planes outboard of the strut-braced bottom centre-section. The divided undercarriage units were set well apart, and Warren girder bracing was employed for supporting the upper centre-section, the outer struts of which were of N form.

A hapless fate eventually overtook the Vickers Type 207 when it disintegrated in mid-air following the collapse of the tail unit during a test dive. The chief test pilot of Vickers—Capt. J. Summers—was flying S1641 at the time with his flight engineer—John Radcliffe—as passenger; both managed to escape safely by parachute.

Maj. Bumpus designed a revised biplane which Blackburn built in 1933 as a Private Venture to Specification M.1/30 under the designation M.1/30A as B-3 K3591. The new machine closely resembled S1640, but detailed inspection disclosed a watertight, metal monocoque fuselage in place of the earlier machine's fabric-covered, metal tubing type and lower wings with a shorter span and narrower chord than the upper planes possessed. The ailerons were different also on the M.1/30A—on S1640 all four had been of broad chord and short span, but those of K3591 were of greatly decreased chord and extended in each case outwards from the centre-section along the entire trailing edges and were inset a short distance from the wingtips. The exhaust pipes fitted to K3591's 825 h.p. Buzzard IIIMS were longer than those of S1640 and extended to the trailing edge of the wings. K3591 received the standard machine-gun armament of one Vickers and one Lewis and was able to carry a total offensive load of 1,900 lb. Eight bomb-racks were disposed beneath the lower wings, four on each side.

Subsequently, Specification M.1/30 was combined with the requirement outlined in S.9/30 and issued in 1933 as Specification S.15/33. The cancellation of M.1/30 resulted in the cessation of any further development of the four prototypes which it had produced.

S1706, the Fairey S.9/30, under test as a floatplane. (*Fairey Photo.*)

Before its amalgamation with M.1/30, Specification S.9/30 had been responsible for the appearance of one prototype each from Fairey and Gloster, besides projects which were not proceeded with but which included the Avro 632 in September, 1932, the three-seat Hawker S.9/30 with a Panther—resembling a cross between the Horsley and Osprey—and the Vickers Type 218 of 1933.

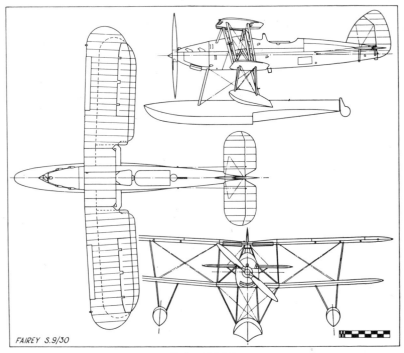

FAIREY S.9/30

Fairey S.9/30

210

The Avro design from Roy Chadwick was based on the use of a radial engine—the Armstrong Siddeley Tiger—and would have had a wing span of 46 ft.

During its life-span Marcel Lobelle's S.9/30 design for Fairey was given little publicity. Constructed under Contract 130845/31 as Fairey airframe F1754, the machine was a three-seat biplane of refined aspect which received the serial S1706. To combat salt-water corrosion in its intended rôle as a fleet torpedo spotter reconnaissance aircraft, the primary structure consisted of stainless steel tubing with a conventional covering of fabric. The two crew members, carried in addition to the pilot, occupied a single large rear cockpit. The fuselage's stainless steel structure was formed from four detachable sections which were bolted together to simplify maintenance and ease replacement of a damaged portion. The S.9/30's wings were arranged to fold rearwards about upper and lower centre-sections of noticeably narrow chord. This feature facilitated the folding arrangement and improved the view from the cockpits considerably. A further aid to a good view for the crew was that the wings were staggered 21° and that the chord of the lower surfaces was less than that of the upper planes. The wings were unequal in span and swept back outboard of the centre-sections, 5° sweep being incorporated in the top planes and 4° in the bottom set. Construction of the wings was by threading the ribs over twin spars braced against intervening compression struts. Frise ailerons of generous area formed part of the upper wings, and Handley Page automatic slots were mounted on the top leading edges. The wing cellules were given single-bay bracing, the inner interplane struts supporting the upper centre-section from the lower centre-section in conjunction with conventional centre-section struts. The wing-folding system—reducing the width to 20 ft. 6 in.—made it possible to dispense with the usual jury struts.

S1706 was completed at the beginning of 1935, powered by the 525 h.p. Kestrel IIMS No. 273/106559 driving a two-blade 11 ft. 9 in. diameter Fairey-Reed metal propeller. Cooling was by evaporation, the two element construction steam condensers being mounted abreast flush with the underside of the upper centre-section. As a landplane, long exhaust pipes reached to the rear on each side of the engine; starting of the Kestrel was by the R.A.E. Mk. II gas starter system. A Fairey Laminar oil cooler with sixteen fins was mounted beneath the engine sump. The landplane undercarriage consisted of divided main units with low-pressure tyres and wheel brakes. For shock absorption the main load was carried by a steel spring in compression with an oleo damping device. A tailwheel supported the rear. The S.9/30 was armed with two guns—a Vickers in the port coaming and a Lewis in the rear on a Fairey high-speed mounting. Alternative under-wing bomb loads were three of 150 lb. each or five 100 lb. plus eight of 20 lb., or one 500 lb. plus four of 250 lb. and eight of 20 lb. Fuel capacity consisted of a main fuselage tank containing 112 gall., another holding 15 gall. in the starboard upper centre-section feeding by gravity and a reserve tank with 14·75 gall. in the port half of the upper centre-section. S1706 took-off from the

Fairey Great West Aerodrome for its maiden flight on 15th January, 1935, with Flt. Lt. C. S. Staniland as pilot.

The Fairey S.9/30 was subsequently converted to a seaplane, attaining significance as one of the very few British designs to utilize the system of a large single central float augmented by a smaller float at each wingtip. Trials with S1706 in this form were recorded in M.A.E.E. Felixstowe Report F/143 of October, 1936. As a seaplane the machine's length increased from the landplane's 34 ft. 1·5 in. to 39·37 ft. mounted on a main float 30 ft. 6 in. long, 4 ft. 11 in. in beam and 3 ft. 9 in. deep, which was divided into six watertight compartments. The float's front pair of struts tapered slightly inwards to the attachment point at the rear of the Kestrel; those at the rear were splayed sharply outwards to the limits of the lower centre-section. No shock-absorbing gear was embodied in the anodized duralumin float system, and a cable control from the cockpit operated the water rudder. An anchor and its cable were stored in a locker in the central float, and in its floatplane form S1706 had its previous long exhausts replaced by a pair of ram's-horn manifolds installed vertically on the flanks of each cylinder bank. At the full loaded weight of 6,500 lb. a depth of water of 2 ft. 2 in. was required to float the machine; at this weight the wing area of 442 sq. ft. resulted in a wing loading of 14·7 lb./sq. ft. The report found that the high position of the pilot's cockpit gave him an excellent view and that his controls and instruments were satisfactory. The rest of the crew accommodation was considered sufficiently roomy. The single drop rudder was found to be very effective in the water, resulting in very satisfactory taxying control at normal speeds and enabling—on a calm sea in a wind of about 4 m.p.h.—the easy execution of turning circles of about three spans' diameter. Prior to—and during—take-off control was very good, with the tip floats rising clear of the water immediately the engine was opened up. The single main float was clean running—throwing water and spray clear of the propeller—and landings were good when made in seas of up to 2 ft., the aircraft always behaving well. One tip float—usually that to starboard—was always well in the water but gave rise to no serious drag effect at up to 20 m.p.h. In flight S1706's control and manoeuvrability were assessed as heavy but positive in all planes. The rudder was thought to need a bias control, as it tended to turn the aircraft to port at all speeds when in the air. At lower flying speeds the S.9/30's controls were found to be much lighter. The machine's take-off run was 430 yd. in 22 sec., the landing run consuming 250 yd. at a landing speed of 50 kt. I.A.S. At 74·5 kt. I.A.S. the climb rate recorded was 880 ft./min. at 2,000 ft., the service ceiling was 14,600 ft., estimated absolute ceiling was 16,200 ft. and the top speed 118 kt. T.A.S. at 2,000 ft.

The Fairey S.9/30's competitor to the same requirement was the Gloster F.S.36, a three-seat, single-bay biplane which Henry Folland designed around the 600 h.p. Kestrel IIMS, starting work on the layout in November, 1931. As was the case with the Fairey contender, one prototype only—S1705—was built by Gloster during 1931. The machine's top speed as a landplane was 157 m.p.h., flight trials taking place late in 1932 before the design was revised to comply with Specification S.15/33.

S1707, the three-seat Vickers Vildebeest Mk. I prototype with full offensive load. (*Vickers Photo.*)

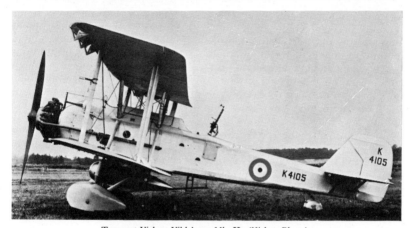

Two-seat Vickers Vildebeest Mk. II. (*Vickers Photo.*)

One of the most prominent of British torpedo-bombers between the two Great Wars was the Vickers Vildebeest designed by R. K. Pierson for its specialized rôle of coastal defence from the outset, whereas the Horsley—its predecessor in the R.A.F.—had originated as a day bomber. During the Vildebeest's development the requirements of Specification M.1/30 were taken into consideration. N230, the prototype of 1929, mounted the 460 h.p. Jupiter VIII engine in its nose, testing being carried out uncowled and also surrounded by a Townend ring. The Vildebeest was a 49 ft. span biplane with single-bay wings, an unusual expedient in a machine of such a size, and displayed the features normally associated with a torpedo-carrier—a divided unit undercarriage and an excellent view for the pilot, in this case situated at the leading edge of the wings. N230 was a two-seater, but later marks which were available alternatively as three-seaters incorporated another cockpit beneath the upper centre-section and adjacent to that of the pilot. The gunner, armed with a Lewis gun, defended the rear from a position in line with the

213

Vickers Vildebeest Mk. II three-seater. (*Vickers Photo.*)

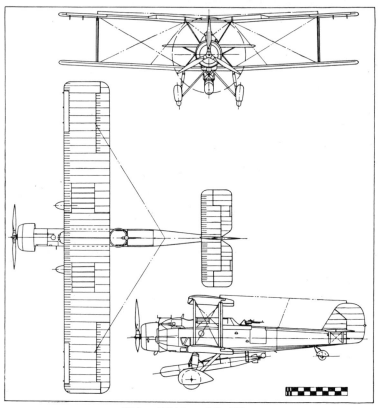

Vickers Vildebeest Mk. IV

214

trailing edge. The Vildebeest's wings were equal in span, square-cut and without stagger. A single strut on each side connected the ailerons, and the upper wingtips were surmounted by Handley Page automatic slots. Armament for the pilot consisted of a Vickers gun housed to port in the coaming. The Jupiter in N230 was replaced later by a 622 h.p. Pegasus I without a cowling. Successful trials were followed by production of the Vildebeest Mk. I powered by the 622 h.p. Pegasus IM3 for the R.A.F., S1707 serving as the prototype Mk. I. No. 100 Squadron was the first to take delivery of the Mk. I in November, 1933.

Development was covered by Specification 22/31, and the Type 252 Mk. II —originally known as the Vildebeest XI—was ordered in December, 1933, with the 660 h.p. Pegasus IIM3 engine. Production of the Type 267 Vilde- beest Mk. III in 1934, also with the 660 h.p. Pegasus IIM3, followed to Specifications 20/33 and 15/34. Specification 21/33 was issued for Vildebeest general-purpose development. By September, 1936, one hundred and fifty- two Mks. I, II and III had been built by Vickers at Weybridge for the R.A.F.

Bristol development of the 825 h.p. Perseus VIII resulted in its adoption for the Vildebeest Mk. IV, thereby introducing the R.A.F. to its first sleeve- valve engine when fifty-seven Mk. IVs were produced to Specification 41/35. At the same time a three-blade Rotol propeller was introduced and a cowling of deep chord provided for the power plant. The previous long exhaust pipes were discarded in favour of a collector around the periphery of the front of the cowling. K4164, the prototype Mk. IV, was evolved by modifying a Mk. II, and No. 42 Squadron was the first to receive production Mk. IVs in 1937. The spat enclosing the Vildebeest's tailwheel was normally retained in service, but often the pair covering the main wheels were removed. N230 was fitted with a tailskid which was replaced by a tailwheel on all Mks. I, II, III and IV; the original prototype also lacked the ventral fin which was added on S1707 and its successors. The Vildebeest's offensive load consisted of either an 18 in. torpedo or a 1,000 lb. bomb load.

Foreign interest in the Vildebeest manifested itself in 1931, when the Type

Three-seat Vickers Vildebeest Mk. IV prototype K4164 with 825 h.p. Perseus VIII. (*Vickers Photo.*)

Westland P.V.3 G-ACAZ/K4048. (*Westland Photo.*)

132 Mk. I civil demonstrator G-ABGE of 1930 was modified during September, 1931, for the Spanish Government to the Type 216 Vildebeest VII by substituting a liquid-cooled 595 h.p. Hispano-Suiza 12Nbr engine for the previous 480 h.p. Jupiter XI. The machine was then equipped with twin floats—fitted on sturdily-braced divided units—for testing in flight at Woolston carrying its torpedo in position. The registration G-ABGE was retained on the wings during these trials, but that on the fuselage was replaced by the marking O-3. K2916, a Pegasus-engine, three-seat Vildebeest Mk. II, was equipped with twin floats in the course of 1936 for trials as a version for the Latvian Government.

During 1931 Westland demonstrated continued adherence to the biplane—with its many virtues—when the P.V.3 was built as a Private Venture prototype torpedo-bomber for operation from the Fleet's aircraft-carriers. Registered P3, the machine was a two-seater conceived by Arthur Davenport to embrace also the rôles of army co-operation and the diverse duties associated with a general-purpose aircraft. As with any large Fleet Air Arm design intended to be stowed aboard an aircraft-carrier, the P.V.3's wings were arranged to fold—reducing to 20 ft. 4 in. in width. From the centre-section outwards, the slightly-staggered wings were given 4° sweepback. An unusual feature was that the inner interplane struts were of N form while those outboard consisted of parallel pairs. Accommodation for the 1,000 lb. torpedo was provided by split undercarriage units, the very wide 12 ft. 10 in. track of which was of great advantage in operations at sea in particular. Spats enclosed the main wheels. P3's engine was an uncowled 575 h.p. supercharged Jupiter XFA, and its armament comprised one Vickers gun for the pilot and a Lewis Mk. III for the observer's Scarff No. 7 ring mounting. In place of the torpedo alternative loads were two 550 lb., four 112 lb. or sixteen 20 lb. bombs. Flt. Lt. Louis Paget took the P.V.3 on its first flight at the commencement of 1931. Although the P.V.3 was not ordered for the Fleet Air Arm, excellent overall performances—especially a service ceiling of 26,000 ft.—was responsible for its selection as one of the pair of machines destined to make the first flight over Everest in 1933. For this purpose it was lightened by the removal of its spats and the replacement of the tailwheel by a skid, the open rear cockpit was transformed into a cabin, and a highly-supercharged 525 h.p. Pegasus IS3, complete with Townend ring, took the place of the Jupiter. P3 received the civil marking G-ACAZ and was named the Houston-Westland after Lady Houston, who was responsible for financing the Everest attempt.

From December, 1932, H. J. Penrose conducted the trials of the converted aircraft and, on 25th January, 1933, undertook—with Air Cdre. P. F. M. Fellowes, the Everest Expedition's leader—a height test from Yeovil during which they reached 37,500 ft., at which altitude the temperature registered was −60° C. The ability of the P.V.3—by virtue of its design layout—to accommodate a propeller of generous diameter to enable the climb to be accomplished, was another decisive factor in its selection for the flight, and that this confidence was not misplaced was demonstrated brilliantly to the world on 3rd April, 1933, when G-ACAZ, piloted by Sqn. Ldr. the Marquess of Douglas and Clydesdale accompanied by L. V. S. Blacker in the cabin, was first across Everest's peak, followed by its companion from Yeovil, the P.V.6 G-ACBR. Shortly afterwards, on 19th April, both aircraft were successful in again conquering the majestic 29,028 ft. mountain by air. The accomplishment of the hazardous flights owed a great deal to the magnificent performance of the Pegasus engines which bore their aircraft safely over the dauntingly dangerous and awesome, peak-studded terrain. Its task completed, G-ACAZ returned to Westland and was delivered later to Bristol for use as an engine test-bed during December, 1933. The serial K4048 displaced the old registration, and the 722 h.p. Pegasus IIIM made its appearance in the nose.

The P.V.6, which—as the Houston-Wallace G-ACBR—kept company over Everest with the P.V.3, started life in 1929 as the second Wapiti Mk. V G-AAWA. With the long fuselage powered by the 550 h.p. Panther II engine installed uncowled and with the undercarriage revised to include additional struts, the machine was shipped to Argentina at the beginning of 1931 for Harald Penrose to demonstrate it at the British Empire Exhibition staged at Buenos Aires; in addition, he flew it in Uruguay, and the machine was tested also on floats.

On its return to Yeovil G-AAWA underwent major modification as a Private Venture to emerge in the guise of the P.V.6 P6 Wapiti Mk. VII. Its new power plant was the cowled 655 h.p. Pegasus IV, and other alterations from the standard Wapiti included installation of a tailwheel, spats, brakes and a cleaner, divided-axle undercarriage, together with an increase in rudder area. Penrose made the first flight with P6 at Yeovil on 30th October, 1931, and tests with the Wapiti Mk. VII disclosed a 20 m.p.h. increase in speed, coupled with improved handling qualities, which encouraged the Air Ministry at once to have twelve existing Wapitis modified to the improved standard.

The Mk. VII prototype K3488 was so different from its precursors in the Wapiti range that it was given the new designation Wallace from 3rd

November, 1931. Its capabilities and design features were such that it was determined to be an ideal machine for Westland to modify as the aircraft to accompany the P.V.3 on its epic flight. Consequently, P6 was registered as G-ACBR and altered to embody a cabin in place of the rear cockpit, military equipment was discarded along with the spats to save weight and a tailskid supplanted the wheel with the same object. For the flight over Everest G-ACBR was piloted by Flt. Lt. D. F. McIntyre, with S. R. Bonnett as his passenger. The historic flight accomplished, the Houston-Wallace was passed back to Westland to revert to K3488, a standard service Wallace, joining the R.A.F. in December, 1933.

Specification 19/32 was issued to cover the conversion of the dozen Wapitis to the first Wallace Mk. Is K3562–K3573. The engine fitted was the 570 h.p. Pegasus IIM3, and No. 501 (City of Bristol) (B) Squadron early in 1933 became the first unit to be equipped. Detail improvements incorporated in the Mk. I included the bulged housing of the pilot's Vickers gun so that it fired along a channel in the port side of the fuselage, easily detachable metal inspection panels covering the fore-fuselage and zipp fasteners for the fabric covering panels of the rear fuselage to facilitate inspection of that part of the airframe. Specifications 7/33 and 9/33 followed for further examples of Wallace Mk. Is.

During 1935 the final—and the best-looking—version of the Wallace appeared with the advent of the Mk. II to Specification G.31/35. Once again K3488 was brought into the picture to be adapted as the prototype Mk. II. Additional power was provided by the 680 h.p. Pegasus IV, and the major external recognition of the Mk. II lay in the installation of a glazed, framed canopy covering both cockpits. The pilot's portion was arranged as a coupé top sliding forwards on rods, and the gunner—whose Lewis was stowed in a trough on the starboard side of the coaming—was protected by a lobster-shell type of canopy consisting of three curved sections which folded upwards inside a fourth outer cover. In emergency, the pilot's canopy could be jettisoned in two halves by splitting it along the centre-line.

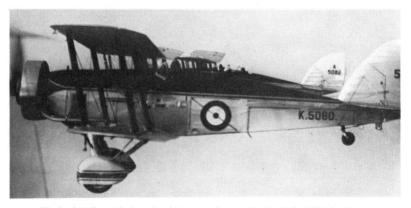

Westland Wallace Mk. I produced by converting the Wapiti. (*Bristol Siddeley Photo.*)

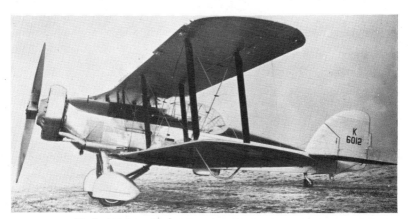

Westland Wallace Mk. II with cockpit canopy. (*Westland Photo.*)

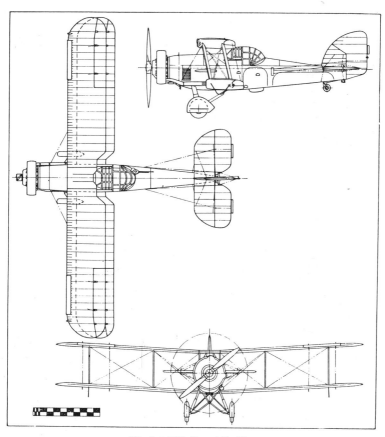

Westland Wallace Mk. II

219

Blackburn Baffin of the R.N.Z.A.F. (*R.N.Z.A.F. Photo.*)

Three Avro projects investigated in the course of 1933 were the 644 small two-seat, 36 ft. span, reconnaissance bomber with a Jaguar for power and the 655 and 656 bombers of low-wing layout, each evolved around a pair of Jaguar VIAs.

Final production of the Ripon was accompanied by the development by Maj. Bumpus at Blackburn of a variant—christened eventually in September, 1933, the Baffin—which went into production to Specification 4/33. The primary alteration in the Baffin lay in the fitting of an air-cooled radial—the Pegasus—the prototype B-5 of 1932 being known as the Pegasus-Ripon. Trials were conducted with the engine cowled with a Townend ring and un-

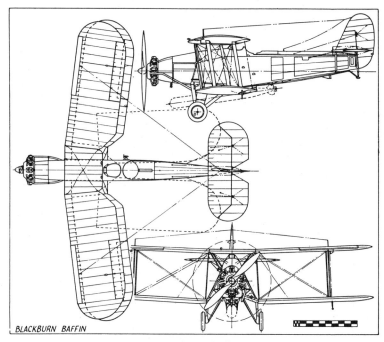

BLACKBURN BAFFIN

Blackburn Baffin

cowled, and the crew of the Baffin remained unchanged as a pilot and observer. Both the Pegasus-Ripon and its companion from Brough, the Tiger-Ripon B-4, were tested at A. & A.E.E. Martlesham, resulting in the adoption of the uncowled Pegasus version, production consisting in the main of conversions of existing Ripons. The extended span of the Baffin was a few inches greater than that of the Ripon, but when folded the Baffin was smaller by 1 ft. 2 in. The Baffin's length was somewhat less than that of the Lion-engine Ripon. The standard Vickers gun armed the pilot, and the observer's Lewis was supplied with the Fairey high-speed mounting. As an alternative to the 1,576 lb. Mk. VIII or Mk. X torpedo a single 2,000 lb. bomb or an equivalent load could be transported. In addition to being supplied to the Fleet Air Arm—in which No. 812 Squadron was the first to use them—Baffins were bought by New Zealand for the R.N.Z.A.F.

The extraordinary versatility of the Gloster design staff under Henry Folland was made plainly evident in 1932 when the company completed its largest aircraft, the T.C.33 bomber transport to Specification C.16/28. A strikingly impressive all-metal biplane with 95 ft. wings of equal span, J9832—carrying a crew of four—was powered by four 600 h.p. Kestrel IIS/IIIS engines installed in tandem pairs at mid-gap and driving two-blade propellers. The Kestrel IIIS units were mounted as tractors, the Kestrel IIS units serving as pushers, each pair being cowled in a commendably clean nacelle. A single steam condenser unit provided evaporative cooling for each pair of Kestrels, being installed to arch prominently above each front engine.

The T.C.33's finely-conceived, oval-section fuselage was metal-covered and was able to accommodate thirty fully-armed troops in a voluminous cabin 27 ft. 8 in. in length, 7 ft. in width and 7 ft. 3 in. in height. Alternatively, as a bomber the bomb load was 6,600 lb. Access to the cabin for loads—other than human—was through openings in the roof and the floor. Stagger was omitted from the fabric-covered wings, but they were swept back from the centre-section outwards. The chord-line of the lower outer wing panels was set at about half-way in the depth of the fuselage, but, to avoid the spars

J9832, the Gloster T.C.33. (*Gloster Photo.*)

Handley Page H.P.43 J9833. (*Handley Page Photo.*)

passing through the cabin, the roots swept upwards at a fairly sharp angle of anhedral. The four ailerons were connected by cables, and Handley Page automatic slots were installed on the upper wingtips. Twin fins and rudders terminated a tailplane mounted on struts above the fuselage.

On completion at Brockworth it was found that the massive biplane was too high to be rolled out through the existing doors of the assembly hangar. Twin channels were thereupon dug to accommodate the main wheels, and the T.C.33 was winched into the open. J9832's maiden flight was accomplished on 23rd February, 1932, and an appearance was made at the Hendon Air Display during the summer of the same year. Flight trials at Martlesham confirmed a satisfactory performance, but the full-depth servo tabs incorporated in the large rudders gave rise to tail flutter.

Bristol interest in C.16/28 extended as far as the preparation during 1929 of two contrasting layouts only for the Types 115 and 116. In both instances the designs were evolved around three Jupiter engines; the Type 115 would have been a monoplane and the Type 116 was planned as an adaptation of an earlier project for Imperial Airways, the Type 113 biplane using also three Jupiters.

The class of aircraft envisaged by C.16/28 was one for which Handley Page, with many years of experience in producing large bombers and commercial transports, were ideally suited to tender. A single prototype of the firm's H.P.43 was completed in 1932 as J9833. Hardly surprisingly, the machine bore the strongest possible resemblance to its immediate predecessor, the H.P.42. In his new design George Volkert reduced the number of engines from four to three, the power plants selected for the H.P.43 being the 600 h.p. Pegasus I without cowlings and driving four-blade wooden propellers. The span of the upper wings was 114 ft., dihedral being applied outboard only of the broad, flat centre-section. The lower wings were of rather shorter span and adopted the same expedient as that used in the Gloster T.C.35 of incorporating sharp anhedral at the roots to leave the cabin unobstructed by the main spars. The parallel-chord wing cellules were braced by pairs of interplane struts set diagonally, wire bracing being absent except between the outermost struts. The H.P.43's fabric-clad metal fuselage was basically rectangular in section, but was faired by a few stringers on each facet. The tailplane was surmounted by twin fins and rudders—disposed above and below—and was carried across the upper longerons, bracing to the fuselage being by struts. The undercarriage was in two halves, with a single wheel on each side installed beneath the pair of lower Pegasus nacelles. Two open positions were provided for Lewis gunners, one at each extreme of the fuselage; an angular, well-glazed canopy covered the cockpit and the main cabin extended fore and aft of the wings. J9833's maiden flight was made on 21st June, 1932, at Radlett with Maj. James Cordes at the controls. In the event, neither the T.C.33 nor the H.P.43 was ordered into production.

In the course of 1932 two examples of the Horsley appeared from Hawker fitted with the 800 h.p. fourteen-cylinder, two-row Leopard II engine. Christened Dantorp, 201 and 202 were ordered in 1930 by the Danish Government following successful trials with Horsley J8620 produced some three years earlier fitted with the Leopard to Specification M.17/27. Composite construction was used on the pair of Danish aircraft, and the machines were built as three-seaters. 201 made its first flight on 19th September, 1932, at Brooklands with Flt. Lt. P. E. G. Sayer as its pilot. Delivery was made with the 805 h.p. Leopard IIIA fitted.

Both machines were convertible to float undercarriages, and 201 and 202 were the subjects of M.A.E.E. Felixstowe Report F/110 of March, 1933, following trials conducted there as floatplanes. 201 was equipped with the geared 800 h.p. Leopard IIIA A.S.7014, the weights being 6,345 lb. empty and 10,420 lb. loaded. The aircraft were identical, but 201 became unserviceable after the start of the trials, which were therefore completed using 202. The complement consisted of pilot, wireless operator and gunner, and, apart from the difference in the number of crew and the power plant, the machines could be considered as standard fully-equipped Horsley torpedo-carriers. When received for test the 13·75 ft. diameter wooden Watts propeller as fitted permitted only 1 ft. 2 in. water clearance from its metal-sheathed tips to the load water-line. Preliminary tests revealed that this propeller picked up water when taxying at moderate speeds and during take-off, resulting in damage to its tips. Replacement was therefore effected with a Watts propeller of 13·51 ft. diameter but without improvement, as its tips also were damaged both in taking-off and landing. A third propeller was then

201, a Hawker Dantorp for Denmark. (*Hawker Photo.*)

fitted, this time a Watts of 12·77 ft. diameter, which allowed 1 ft. 8 in. water clearance. 1·5 in. chine strips were then attached to the inboard surfaces of the floats, but, despite these modifications, the metal sheathing of the propeller was slightly damaged at the tips while taxying. Following repair, another identical Watts propeller was then supplied but with the sheathing increased from 24 S.W.G. to 20 S.W.G. The depth of the chine strips was increased to 2·25 in., and their starting point was extended nearer to the bows. Further damage to the propeller was now eliminated, and no alteration in performance was detectable.

The Dantorp was assessed as highly manoeuvrable and comfortable to fly, the controls being very good, reasonably light, well harmonized and responsive. Low-speed control was also excellent, without loss of lateral control when the elevators became ineffective. The machine was thought unlikely to spin inadvertently and was able to fly hands off at any rate over the speed range. A marked change of trim was noticeable between engine on and off, but handling with and without the torpedo was about the same. The installation of larger chine strips reduced the amount of water thrown up, but manoeuvrability while on the surface was poor, as the floats' rudders were not low enough in the water. Fault was found with the control gear fitted to engage and disengage the water rudders as it tended to lodge in the open or closed position. Take-off and landing were easy, without signs of porpoising or swinging. Tests were made with a Danish torpedo and with one fixed gun and one movable gun. The wing area was 692 sq. ft., giving a wing loading of 15·1 lb./sq. ft. The climb was 670 ft./min. at sea level at 69·3 kt. I.A.S., service ceiling 12,450 ft., estimated absolute ceiling 14,400 ft., top speed 111·2 kt. I.A.S. at sea level, landing speed 58·7 kt. I.A.S. and take-off time 20 sec. at 10,420 lb. in a wind of 5 kt.

Another seaplane conversion of a type ordered by a foreign air force which was tested on the East Coast was the Hawker Swedish Hart floatplane, the trials of which were recorded in M.A.E.E. Felixstowe Report F/124 of May, 1934. The aircraft was 1303, powered by the cowled Pegasus IM2 delivering 590 h.p. at 2,000 r.p.m. at 4,500 ft. and driving a two-blade wooden Watts L.H.T. 10·75 ft. diameter propeller. The machine was mounted on twin floats and received at M.A.E.E. on 23rd February, 1934, erection being undertaken by Hawker personnel. The tests were made at a loaded weight of 5,160 lb. to assess speeds and rates of climb up to 18,000 ft. and also water and air handling qualities; the empty weight was 3,192 lb. The service ceiling was established as 20,300 ft., top speed 144·5 kt. at 7,000 ft. and take-off time as 22 sec. in zero wind with a run of 460 yd. Control was easy under all conditions, both in the air and on the water. In normal flight the controls were extremely pleasant and harmonized satisfactorily. In aerobatics the nose tended to rise relative to the ground when inverted during a slow roll, but this tendency was eliminated by adjusting the tail trim before executing the manoeuvre. The controls were effective down to the stall at 53 m.p.h. I.A.S., but longitudinal instability was experienced at 90 m.p.h. and over. The take-off was easy without signs of porpoising; the machine swung to the

Gloster T.S.R.38 S1705. (*Gloster Photo.*)

right, but was checked satisfactorily by use of the rudder. Landings were normal without porpoising; 1303 handled very well on the water, and no difficulty was encountered in turning in winds of up to 20 m.p.h. The foreign airspeed indicator was difficult to see, being set too high and half hidden by the edge of the cockpit. The tail trim indicator also was difficult to read in the air. The machine's wing area of 348 sq. ft. gave a wing loading of 14·8 lb./sq. ft. Offensive load consisted of two 100 lb. bombs, the armament comprising one Vickers gun and one Lewis gun. 1303's best climb rate was 1,290 ft./min. at 4,000 ft., that at sea level being 1,210 ft./min., both rates being at a climbing speed of 85 kt. I.A.S. Estimated absolute ceiling was 21,700 ft. The landing run was 260 yd., taking 13 sec. at a landing speed of 49 kt. I.A.S.

In the course of 1933, S1705—originally the Gloster F.S.36 to S.9/30—made its reappearance as the T.S.R.38 following modification to Specification S.15/33. The new requirement represented the combination and amendment of Specifications M.1/30 and S.9/30 and was issued to produce an experimental general-purpose, torpedo, spotter and reconnaissance aircraft. Folland's revision of the F.S.36 resulted in a three-seat, single-bay biplane with unequal-span folding wings which were swept back 10° 16′ on upper and lower planes outboard of the centre-section, equal dihedral of 4° being applied to both sets of wings. The 600 h.p. Kestrel IIMS was cowled so that it blended very cleanly into the fuselage, its pair of radiators being mounted one on each side flush beneath the slightly-anhedralled lower wing roots. The slim fuselage combined with the sweptback wings and well-rounded control

225

K4295, originally the Blackburn Shark prototype B-6, converted to a Shark Mk. II. (*Blackburn Photo.*)

surfaces to produce a biplane of undoubted elegance. The M.6 aerofoil section selected for the wings—used at its standard thickness/chord ratio of 0·12 for the lower planes but thinned to 0·1 for the upper—resulted in fairly thick surfaces conferring good lifting and slow-speed qualities on the aircraft. The crew were seated one behind the other; the pilot was armed with a

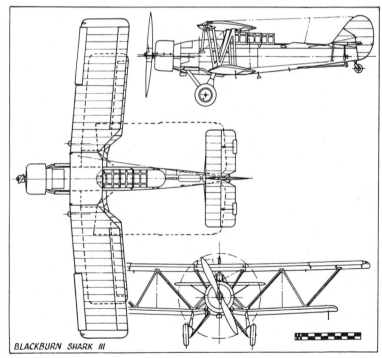

BLACKBURN SHARK III

Blackburn Shark Mk. III

226

Vickers firing through a channel in the port side of the cowling while the observer used a Lewis stowed in the top decking. An 18 in. torpedo was accommodated between the divided main wheel units; the tailwheel was given the refinement of a spat. For deck landing S1705 was equipped with an arrester hook hinged to the rear of the fuselage. Construction was of metal throughout with a covering of fabric. Other modifications made to the machine after it was constructed to its original S.9/30 formula included revision of the control circuits and the addition of flotation gear in the wings. As an alternative to the torpedo the T.S.R.38 was able to transport a bomb load of 1,700 lb. In place of the Kestrel the evaporatively-cooled 690 h.p. Rolls-Royce Goshawk VIII was installed later in S1705. The sole prototype constructed went to A. & A.E.E. Martlesham in 1933 for assessment and underwent trials also on H.M.S. *Courageous* during 1934.

Although the Gloster T.S.R.38 faded into the limbo, the general intensification of activity in the T.S.R. category during the first half of the 1930s was eventually to produce new torpedo-carrying designs which were ultimately to prove of the greatest importance to the Fleet Air Arm. Concerns already well experienced in the art of designing and constructing the highly specialized torpedo-bomber were able repeatedly to submit newer, more advanced designs in the particular class demanded and were usually the firms to have their prototypes selected on their merit for production.

May, 1934, was the month in which a new Private Venture torpedo bomber to S.15/33 from Blackburn made its first flight. The machine was the B-6, designed by Maj. F. A. Bumpus to seat either two or three. Generous cut-outs were made in the centre portions of both upper and lower wings, a feature which facilitated folding and aided the view for the crew. The two-bay wings were of unequal-span, swept back outboard of the centre-section and utilized a substantial diagonal strut on each side between the N interplane struts in place of the conventional wire bracing. The horizontal flying surfaces on the B-6's immediate predecessors from Blackburn had borne well-rounded tips, but those of the new prototype were square-cut. A notable technical advance was the construction of the fuselage as a metal watertight monocoque designed to assist flotation in the event of a forced landing on water. The B-6 was powered by the twin-row, fourteen-cylinder 700 h.p. Armstrong Siddeley Tiger IV installed in a deep-chord cowling. Armament consisted of the standard Vickers gun for the pilot and a Lewis for the observer, and the usual divided undercarriage allowed suspension of the 1,500 lb. torpedo beneath the fuselage. Under-wing racks could carry an equivalent weight of bombs in place of the torpedo.

B-6 was allotted the serial K4295 and was successful enough to bring in August, 1934, an order to Specification 12/34 for sixteen examples designated Shark Mk. I, No. 820 Squadron, F.A.A., becoming in May, 1935, the first to introduce it into service. The Mk. I continued to use the Tiger IV, but the Shark Mk. II—K4295 again being used as the prototype—received the 700 h.p. Tiger VI as its power plant, together with stronger fuselage, wings, tail and engine mounting. Specification 13/35 was drawn up to cover development of the Shark Mk. III, in which the crew were enclosed in a glazed canopy. Specification S.19/36 was issued on 16th June, 1936, for production of the Shark Mk. III, but was subsequently amended on 7th July, 1936, to read Shark Mk. II. Production of twenty-six Shark Mk. IIIs in Canada by Boeing for the R.C.A.F. was covered by Specification 31/37, the engine used being the Pegasus IX. The Shark was able to operate on twin floats, and K4295 performed the rôle as test vehicle for the type in this form. The six Shark Mk. IIs sold to Portugal were fitted with de-rated Tiger IVC engines. Despite several attributes, including the monocoque watertight fuselage, fixed struts for wing rigging, the use of hydraulically-operated latch pins in the wing folding system and the elimination of jury struts, the Shark was destined to be overshadowed by its illustrious contemporary from Fairey, the Swordfish.

When Specification S.9/30 was issued Fairey prepared an alternative project of the S.9/30 biplane S1706. Under the designation T.S.R.I, Marcel Lobelle designed the machine from the start to transport a torpedo in addition to its duties of spotting and reconnaissance. The three-seat aircraft was built as a Private Venture, being completed in 1933; not unnaturally it was strongly reminiscent of S1706, but a sharp contrast was provided by the use of an air-cooled radial—both the 635 h.p. Pegasus IIM and the Tiger were tried—as opposed to S1706's inline Kestrel. The fin and rudder were of high aspect ratio, and spats at first covered the main wheels. The Fairey airframe number was F1875, and the T.S.R.I followed the current Fairey formula of two-bay wings of differing span and chord, embodying stagger and a pilot's cockpit set high in the fuselage as an aid to accurate torpedo aiming. Flt. Lt. C. S. Staniland conducted the T.S.R.I's maiden flight from the Great West Aerodrome on 21st March, 1933. The prototype proved satisfactory in its trials until, on 11th September, 1933, Staniland found it impossible to extricate the machine from a flat spin in which it was trapped. He then underwent the unnerving and unpleasant experience of finding himself in the rear compartment, having been blown there after baling out of the front cockpit,

Fairey T.S.R.II K4190. (*Fairey Photo.*)

228

K4190, the Fairey T.S.R.II, modified as the prototype Swordfish. (*Bristol Siddeley Photo.*)

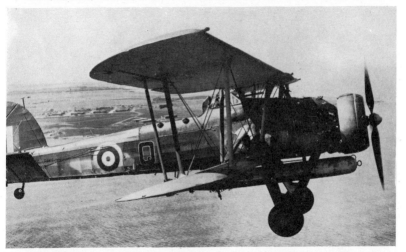

L2781, a Fairey Swordfish Mk. I equipped as a single-seater. (*Bristol Siddeley Photo.*)

NS204, the last Fairey Swordfish Mk. III, built by Blackburn. (*Blackburn Photo.*)

and was forced to jump again from the opposite side to make a safe escape from the doomed aircraft.

The T.S.R.I had established itself as sufficiently promising for a second prototype—the T.S.R.II—to be constructed. This was completed in the spring of 1934 and had been revised to incorporate an additional bay in the fuselage to eradicate any tendency to spin. As a result, it was necessary to introduce compensatory sweepback of 4° in the upper wings. The T.S.R.II, Fairey airframe F2038, was allotted the serial K4190 and was taken on its first flight from the Fairey testing ground by Chris Staniland on 17th April, 1934. The new machine's engine was the 690 h.p. Pegasus IIIM3, and K4190 had been developed by Lobelle to comply with Specification S.15/33. Other significant external alterations compared with the T.S.R.I were K4190's new fin and rudder of much lower aspect ratio, revised upper wing-tips and the addition to the rear fuselage of anti-spin strakes of considerable length. A broad-chord Townend ring cowling enclosed the Pegasus, and K4190 was tested with a wooden Watts propeller and a metal Fairey-Reed—both with two blades. Trials were made on floats at Hamble from 10th November, 1934, followed by catapult launches from H.M.S. *Repulse*.

A. & A.E.E. Martlesham testing was successful, and the T.S.R.II was ordered for the Fleet Air Arm as the Swordfish Mk. I, No. 825 Squadron receiving the first in July, 1936. Development was to Specification 38/34, a

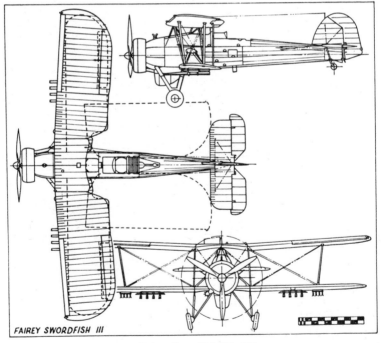

FAIREY SWORDFISH III

Fairey Swordfish Mk. III

230

three-blade Fairey-Reed metal propeller replacing the previous two-blade unit. As a torpedo-carrier the crew numbered two, but was increased to three for spotting and reconnaissance duties. Under-wing racks accommodated a bomb load of 1,500 lb. in place of the torpedo. The Swordfish Mk. II appeared in 1943, fitted with stronger lower wings to enable batteries of rocket projectiles to be fired from their undersides. These loads could alternate between eight 60 lb. high-explosive type or eight 25 lb. armourpiercing. Depth charges were another possible offensive load. The Pegasus IIIM3 engine was fitted to the first Mk. IIs, but the 750 h.p. Pegasus XXX took its place in later batches of the Mk. II. 1943 saw also the last major production model, the Mk. III, appear. This version was distinguished by the ventral A.S.V. Mk. X radar scanner installed beneath the fore fuselage. A number of Swordfish were converted for use as Mk. IVs in Canada, being equipped with a glazed canopy over the cockpits as protection against the extreme cold.

M.A.E.E. Felixstowe Report F/138A of September, 1936, dealt with trials carried out with Swordfish K5662 completed to Specification 38/34 as a fleet spotter, reconnaissance and torpedo seaplane powered by Pegasus IIIM3 P.15844/110329 developing 673 b.h.p. at 2,200 r.p.m. at 3,500 ft. The machine's weight empty was 4,997 lb. and loaded 8,015 lb., span 45 ft. 6 in., length 40 ft., height 16 ft. and width folded 17 ft. 3 in. The divided twin dural floats had a track of 9·8 ft. and were 26 ft. 9·7 in. long, 3 ft. 6·75 in. in beam and 3 ft. 1·3 in. deep. The wing area of 549 sq. ft. gave a wing loading of 14·6 lb./sq. ft. At the full loaded weight of 8,900 lb. a depth of water of 1 ft. 9·5 in. was required to float the aircraft. Frise ailerons were fitted to all wings and automatic Handley Page slots to the upper wingtips. The fuselage was of steel tubing, the same medium forming the primary structure of the wings, dural being used for their secondary structure. Covering was of fabric. The floats had two water rudders with pivoting blades raised and lowered by tricing line, each of these rudders being controlled pneumatically by a servo tab hinged to the air rudder's trailing edge and operated by a small servo motor. The propeller was a three-blade Fairey-Reed L.H.T. of 11·83 ft. diameter.

At all speeds longitudinal stability was light and positive, and lateral and directional stability were heavy but positive. While taxying the water rudder control was not very good at low speeds. At 1,000 r.p.m. and above rudder control was more positive. With tip slots operating, the stall was satisfactory. The ailerons could be lowered from 0° to 8° to act as flaps, but were not so used during the trials. In diving tests the machine was stable both laterally and longitudinally and without undue vibration. While diving no flutter of the control surfaces was recorded. With the c.g. forward K5662 came out of a dive easily and quickly; with the c.g. aft definite pressure was needed on elevators and the response was slow. The floats were fitted with vertical plungers for attachment to the struts. The cockpit layout of controls and instruments was satisfactory, and the W/T installation was fitted under remote control in a crate as a complete unit in the aft end of the rear cockpit. The rear fuselage contained the large rubberized fabric flotation bag with a

K3602, a Vickers Valentia. (*Vickers Photo.*)

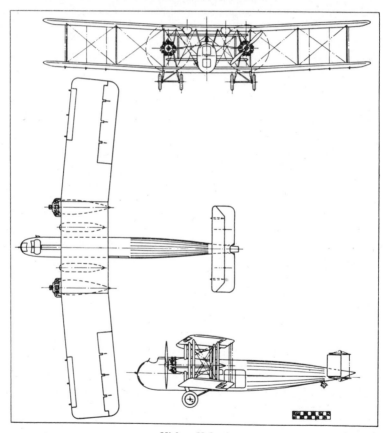

Vickers Valentia

232

buoyancy of 1,600 lb., and the dinghy was housed in the root of the port upper wing, inflation by carbon dioxide taking place on immersion in 30 in. of water. K5662 took a considerable time to get on to the step compared with other seaplanes of similar size, and during this period the propeller picked up a lot of water. The best approach speed was 80 kt. Even under very choppy conditions the machine's behaviour was very good, without porpoising or swing. At the full load of 8,900 lb. the floats were very low in the water at low speeds, and considerable water was picked up by the propeller and thrown over the windscreen and starboard side of the aircraft. In a slight chop the tips of the propeller appeared at times to touch the water. The water rudders dropped easily to take effect at about 1,000 r.p.m. Opening up to 1,200 to 1,400 r.p.m. made the floats become dirty and gave the impression that K5662 wanted to dive below the surface. At above this speed the nose of the aircraft came up, the propeller cleared the water and control was very good. The floats were then reasonably clean. Once on the step, a slight pounding ensued before reaching enough flying speed. On take-off and landing the controls were satisfactory. Stability on the water was good without any tendency to dip a wingtip even in a strong cross-wind. As a spotter recon-naissance type the Swordfish Mk. I recorded a top speed of 118 kt. at 4,600 ft. full throttle height, a maximum rate of climb of 850 ft./min. at 800 ft. and a service ceiling of 14,250 ft.

The bomber transport was an aircraft of some consequence in the R.A.F. during the early 1930s, finding particular application in the Middle East, where the Service had special commitments in its appointed rôle as aerial peace-keeper. Steady development in this class of aeroplane resulted in the appearance periodically of an improved version of existing equipment, so that the Vickers Victoria Mk. VI was developed to Specification 25/33 as the Type 264 Valentia. First ordered in July, 1933, the machine was produced to Specification 30/34, initial deliveries being made to the R.A.F. during May, 1934. The new bomber transport was basically the same as the Victoria Mk. VI and was powered by a pair of 650 h.p. Pegasus IIL3s, or with IIM3s for use in India with one flight of No. 31 Squadron in 1938. An external difference was the installation of a swivelling tailwheel in place of the Victoria's skid, many of the Valentias being produced by converting Victoria Mk. Vs. The bomb load of 2,200 lb. was carried beneath the lower wings.

The unequivocal success of the Hawker Hart as a day bomber led to its consideration for adaptation as a high-performance general-purpose type as the Hart General Purpose, a designation then changed to Hardy. The development was to Specification G.23/33, the prototype being a modified Hart K3013 which, in its new form, made its first take-off on 7th September, 1934, at Brooklands piloted by Flt. Lt. P. E. G. Sayer. The Hardy's power plant was the 530 h.p. Kestrel IB or the 585 h.p. Kestrel X, and the standard armament of one Vickers and one Lewis was retained. The bomb load was carried in racks beneath the lower wings, the machine's appearance resembling that of an Audax with its long exhaust pipes and a horizontal gun-ring. The forty-seven production Hardys of 1936 were constructed by Gloster; the examples used in the Middle East for giving close support to ground troops, army co-operation, dive-bombing and reconnaissance were later equipped with low-pressure, heavy duty tyres to cope with the terrain encountered. No. 30 Squadron in Iraq during April, 1935, was the first unit to receive the Hardy.

At the same time as the advent of the Hardy, another development of the ubiquitous Hart emerged from Hawker. This was the two-seat Hind, the prototype of which—K2915—after revision from its original preparation to Specification 25/31 was designed to Specification G.7/34 to take advantage of the performance conferred by the fully-supercharged 640 h.p. Kestrel V. Noticeable external alterations compared with the Hart were the adoption of a tailwheel, the canting of the gunner's ring mounting and the fitting later on of ram's-horn exhaust stubs. K2915's maiden flight was from Brooklands on 12th September, 1934, and the Hind was subsequently ordered to Specification 11/35, a total of five hundred eventually being produced by the time that the termination of production came in September, 1938. No. 21 Squadron in December, 1936, was the first to receive the Hind. Specification 31/36 was prepared for a general-purpose version Hind Mk. I, but was abandoned, 46/36 was to Royal Australian Air Force requirements, and 13/37 of 31st May, 1937, covered conversion of the Hind with Kestrel V and various modifications to the radiator's retracting gear, controls, bomb-release gear, tanks, ammunition feed, etc. The Hind's primary claims to distinction are that it was the last of the R.A.F.'s biplane light bombers and that it played an important part in equipping many of the new squadrons hurriedly formed during the early expansion period once the country had begun to awaken to the growing danger surrounding it.

The Hind found itself in demand for export and went into service with several foreign air forces. The first of four for Portugal in 1936 with Kestrel Vs made its initial flight on 5th June, 1937. Yugoslavia bought three Hinds, the first of which was taken on its maiden flight from Brooklands by John Hindmarsh on 3rd June, 1937. This machine and the second were fitted with the 690 h.p. Kestrel XVI, but the third Yugoslav Hind received the air-cooled nine-cylinder Gnome-Rhône K-9 Mistral installed uncowled. The second example was tested at M.A.E.E. Felixstowe as a seaplane before dispatch to Yugoslavia. A radial power plant, the 840 h.p. Mercury VIII with cowling and a three-blade propeller, was selected for the batch of thirty-five Persian Hinds, No. 601—the first—making its initial take-off on 28th April, 1938, in P. G. Lucas's hands. Afghanistan ordered eight Hinds, the first four of which had the Kestrel V delivering its full power; the Kestrel Vs of the others were de-rated. A further twelve ex-R.A.F. Hinds were supplied to the Afghan Air Force. During January, 1938, Latvia placed an order for three Hinds, the first—176—making its initial flight some four months afterwards on 4th May. The Latvian version used the cowled 840 h.p. Mercury IX driving a two-blade wooden Watts propeller. The third machine—178—was tested also with a Pegasus in place of the Mercury. In the course of 1939 and 1940, Eire purchased six ex-R.A.F. Hinds. Although the Swiss Govern-

K3013, the prototype Hawker Hardy. (*Hawker Photo.*)

ment was the first of the foreign customers to evince interest in the Hind, one example only—HB-HAL—was supplied.

In spite of official reluctance to equip more than one squadron with the excellent Sidestrand, development of the big biplane continued at Boulton and Paul under John North's inspired direction. A Sidestrand Mk. III J9186 had served already as a development aircraft for the testing of various

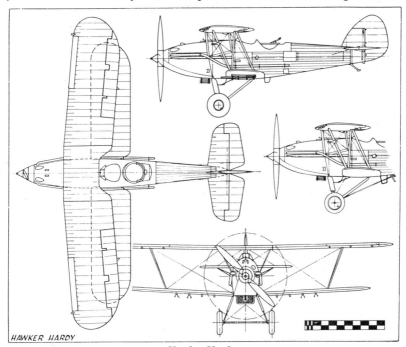

Hawker Hardy

235

Hawker Hind Mk. I. (*Hawker Photo.*)

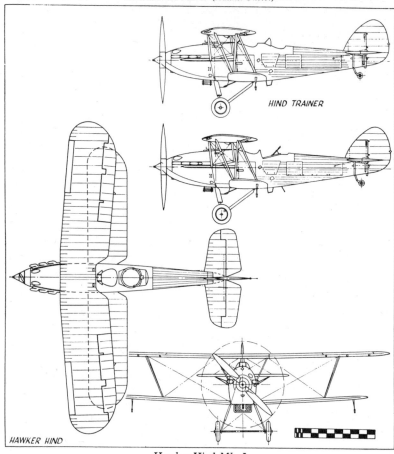

HIND TRAINER

HAWKER HIND

Hawker Hind Mk. I

236

Hawker Persian Hind. (*Bristol Siddeley Photo.*)

HB-HAL, the single Hawker Swiss Hind. (*Hawker Photo.*)

The third Hawker Latvian Hind 178. (*Hawker Photo.*)

innovations and was prepared in 1933 to be the P.29 Sidestrand Mk. V still equipped as a three-seater, but with a pair of 555 h.p. Pegasus IM3 engines fitted with polygonal Townend cowling rings containing nine facets each.

The spirited performance of the Sidestrand had brought into sharp prominence one particular problem associated with higher speed. This was the difficulty being experienced by the gunners in aiming their Lewis guns satisfactorily in the increasing pressure of the slipstream. North was convinced that the stage had now been reached at which the only solution lay in enclosing the gunner in a protective turret, at the same time providing power for its propulsion. He thereupon set about evolving a power-operated turret for installation in the nose of the new version of the Sidestrand. The cylindrical turret with dome ends contained a single Lewis gun and was driven in rotation by compressed air at 120 lb./sq. in., tapped from storage bottles charged by a compressor fitted to one of the Pegasus engines and taken to a revolving joint at the turret's base. Elevation and depression of the weapon in the long vertical slit was manual, its weight being counter-balanced by that of the gunner through hydraulic connection with his seat. The arc of rotation for aiming was about 240° and an external pivot gave some degree of additional movement to the gun, the blast of the air against the barrel being taken into account in the balancing of the gun. Pressure of the gun to either side against a pair of plunger valves, caused by the gunner aiming at his target, controlled the rotation of the turret. Other aids to crew efficiency were the provision of a fully-enclosed pilot's cockpit, heating by a controllable hot air supply provided by a heater embodied in the exhaust system of one of the Pegasus units, an automatic pilot and a windscreen of generous area to shield the dorsal gunner. Strengthening of the airframe allowed the machine to operate at a gross weight of 12,000 lb. and with a bomb load of 1,500 lb. Additional strut bracing was incorporated in the main undercarriage units, and the aircraft was endowed with complete equipment to cover operations by day or by night.

Sqn. Ldr. C. A. Rea conducted J9186's first flight in its new form from Mousehold Aerodrome in 1933; its conversion was an unqualified success, and three more Sidestrands were modified, using the 580 h.p. Pegasus IIM3, to Specification 29/33 as development aircraft for the production version to be designated Sidestrand Mk. V. Specification 23/34 was drawn up for the construction of twenty-four examples for the R.A.F., the name of Overstrand —another Norfolk village near the type's birthplace—being selected in March, 1934, in place of the earlier title.

Once more one unit only was destined to be equipped with the new Boulton and Paul product, and this was again No. 101 Squadron, which took over its first Overstrand, the converted Sidestrand J9185, on 24th January, 1935, its true production P.75 Overstrand Mk. Is starting to arrive a year later, early in 1936. No. 101 thus qualified for distinction as the first R.A.F. squadron to operate an aircraft equipped with a power-operated gun turret. J9770, a P.75 Overstrand, was tested in 1935 with increased power in the form of a pair of 720 h.p. Pegasus IV engines.

Boulton Paul P.75 Overstrand J9186, originally a Sidestrand. (*Boulton Paul Photo.*)

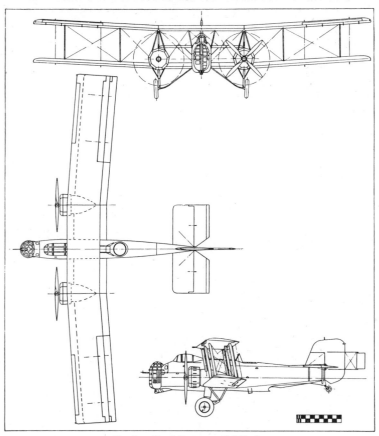

Boulton Paul Overstrand Mk. I

239

804, fourth Hartbees constructed by Hawker. (*Hawker Photo.*)

Although it was very late in the era of the biplane, an improved model of the Overstrand—named the Superstrand—was designed to utilize a retractable undercarriage together with other refinements and to attain a top speed of 191 m.p.h. The day of the large biplane with its lack of sufficient speed was, however, finally over, and the project was abandoned.

In the course of production of the Overstrand major changes occurred in the firm when Boulton and Paul Ltd. became a public company known as Boulton Paul Aircraft Ltd., with a move taking place eventually by August, 1936, to Wolverhampton from Norwich.

During 1934 the Air Ministry issued Specification B.3/34 for an experimental twin-engine, landplane heavy bomber. Frank Barnwell at Bristol prepared in 1934 the Type 144 monoplane project with two Bristol Perseus engines to meet the requirement, the design being an adaptation of the Type

805, first Hartbees Mk. I of sixty-five constructed in South Africa. (*S.A.A.F. Photo.*)

240

130 troop carrier to C.26/31—later known as the Bombay. J. Lloyd evolved a layout for the Armstrong Whitworth B.3/34 to the requirement, the design emerging later as the Whitley Mks. I and II to Specification B.21/35.

South African interest in procuring a version of the Hart manifested itself during 1934 when discussions took place which resulted in Specification 22/34 being drawn up to cover development of the design of four sample aircraft which evolved as the Hawker Hartbees. 801, the first machine, made its initial flight on 28th June, 1935, and subsequent production of sixty-five Hartbees Mk. Is was undertaken at Pretoria. The type was basically an

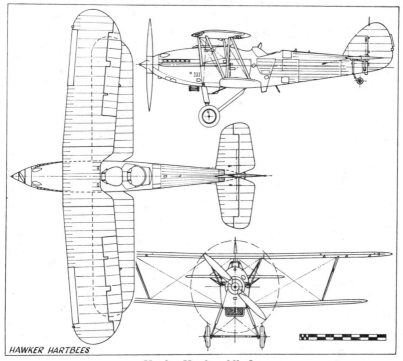

HAWKER HARTBEES

Hawker Hartbees Mk. I

adaptation of the Audax using the 608 h.p. Kestrel VFP and armed with the standard pair of guns, one Vickers and one Lewis. Light bombs for close support work were carried under the lower wings.

Among the specifications issued during the hey-day of the general-purpose aircraft, G.4/31 was significant in producing the largest number of proto-types and projects and the greatest variety of design concepts in answer to its requirements. The Air Ministry announced the new specification for an experimental general-purpose type in July, 1931, amending the requirement in October, 1931, to extend the scope of the duties of the resulting aircraft to include—besides light bombing by day and by night, army co-operation, dive-bombing, land reconnaissance, photography and casualty evacuation, originally demanded—the additional rôles of torpedo-bomber and coastal reconnaissance. Outstanding versatility was therefore called for in any project prepared to satisfy G.4/31, the specification constituting a bold challenge to the aircraft industry's designers—men who had, however, by now accumulated a considerable fund of experience to enable them to meet it with a fair chance of success.

Plenty of interest in submitting tenders was displayed by the larger companies equipped to undertake the task; few, indeed, refrained from putting forward their proposals with alacrity for a replacement aircraft—for the Gordon and Wapiti—which could, in varying climates and temperatures, be operated with equal efficiency in numerous rôles carrying a torpedo or a 1,000 lb. bomb and fly from all types of aerodrome and temporary landing strip.

Bristol's Frank Barnwell prepared several layouts to G.4/31, submitting also the Type 120 R-6 for testing at Martlesham as a contender. The Air Ministry's revision of the Specification's demands, however, rendered the Type 120 incapable of meeting G.4/31, resulting in Barnwell drawing up the Type 121—a revised version of the Type 120 with larger, equal-span wings for greater lifting power—and the Type 122, a biplane based on the Type 121, in which the pilot was situated high in the nose ahead of the upper wings. Both projects were prepared in 1931 around the Pegasus engine. During the same year, and again evolved around the Pegasus, two stressed-skin cantilever monoplanes—the low-wing Type 125 and the high-wing Type 126—were devised by Barnwell as G.4/31 alternatives. No progress was made with any of these ideas, and Bristol interest in the requirement soon lapsed in favour of the firm's many other design activities.

The Blackburn contribution to the field for G.4/31 was a Private Venture adaptation in 1934 of the earlier B-6 biplane, G. E. Petty's modification resulting in the B-7 with wings of slightly increased area and from which the ability to fold had been deleted. B-7 was powered by a cowled 700 h.p. Tiger IV driving a two-blade propeller and could be operated with a crew of two or three.

Hawker decided to join the list of companies preparing designs to meet G.4/31, and Sydney Camm also set about producing a new Private Venture version of a successful existing design—in this case that of the Hart. The new

B-7, the Blackburn G.4/31 Private Venture. (*Blackburn Photo.*)

IPV4, the Hawker P.V.4 to Specification G.4/31. (*Hawker Photo.*)

machine, the P.V.4 IPV4, stopped short of the torpedo-carrying requirement and was designed with particular attention to the dive-bomber aspect of the specification. Significant alterations from the basic Hart layout were an overall strengthening of the airframe, the increase in the span of the upper wings to 40 ft., the addition of a pair of diagonal struts in the centre-section cabane and the substitution of a cowled 800 h.p. Pegasus III engine for the

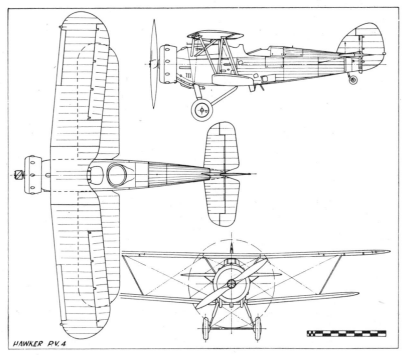

Hawker P.V.4

243

Westland P.V.7 in its later form with covered cockpit and revised fin and rudder. (*Westland Photo*.)

Kestrel. Crew capacity remained two, and the P.V.4 was taken on its maiden flight from Brooklands on 6th December, 1934. The port side of the nose accommodated the pilot's Vickers Mk. III gun, and a Somers ring mounting —installed at an angle in the rear cockpit—bore the observer's Lewis. The total bomb load of 570 lb. was housed beneath the lower wings. For assessment at A. & A.E.E. Martlesham in June, 1935, the P.V.4 was equipped with the 820 h.p. Pegasus X with which it reached a top speed of 183 m.p.h. at 6,600 ft. At the end of its A. & A.E.E. trials in October, 1935, the P.V.4 became K6926 with a new rating of some 900 h.p. for the Pegasus and was passed to Bristol as a test-bed at Filton for its engine. Later trials there included the fitting of the Bristol Perseus and Taurus power plants.

The majority of the designers engaged in evolving the machines to be built by their firms to compete in the G.4/31 tests of 1935 adhered to the biplane formula, but Westland's chief designer Arthur Davenport—always a staunch advocate of the monoplane—chose a high-wing layout for the Yeovil firm's Private Venture prototype P.V.7 P7. Completed in the autumn of 1933, the machine was a handsome two-seat design with a generous wing span of 60 ft. 3 in. The parallel-chord mainplanes, mounted at shoulder level, featured roots tapering down in thickness to improve visibility from the cockpit set at the leading edge, Handley Page slots and Westland electroscope trailing-edge split flaps set inboard adjacent to the ailerons. These flaps were fitted to limit the diving speed when dive bombing. Sturdy struts braced the wings— contributing a degree of lift—and were attached to the divided undercarriage units. The gunner and his Lewis were located in a recess in the top decking just aft of the trailing edge of the wings, covered with a hinged, segmented canopy which retracted forwards for action. Power for the P.V.7 was provided by the 722 h.p. Pegasus IIM3 complete with Townend ring. A Vickers gun in the port side of the nose armed the pilot.

Harald Penrose took P7 on its first flight on 3rd October, 1933, from the Westland field at Yeovil and found that some modifications were necessary. Revisions made included the fitting of a new fin and a larger parallel-chord rudder without the previous angled horn balance, strengthening of the

244

bracing of the wing panels, which had displayed a disconcerting tendency to twist under the application of the ailerons while diving, and the provision of a canopy to enclose the hitherto open pilot's cockpit. Development flying continued for nearly a year, and the large, graceful monoplane was eventually delivered to Martlesham for further trials. Westland entertained high hopes for its adoption by the R.A.F., but they were dashed when, on a day in the late summer of 1934, the machine crashed while Penrose was putting it through diving tests from the A. & A.E.E. Unknown to him, after taking-off a telegram arrived from Westland instructing postponement of the flight as the P.V.7 possibly did not meet the necessary strength requirements at the loading proposed for the flight. In overload conditions in a dive at about 215 m.p.h. in turbulent air, the port rear main bracing strut failed and the wing was torn off, carrying the tail with it in its passage. Harald Penrose went through the frightening experience of being trapped inside the cabin, but was fortunately able to extricate himself through a small side exit to make one of the first successful parachute escapes from a military aircraft with an enclosed cockpit. With a 722 h.p. Pegasus IIIM3 engine fitted, P7 had demonstrated a top speed of 173 m.p.h. at 5,000 ft., but, despite the promise which the design had shown, on the grounds of cost it was decided that a further prototype would not be built as a Private Venture.

Thus ended Westland aspirations to an order from G.4/31, but the monoplane layout was also adopted by Handley Page for the H.P.47, which Dr. Gustav V. Lachmann designed as the Cricklewood company's entry to comply with the specification's dicta. The firm was strongly placed to produce a successful design for the stated duties of the requirement and evolved an elegant two-seat, cantilever low-wing aircraft of strikingly advanced concept and businesslike aspect. The pilot was situated in an advantageous position towards the nose in the narrow, deep fore portion of the fuselage; the rear of the body diminished abruptly at the trailing edge into a tapering boom carrying the tail unit, thereby providing the well-protected gunner with an excellent field of fire for his Lewis gun. To retain sufficient control at high climbing angles, the fin and rudder were mounted in advance of the horizontal tail surfaces. Generous use of high-lift devices—another Handley Page *forte*—conferred good take-off and landing qualities on the H.P. 47, those installed including full-span, leading-edge slots, slotted ailerons and hydraulically-operated trailing-edge flaps. Lift spoilers were installed on the leading edges adjacent to the slots to aid manoeuvrability. Spats enclosed all three undercarriage wheels, those over the main wheels forming a prominent feature of the design. The sturdy inverted tripod struts were set wide apart, allowing the torpedo to be carried easily between them. Provision was made for operation on floats. Three passengers could be carried in the compartment between the two open cockpits; for ambulance work stretchers were borne in the same space. The bomb load was housed in under-wing racks; aiming was by the gunner from a prone position in the base of the fuselage, accuracy being assisted by a plate to deflect the slipstream. A groove in the port side of the nose housed the pilot's Vickers gun.

The single H.P.47 prototype K2773 carried a 695 h.p. Pegasus IIMS engine in its nose, surrounded by a Townend ring incorporating a collector ring feeding a pair of lengthy exhaust pipes. All-metal construction and covering was used, with the exception of portions of the upper and lower surfaces of the wings which received fabric covering.

K2773's first flight was made in November, 1933, from Radlett with Sqn. Ldr. T. H. England at the controls, subsequent testing to Air Ministry requirements being conducted by Maj. J. L. B. H. Cordes. On trial the rear boom of the fuselage was found to twist and was consequently strengthened. Eventually, despite a highly promising appearance, K2773 passed the remainder of its life at Farnborough as a test-bed.

In most of the prototypes constructed to G.4/31 particular emphasis was laid on the provision of a commanding view for the pilot, a point of primary importance in successful torpedo attack. In several instances the expedient was adopted of locating the pilot's position—either open or enclosed—just ahead of the leading edge of the wings. This idea was eventually resorted to by J. Lloyd in designing the A.W.19 A-3, Armstrong Whitworth's Private Venture two-seat biplane prepared to the requirement, following first thoughts which resulted in a layout for a machine which would have resembled a scaled-up Atlas with a fin and rudder outline akin to that of the A.W. Atalanta civil monoplane and equipped with spats over the main wheels and the tail-wheel.

The designation A.W.19—conferred on this original design—was employed also for the final machine, which was completed at the commencement of 1934 as a single-bay biplane with moderately staggered wings, the upper planes of which were—at 49 ft. 8 in.—very slightly greater in span than the lower surfaces. The four Frise mass-balanced ailerons were connected by struts, and Handley Page automatic slots occupied the upper outer leading edges. A cabin filled the gap between the wings, the lower wing roots incorporating slight anhedral which increased the gap between the mainplanes and served to shorten the undercarriage, which was fitted with semi-low-pressure tyres. A detachable crutch carrying the 18 in. Mk. VIII or Type K torpedo was installed between the divided-axle main wheel units. The pilot's ·303 Vickers gun fired from an orifice in the starboard nose decking beneath the cockpit, and the observer's ·303 Lewis was mounted in the mid-upper position on an Avro gun-ring, set at an angle in the coaming. A bomb load of 1,000 lb., released electrically, was carried in racks beneath the lower wings, as an alternative to a single 1,000 lb. Type B bomb in place of the torpedo. The A.W.19, which flew for the first time on 28th February, 1934, from Whitley Abbey, piloted by A. C. Campbell Orde and powered by the 810 h.p. Tiger VI driving a two-blade wooden propeller, was designed to carry an extremely comprehensive range of service equipment.

Among the bevy of biplanes built as G.4/31 prototypes, in its final Mk. II form Marcel Lobelle's design for Fairey was undoubtedly the most elegant in appearance. Before the machine which subsequently emerged was finalized as a design, several alternative layouts were given extensive consideration. The initial proposals contrasted sharply with each other—one was a two-bay biplane and the other a monoplane. Each was intended to use a retractable undercarriage, and both projects were evaluated in the R.A.E.'s wind-tunnel

Armstrong Whitworth A.W.19 A-3. (*Bristol Siddeley Photo.*)

247

at Farnborough. Tests were made with the biplane using a conventional centre-section supported by struts and also with the identical centre-section connected to the fuselage at an acute dihedral angle. The pilot was given a cockpit at the leading edge of the upper mainplanes, his view being assisted by deep cut-outs in the front of the wings on each side. A fairing beneath the fuselage was proposed as a housing for the bomb load, and this idea applied also to the 58 ft. span monoplane design which was tested in model form. The monoplane's mid-wings were joined to the fuselage at shoulder level. A straight leading edge was used, but acute taper was embodied by sweeping the trailing edge forwards from the roots, which were of very broad chord. To improve the gunner's field of fire these roots contained a deep cut-out. The pilot's cockpit was offset to port and was lined up with the wings' leading edge.

The next Fairey G.4/31 proposal of October, 1932, differed greatly from the first two projects. The new design was that of a conventional two-bay biplane with staggered, unequal-span wings and with the crew in tandem cockpits mid-way along the fuselage. The divided undercarriage was fixed, and streamlined bomb-containers were to be set flush with the underside of the lower wing roots, which were set with anhedral, the lower halves of the missiles protruding into the slipstream. The torpedo was intended to nestle against the underside of the fuselage. The engine proposed was a cowled Tiger II. This scheme was superseded by yet another for a single-bay biplane with extensive cut-outs in the trailing edges of the wings at the roots. An uncowled Pegasus IIIM was to power the machine. A model was submitted to the R.A.E. assessment in the tunnel, as a result of which the fuselage was lengthened by 20 in. in the final design and horizontal strakes were incorporated in the fuselage ahead of the tailplane.

The Fairey G.4/31 design was ultimately finalized so that, in 1934, the two-seat Mk. I, Fairey airframe F1926, made its début as a Private Venture.

Fairey G.4/31 Mk. I. (*Bristol Siddeley Photo.*)

The Fairey G.4/31 Mk. II F-1/K3905. (*Fairey Photo.*)

The machine was powered by the 635 h.p. Pegasus IIM3 mounted uncowled in the nose of a deep fuselage containing a cabin reached through an external starboard door and internally from the rear cockpit along a passage provided by off-setting the pilot to port at the trailing edge. Modifications were subsequently effected, and the machine appeared in its Mk. II version during 1935 with a 750 h.p. Tiger IV in a broad-chord Townend ring, long exhaust pipes, spats on its main wheels and a new fin and rudder but without the earlier ventral fin. A Fairey high-speed mounting carried the observer's Lewis gun, and a Vickers in the port decking armed the pilot. A wooden propeller was tried as well as a Fairey-Reed duralumin type. During the design stages alternative engines discussed included the Panther II, Jupiter XF, Pegasus IIIM3 and the Kestrel IIMS. The aircraft bore the marking F-1 and was later allocated the serial K3905. In its Mk. II form the Fairey G.4/31 presented a greatly refined appearance; nevertheless, no progress was made towards a production order.

Parnall of Yate, although but a relatively small concern and one which, apart from other related activities, had been responsible in the main for a succession of extremely diverse prototypes during its time in the aircraft industry, took the decision to proceed with the construction of a prototype to G.4/31. The design of K2772 was undertaken by H. V. Clarke, and the machine was the last of the group of G.4/31 aircraft to be completed, making its appearance during 1935 to undergo its maiden flight at Yate piloted by Capt. Howard John Saint. Among the G.4/31 biplanes the Parnall prototype's upper span of 57 ft. made it the largest. The Pegasus IM3 with Townend ring, developing 690 h.p., was chosen to power the big, unequal-span biplane, the two-bay wings of which were braced by N interplane struts fitted from opposite corners compared with the usual form, thus giving a reversed effect.

K2772, the Parnall G.4/31. (*Flight International Photo.*)

K2772 was built embodying recommendations made by the R.A.E. at Farnborough following tests in the wind-tunnel with models. Spinning trials, with and without the automatic Handley Page slots, operating at an equivalent height of 8,500 ft. were recorded in Report B.A.1003 of January, 1933, which suggested revision of the disposition of the fin area and an overall improvement in the tail surfaces. Two years later, in January, 1935, Report B.A.1003A was issued following additional spinning trials with a revised model which incorporated modified rear fuselage, fin, rudder and elevators, as well as a small increase in the span of the slots.

The Parnall G.4/31 accommodated a crew of two, the pilot occupying a covered cockpit high above the nose at the upper leading edge; the gunner used a cockpit at the rear of the wings aft of the unglazed cabin which filled the entire gap between the mainplanes. At the upper wing roots the dihedral angle increased sharply, the aerofoil section being the Parnall 3. Four cable-connected ailerons provided lateral control. The bomb load was carried externally in under-wing racks; the standard armament was fitted consisting of a Vickers set to port for the pilot and a ring-mounted Lewis for the gunner.

To G.4/31, in addition to a projected Type 246, Vickers prepared the Type 253 biplane which was subsequently constructed, being completed in the summer of 1934. In its earlier proposed form of 1932 the biplane was to be a machine with unequal-span, two-bay wings of 571 sq. ft. area, using an R.A.F.34 aerofoil. Ailerons were to be a part of the upper wings only, and the interplane struts were to be of inverted V form for the inner bracing and single I type outboard. Slight stagger of 1·5° was envisaged, the scheduled engine was a Pegasus IM3 without cowling, and prominent trousers were to fair the main wheel units, which raked forwards sharply.

On being rolled out, the Type 253 displayed considerable modification. R. K. Pierson had been responsible for the overall design, which embodied an elegant, slim, oval-section fuselage constructed on the radical geodetic system evolved for Vickers by Dr. Barnes Neville Wallis a few years previously as part of the structure of the airship R-100. As in the A.W.19 and the Parnall G.4/31, the fuselage filled completely the wing gap, and the pilot and observer were respectively in front of and behind the upper wings. Normal pairs of splayed parallel interplane struts connected the two-bay wings of un-equal span, and anhedral was employed in the lower roots. Both upper and lower wing roots were swept forwards, and the aerofoil was the R.A.F.15. Handley Page slots and four cable-connected ailerons were used, under-wing racks taking the bomb load. The divided-axle undercarriage embodied large, shapely spats, a third spat covering the tailwheel. K2771 was fitted with the 690 h.p. Pegasus IIIM3 in a Townend cowling incorporating a collector ring and turning a 13 ft. 2 in. diameter two-blade wooden propeller. The pilot's ·303 Vickers gun was buried in the port nose decking, and the observer was armed with the usual ·303 Lewis.

Capt. Joseph Summers was responsible for the Type 253's first flight, which took place from Brooklands on 16th August, 1934. Revisions then made to K2271 included the enclosure of the open cockpit by a rearwards-sliding canopy and the deletion of the cut-outs in the upper wings by extend-ing the chord to its full depth, in which form it appeared in 1935.

The Vickers Type 253 was an eminently businesslike design, and A. & A.E.E. Martlesham assessment finally brought an order for one hundred and fifty for the R.A.F. Subsequently, however, on 10th September, 1935, the order was cancelled on the suggestion of Vickers in favour of a contemporary

Vickers Type 253 K2771 in its original form with open cockpit and reduced chord in upper centre-section. (*Vickers Photo.*)

The Armstrong Whitworth A.W.19. (*Whitworth Gloster Photo.*)

monoplane design of more advanced concept which was to attain production status as the Wellesley.

The progressive development of the British bomber through the first five years of the 1930s had proceeded against a background of frustrating and dangerous political doctrines and in the face of the direst economic depression in which the United Kingdom lay submerged. Consideration and awareness of the serious factors militating against the evolution of the bomber at the time emphasize the praiseworthy virility of the industry during this period of economic stress, and renders all the more remarkable the fact that the era was such a prolific one in the range of prototype and production bombers and torpedo-carrying aircraft designed and produced in a comparatively brief period.

K3583, the prototype Bristol Type 130 Bombay. (*Bristol Photo.*)

CHAPTER SIX

SPURRED TO SURVIVE

The system instituted by the Air Ministry of drawing up the requirements of the Royal Air Force and the Fleet Air Arm for aircraft in various classes and issuing the resulting specifications to the industry for tender had served well since it was adopted towards the close of the 1914–18 War. In retrospect, the era of the early and middle 1930s is seen as one which produced a remarkable proliferation of prototypes, a relatively small percentage of which ultimately reached squadrons as their equipment after competitive trials.

In each category design had become fairly stable, with the biplane still resolutely occupying first place and being subjected to continuing evolution. The monoplane, however, was asserting its claims to serious consideration, recognition and adoption with increasing vigour and pressure. In the face of urgent demands for modern aircraft to equip existing and new squadrons there was no place for opposition to the incorporation by designers of technical advances of every conceivable nature. A sense of strident urgency had descended upon the nation once the unsavoury truth had seeped into the minds of the politicians, who for fifteen years had been incapable of assimilating the simple fundamental fact that the key to survival at that time—and, indisputably, at any period in man's history—was armed strength. The obvious and bitter truth was now forcing itself home, and the factor of German rearmament was decisive in stimulating the frantic programmes to put the British Services in fighting order. The proposed increases in bomber strength were catered for by the preparation and issue of new specifications intended to produce advanced new designs in various classes. The requirements were settled not a minute too soon and brought forth the best that British design and engineering ability could offer—machines in all categories which were destined to achieve undying fame but a few years hence when they were called upon to demonstrate their prowess in action.

Both in Great Britain and abroad funds for military aircraft procurement were far from plentiful prior to the rearmament period, and a few attempts were made to adapt existing commercial designs to carry guns and bombs. The idea was successful in several instances, but the batches turned out were necessarily quite small, with but one main exception—that of the Anson. The de Havilland Aircraft Company attained some minor reward in this field with the D.H.84 Dragon biplane when eight were produced early in 1933 for the Iraqi Air Force. The military Dragon for Iraq was essentially the same as the normal civil version, but was able to carry sixteen 20 lb. bombs under the fuselage and was armed with twin Vickers guns fixed in the nose and a dorsal Lewis gun to the rear of the cabin. The fin incorporated a long curved extension reaching mid-way to the wings, and a metal rail structure behind the gunner's cockpit acted as a guard to prevent the gun firing into the tail unit. In March, 1934, the Danish Army Air Force took delivery of two additional military Dragons, and another three went to the Portuguese Air Force in 1937.

One of the most refined and elegant of British civil aircraft of the 1930s, the Airspeed Envoy, formed the subject of a profitable conversion to an operational military machine in late 1935 when the Government of the Union of South Africa ordered seven 6JM Series III Convertible Envoys for delivery during 1936. Three were for the direct use of the S.A.A.F. and carried a manually-operated Armstrong Whitworth turret in the dorsal position from which a single Lewis gun was fired. Another gun, a Vickers, was installed in the starboard side of the nose to fire forwards. Attachment points beneath the fuselage held the racks for three 100 lb. or sixteen 20 lb. bombs. The remaining four Convertible Envoys were supplied to South African Airways, conversion to light bombing or reconnaissance being effected in four hours by four men. The South African machines each used a pair of 355 h.p. Armstrong Siddeley Cheetah IX engines, but Czechoslovak Walter Castor IIs were specified for the two Convertible Envoys ordered by Czechoslovakia.

Far less beauteous than the Envoy but destined for immeasurably greater prominence was the Avro Anson, another civil design selected for adaptation as an operational service type. By the mid-1930s the twin-engine, retractable-undercarriage monoplane had made its impact upon the British aeronautical scene by virtue of its several design advantages in the relentless quest for improved efficiency. An Air Ministry requirement of May, 1934, for a general reconnaissance landplane drew proposals from Avro and de Havilland. The Avro project was designated 652A and was designed by Roy Chadwick in parallel with the 652 civil version. The firm's proposals went to the Air

K4771, the prototype Avro 652A Anson. (*Avro Photo.*)

Ministry on 19th May, 1934, and suggested a modified 652 to carry a 360 lb. bomb load housed in the centre-section, a pilot's fixed Vickers gun to port in the nose and a Lewis gun either on an open ring above the cabin or farther aft

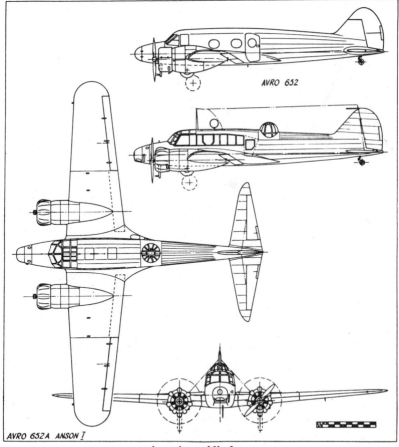

AVRO 652

AVRO 652A ANSON I

Avro Anson Mk. I

141, first of three Avro Anson Mk. 19 Ser. 2 bombing and reconnaissance aircraft supplied to the Irish Air Corps. (*Irish Air Corps Photo.*)

in a manually-operated Armstrong Whitworth cupola. Large rectangular windows were to replace the civil machine's oval type, and a pair of 295 h.p. Cheetah IXs were specified as the power plants. A single prototype—K4771—of the 652A with the cupola was ordered for competitive trials with the D.H.89M in 1935; S. A. Thorn took K4771 on its first flight at Woodford on 24th March, 1935.

The Hatfield offering for the same requirement, K4772, consisted of a standard Rapide airframe to which had been added a curved extension to the fin, a Vickers Mk. V gun housed to starboard in the nose, a Lewis Mk. III on a dorsal de Havilland mounting at the rear of the cabin and a bomb-bay able to take two 100 lb. and four 20 lb. bombs. Three revised D.H.89Ms were subsequently sold to the Spanish Government in December, 1935, and two additional examples went to the Lithuanian Government in 1936.

Meanwhile, the Air Ministry requirement was satisfied by the Avro 652A following Service Trials during April and May, 1935, at Martlesham and Gosport, but further modifications took place before the machine joined the R.A.F. as the Anson Mk. I to Specification G.18/35 of August, 1935. No. 48 Squadron in March, 1936, became the first to operate the new type, at the same time achieving two distinctions as the initial R.A.F. unit to be equipped with advanced monoplanes as well as being the first in the Service to fly with retractable undercarriages. The ultimate selection of the 652A for the R.A.F. ended further development of an alternative project, the Avro 664, considered for the same purpose. When it first entered service the Anson carried a crew of three and an offensive load of two 100 lb. and four 20 lb. bombs; this capacity was increased later to a complement of four and two 250 lb. bombs.

During this period the bomber transport was not neglected, and Specification C.26/31 was drawn up to bring into being a replacement in this class of aircraft. Three prototypes and a project resulted; the project was the Type 231 of 1933 from Vickers, and monoplane designs appeared from Handley Page, Armstrong Whitworth and Bristol. Although the H.P.43 of 1932 to Specification C.16/28 had not progressed beyond the prototype stage with the single example J9833, it was considered at Handley Page that the basic concept warranted an extension of development to endeavour to satisfy C.26/31. Hitherto engaged in experimental work for the company—particularly in

256

connection with slots and associated research—Dr. Lachmann took over as chief designer for some four years from 1932 until 1936, being responsible for several new designs—among them the H.P.51 to C.26/31. A significant feature embodied in the H.P.47 had been the cantilever wings of sharply tapered planform combined with fairly blunt tips and high-lift devices. The H.P.51 was a modification of the H.P.43 biplane, which Dr. Lachmann transformed into a sturdy cantilever high-wing monoplane with a crew of five by utilizing J9833's fuselage, to which were attached mainplanes of his own distinctive style with a broad chord at the roots reducing drastically towards the tips. Slots and flaps occupied about 50% of leading and trailing edges respectively. A pair of cowled 700 h.p. Tiger IV engines were installed fairly close to the fuselage to drive two-blade propellers. The main undercarriage was a fixed assembly of clean design incorporating large spats. The basic form of the H.P.43's tail unit was retained, but the twin fins and rudders exhibited reduced aspect ratio.

The H.P.51 kept the original serial J9833 and was taken on its first flight on 8th May, 1935, from Radlett by Maj. Cordes. The machine demonstrated its parent firm's final acceptance of Dr. Lachmann's theories on cantilever wing design and construction, which had first been allowed the opportunity to prove themselves in the H.P.47, and marked also the Handley Page concern's final rejection of the biplane on which its fortunes had depended for two decades.

On 4th June, 1935, just under a month after the H.P.51's maiden flight, K3585—the Armstrong Whitworth A.W.23 bomber transport to C.26/31—made its initial take-off. John Lloyd's design was a low-wing monoplane of portly aspect occasioned—and dominated—by its voluminous, fabric-covered, steel-tubing fuselage which was able to carry twenty-four troops. The flying surfaces were of relatively low aspect ratio, the wings—evolved around the massive light alloy box spar—possessing a remarkably thick section and carrying the two 840 h.p. Tiger VIII power plants in nacelles which housed also the retractable undercarriage, the first to be incorporated in an Armstrong Whitworth design. Nose and tail Lewis guns were installed in Armstrong Whitworth turrets, that at the rear being situated aft of the twin fins and rudders mounted on a low-set tailplane.

Nearly four years after its appearance the A.W.23 was acquired by Sir Alan Cobham's Flight Refuelling Ltd., in April, 1939, as G-AFRX for use in the development of in-flight refuelling techniques until its destruction on the ground at Ford, Sussex, in June, 1940, during an air raid.

Handley Page H.P.51 J9833. (*Handley Page Photo.*)

257

The demands of C.26/31 were eventually fulfilled by a design from Bristol, the Type 130 by Capt. F. S. Barnwell. The machine was akin in layout to the H.P.51, being a twin-engine, cantilever high-wing monoplane with fixed, spatted undercarriage and twin fins and rudders. The mainplanes were less highly tapered than those of the Handley Page design, and the Type 130 differed further in using advanced all-metal, stressed-skin construction. The aircraft's design gained considerable benefits from the amount of research initiated at Bristol following the trouble encountered with aileron reversal in the wings of the Type 95 Bagshot caused by flexing of the surfaces. Subsequent Bristol development of the cantilever type of wing to incorporate multiple spars and other features to combat twisting led to the suggested use of such wings for the Type 115 monoplane proposed with three Jupiter engines in 1929 to meet Specification C.16/28.

When C.26/31 was promulgated the Type 115 layout was revised and resulted in an order during March, 1933, for K3583, the prototype Type 130 which Cyril Uwins took into the air at Filton for its maiden flight on 23rd June, 1935. Two 750 h.p. Pegasus IIIM3 engines powered the Type 130, which accommodated a crew of three and twenty-four troops and, despite the fairly bulky fuselage dictated by its intended rôle, possessed a certain elegance of line. Armament of the Type 130 consisted at first of a Lewis gun in a revolving turret in the nose and another Lewis on a Scarff ring in the extreme tail, a position which was improved later by the addition of a cupola. Further development of the Type 130 took place in the course of 1936 both at Bristol and at A. & A.E.E. Martlesham, modifications—including the fitting of 1,010 h.p. Pegasus XXIIs with variable-pitch Rotol propellers and Bristol hydraulically-operated turrets at front and rear—bringing a new Type 130 Mk. II designation. An initial order for fifty was received, the type going into production as the Bombay Mk. I following rejection of the name Bedford at first suggested.

Pre-occupation with the Blenheim precluded construction of the Bombay by Bristol, and Short & Harland of Belfast were therefore selected to undertake production, design revision taking place to Specifications 38/36 of 5th March, 1937, and 47/36 of 7th July, 1937. Fifty production Bombays were built, the first—L5808—accomplishing its initial flight from Belfast in March, 1939. The Bombay's bomb load of 2,000 lb. was borne in external

K3585, the sole A.W.23. (*Armstrong Whitworth Photo.*)

First production Bristol Type 130A Bombay Mk. I L5808 constructed by Short & Harland. (*Short Photo.*)

racks installed beneath the belly, aiming being from a glazed position in the nose below the front gun station. The production Type 130A Bombay Mk. I was distinctive in lacking spats, possessing revised nose- and tail-gun positions and in having additional glazing in the cockpit canopy.

Despite the fact that the Air Ministry had ordered the Vickers Type 253 K2771 biplane prototype for evaluation to G.4/31, the Vickers directors were so convinced of the eventual superiority of the alternative Type 290 monoplane—designed to the same specification—that the decision was taken on 12th

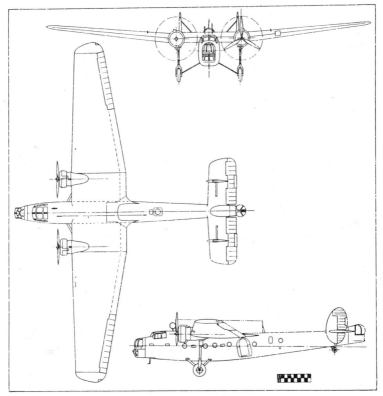

Bristol Bombay Mk. I

259

Vickers Wellesley Mk. I K7772. (*Bristol Siddeley Photo.*)

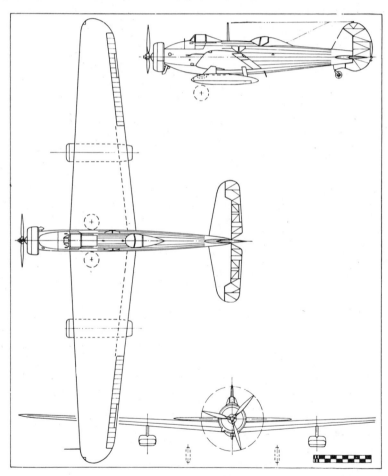

Vickers Wellesley Mk. I

April, 1932, to proceed with its construction as a Private Venture. The resulting O-9 K7556, which made its first flight fromBrooklands on 19th June, 1935, was a two-seat low mid-wing monoplane of outstanding elegance of line for a military general-purpose aircraft. R. K. Pierson's superb new creation again employed Dr. B. N. Wallis's ingenious system of geodetic construction, which was still looked upon askance by Air Ministry officials, for so long schooled in conventional methods of construction.

Geodetics permitted the Type 290 to be given 73 ft. 6 in. span tapered wings of high aspect ratio in the interests of long range. They were joined to a fuselage which differed but little from that employed in its Type 253 biplane counterpart. The nose bore a supercharged 925 h.p. Pegasus XX engine complete with Townend ring cowling and driving a three-blade metal propeller. The main undercarriage units were equipped with Vickers oleo-pneumatic shock absorbers and brakes, retraction taking place inwards into the wings; a spat faired the fixed tailwheel. Frise ailerons and split flaps occupied the trailing edge of the wings, and the machine's 2,000 lb. bomb load was housed in a pair of streamlined panniers mounted on pylons beneath the mainplanes. The Type 290's pilot was seated in a covered cockpit in line with the wings' leading edge and was armed with a Vickers gun concealed in the inboard panel of the starboard wing; the gunner was situated some distance aft in a streamlined fairing, the glazed portion of which retracted to enable him to use his Vickers K gun. A cabin between the two cockpits was provided for navigation.

In its initial tests K7556 swiftly justified its parent firm's faith and confidence by revealing a performance far in excess of that possessed by the G.4/31 biplane, the outcome of this manifestation being the strongest representations by Vickers to the Air Ministry—shortly after K7556 first took to the air—that the production order for the Type 253 should be switched to the Type 290. The Air Ministry finally bowed to the Vickers demands, cancelling the biplane order on 10th September, 1935, and replacing it with a contract for seventy-nine of the graceful monoplanes under the designation Wellesley Mk. I. Production was to Specification 22/35, and No. 76 Squadron at Finningley in April, 1937, gained the distinction of becoming the first to be equipped with an aircraft of geodetic construction.

The Wellesley's inherent long range made it a natural choice as the instrument to attack the world's long-distance record, and five were accordingly modified at the close of 1937 for delivery to the Long-range Development Flight of the R.A.F., which was formed in January, 1935, to make ready for the attempt. The principal revisions were the addition of a third member to the crew of each machine, the fitting of the Pegasus XXII engine in a cowling of increased chord faired into the nose, the use of a constant-speed propeller and the incorporation of extra fuel tanks—a requirement which the Wellesley's geodetic wings made relatively simple to execute. Three aircraft—L2638, L2639 and L2680—were selected out of the five prepared for the venture and took-off, led by Sqn. Ldr. R. Kellett, from Ismailia early on 5th November, 1938, with the object of reaching Darwin non-stop. L2639, with but a marginal supply of petrol to complete the scheduled flight, landed at Koepang for fuel, while the remaining two pilots of the trio, Sqn. Ldr. Kellett and Flt. Lt. A. N. Coombe, flew on to Darwin to land there on 7th November after 48 hr. 5 min. airborne and with the satisfactory knowledge that they had recaptured the record for Britain with a figure of 7,162 miles. L2639 followed the triumphant Wellesleys to Darwin to land some three hours after their arrival.

Later models of the Wellesley went into service with a glazed extension of the front cockpit canopy which reached to the rear to cover the navigator's cabin, a modification which was detrimental to the machine's purity of line. Provision was made in the Wellesley's design for the carriage of a torpedo beneath the fuselage, but the type was employed in the rôle of long-range bomber.

NZ341, a three-seat Vickers Vincent of the R.N.Z.A.F. (*R.N.Z.A.F. Photo.*)

A specification which was not proceeded with in its original form was M.15/35 for an experimental shore-based, twin-engine torpedo-bomber with internal housing for the torpedo, to which Frank Barnwell prepared the Bristol Type 150 project in 1935 evolved around a pair of Perseus VI engines. The layout was derived from the Blenheim with the pilot located 4 ft. 6 in. towards the front, balance adjustment being effected by moving the dorsal turret rearwards. Subsequently the requirement was amalgamated with G.24/35 to become Specification 10/36.

By 1934 the selection of a new type to replace the well-worn IIIFs and Wapitis which had been serving in the general-purpose capacity in the R.A.F. abroad had become a matter of urgency. The Vildebeest was proving an effective machine in its particular rôle and offered an obvious solution to the problem. S1714 was consequently modified and sent out to the Middle East to test its suitability for adoption. It proved satisfactory and was ordered for the Service as the Vincent to Specification 16/34. The space hitherto reserved for the torpedo was occupied by an external auxiliary fuel tank which gave it a total range of 1,250 miles. Comprehensive service equipment was stowed aboard to cope with the multifarious duties of a general-purpose aircraft and included the fitting of a message retrieving hook and under-wing racks to

S1715, a three-seat Vickers Vildebeest Mk. I converted to Vincent standard for experimental work.
(*Bristol Siddeley Photo.*)

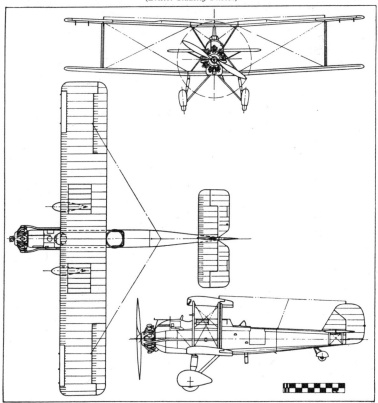

Vickers Vincent

263

The second prototype Fairey Seafox K4305. (*Fairey Photo.*)

transport a bomb load of 1,000 lb. The standard Vickers gun—mounted in the port nose-decking—for the pilot and a Lewis gun in the rear cockpit were carried; a third seat was available just behind the front cockpit. The Vincent's power was provided by a 660 h.p. Pegasus IIM3 installed without cowling. Some Vincents were derived by converting Vildebeests, and No. 8 Squadron at Aden in February, 1935, became the first Vincent unit. In service the machines were frequently flown without spats.

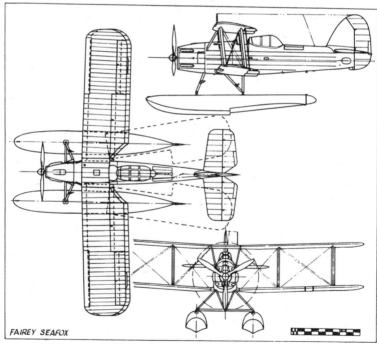

Fairey Seafox

264

Even as late as the mid-1930s the biplane was still considered to possess sufficient virtues to justify consideration as the formula for a new Fairey design to meet Specification S.11/32 for a Fleet Air Arm two-seat, light spotter reconnaissance seaplane to be launched from cruisers by catapult. Marcel Lobelle's ideas resolved themselves into a dainty two-bay biplane with 40 ft. equal-span, folding wings which were slightly staggered and incorporated a few degrees of sweepback. The metal frames of the flying surfaces were fabric covered, but the fuselage consisted of a watertight all-metal monocoque structure which was sealed entirely except for the cockpit apertures and the usual drain holes. The observer was given the luxury of a glazed canopy, but the pilot remained in the open to improve his view during launching and to facilitate recovery by ship's derrick after landing alongside the vessel. The view from the front cockpit was enhanced by the selection as power plant of the air-cooled 395 h.p. Napier Rapier VI, the sixteen cylinders of which were disposed in four inline banks to form an H layout resulting in a very slim compact unit.

Christened Seafox, the prototype K4304 made its first flight from the Fairey seaplane base at Hamble on 27th May, 1936. Some five months later a second Seafox prototype, K4305, made its appearance as a landplane to accomplish its first flight on 5th November, 1936. The neat Seafox was ordered for the Fleet Air Arm in January, 1936, a few months prior to the prototype's début, sixty-three out of sixty-four production examples being seaplanes. The Seafox's pilot lacked armament, but the observer used a ·303 Lewis on a Fairey special rocking pillar mounting stowed complete and flush with the rear decking in a covered recess; bombs were carried on one universal No. 1 rack under each lower wing, the capacity being two 100 lb. anti-submarine, or one 100 lb. anti-submarine and four 20 lb., or eight 20 lb., or smoke floats. No provision was made for a bomb-sight, and all aiming was carried out by estimation. Strut-connected Fairey camber-changing flaps on the four mainplanes and upper wing slots assisted low-speed performance.

Apart from being the sole aircraft to use the Rapier in service, the Seafox's main claim to distinction is the part played during the Battle of the River Plate on 13th December, 1939, when one from No. 718 Catapult Flight launched from H.M.S. *Ajax*—with Lt. E. D. G. Lewin as pilot accompanied by Lt. R. E. N. Kearney as his observer—spotted for the guns of H.M.S. *Achilles, Ajax* and *Exeter*, enabling them to defeat the German pocket-battleship *Admiral Graf Spee*, which was subsequently scuttled in Montevideo harbour a few days later on 17th December.

Report F/145A of April, 1937, recorded the results of tests carried out at M.A.E.E. Felixstowe on K4305, the second prototype Seafox on twin production floats. Comparative trials were conducted for take-off at a flap setting of 10° with a two-blade wooden Watts propeller with Schwartz finish and with a three-blade metal fine-pitch Angles X·5 propeller to represent the fine-pitch setting of a controllable two-pitch type. Both were 9 ft. 6 in. in diameter and driven by Rapier VI 75021/114072. K4305's all-up weight was 5,730 lb., about 300 lb. above the Seafox's normal A.U.W. Handling with the wooden propeller was assessed as very manoeuvrable on the water, the water rudders being very effective in a choppy sea in a 20 m.p.h. wind, enabling taxying to be conducted easily in any direction. Alighting with 35° of flap to check safe landing speed was particularly easy, without evidence of swing on take-off or landing. On the water K4305 was stable longitudinally and laterally. Using the metal propeller, take-off time was 50 sec. as opposed to 64 sec. with the wooden type. All-up weight of the production Seafox was expected to be 5,400 lb., resulting in a take-off time of 36 sec. equipped with the metal propeller. Even with a two-pitch type fitted, this was considered as too long. Specification S.11/32's requirement of 40 kt. alighting speed was not met, as it was recorded by M.A.E.E. as 53 kt. T.A.S.

A later report—F/145K dated 20th October, 1938—from M.A.E.E. Felix-stowe dealt with armament trials conducted with K4305. The single Lewis gun in the rear compartment was supplied with six magazines on pegs. Firing trials at 2,000 ft. revealed satisfactory gun behaviour with a fairly acceptable field of view for firing, but limitations downwards were imposed by the floats. The cupola exerted an adverse effect on the Norman Vane sight, making it unreliable when firing aft. When closed the Perspex canopy had a gap of up to 6 in. between its lower edge and the fuselage side, resulting in unpleasant draughts; the gunner was more comfortable with the hood up, whether firing or not.

Activity in the field of commercial aviation continued to expand swiftly as Great Britain managed to draw away from the devastating effects of the depression. The indisputable qualities of the twin-engine monoplane—embodying retractable undercarriage, flaps, variable-pitch propellers and associated advances in power plants—were recognized and accepted as the formula to be adopted for the generation of projected new civil designs. At Bristol Frank Barnwell was quick to adopt the layout for a new transport which eventually manifested itself in 1935 as the Type 142 created for Lord Rothermere and which—as the *Britain First*—astounded the aeronautical world by its magnificent performance, which included a top speed some 50 m.p.h. higher than that of the latest fighter then in production for the R.A.F. Acceptance trials at Martlesham as R-12, and subsequent evaluation as K7557 brought recognition of the design's potential as a fast bomber, ideal to take its place in the expanding strength of the Royal Air Force.

No time was lost by Barnwell in revising the Type 142 as the Type 142M three-seat medium bomber, the wings being raised to a mid-wing position and a pair of Mercury engines selected as power plants. At an Air Ministry conference convened on 9th July, 1935, to consider the layout, the proposals were impressive enough for Specification B.28/35 to be prepared for the bomber's development, a step which resulted in producing in a single stage a machine embodying prodigious technical advances over the biplane which it was shortly to supplant. An initial production order was placed in September, 1935, some ten months before the maiden flight of the prototype Type 142M K7033 on 25th June, 1936, at Filton piloted by Cyril Uwins.

The brilliant new bomber received the name Blenheim Mk. I and was a compact, sturdy design with the pilot seated in a generously glazed nose flanked by a pair of 840 h.p. Mercury VIII engines, into the nacelles of which the main wheels retracted rearwards. The raised position of the wings allowed the insertion of the bomb-bay—with a 1,000 lb. capacity—in the space vacated by the centre-section. A fixed Browning gun was fitted in the nose for the pilot, and a bomb-aiming position was provided in the same location. The Bristol B.I Mk. I dorsal turret containing a single Vickers K or Lewis gun was semi-retractable. Further modifications to the design before it entered production were the deletion of the retraction system of the tailwheel, the incorporation of controllable cooling gills around the periphery of the engine cowlings and the installation of more efficient air intakes.

No. 114 Squadron at Wyton in March, 1937, was the first to receive the new 285 m.p.h. Blenheim Mk. I, the fastest medium bomber in service in any air force at that time. Foreign interest soon arose once the Blenheim's superlative performance was publicized, and exports were made to Finland, Turkey and Yugoslavia. To cope with the demand to re-equip the R.A.F., production of the Blenheim Mk. I was sub-contracted to Rootes Securities Ltd., under Specification 33/36 of 23rd October, 1936, and to A. V. Roe Ltd., under Specification 2/37 of 22nd February, 1937.

As successful a new design as the Blenheim obviously possessed great inherent potential for development, and the Bristol design team were quickly at work with several schemes. A derivative, the Type 149 of November, 1935, planned to meet Specification G.24/35 issued in August, 1935, to produce an advanced general reconnaissance and coastal bomber, was rejected for its original purpose but transferred instead to give a general reconnaissance variant of the Blenheim under Type 149. The basic Type 142M layout was retained, but the nose was extended by 3 ft. to provide space for navigation and radio operation in front of the controls. The necessary increase in range was accomplished by inserting extra fuel tanks in the outer wing panels. L1222, a short-nose Blenheim Mk. I, was modified as the Mk. II prototype to house the additional tanks and was fitted with external bomb-racks and a stronger undercarriage, but the version was abandoned in favour of the lengthened nose model. A Mk. I—K7072—was utilized as the prototype Type 149, the name Bolingbroke Mk. I being selected for its production to Specification 11/36 of 14th July, 1936, for an interim general reconnaissance landplane with Mercury MEIIIM engines, and to Specification 34/36 of 23rd October, 1936, for production by Rootes.

Capt. Uwins took K7072 on its initial flight at Filton on 24th September, 1937, and found that the lengthening of the nose with the retention of the Mk. I profile had taken the windscreen too far in advance of the pilot's seat, which had not been moved. The shape of the nose was therefore modified by moving back the upper windscreen portion nearer to the pilot's position while retaining the extended lower nose. The glazed framework ahead of the pilot still obstructed his landing vision, and the expedient which finally resolved the problem was the reduction in height of the port section of the nose in line with the controls, which were on the left. The practicability of combining

K7072, the prototype Bristol 149 Bolingbroke Mk. I, was a converted Blenheim Mk. I.
(*R.C.A.F. Photo.*)

the extended nose and the long-range tanks in one model brought the decision to use the designation Blenheim Mk. IV for the new Type 149 variant with 920 h.p. Mercury XVs, and the name Bolingbroke was thereupon applied to the version of the Mk. IV built under licence in Canada for the R.C.A.F. by Fairchild at Longueuil, P.Q. K7072 was used by Fairchild as the model for the production of a batch of eighteen 840 h.p. Mercury VIII-powered Bolingbroke Mk. Is, which were followed by one hundred and twenty-five Mk. IVs fitted with the 920 h.p. Mercury XV. A Mk. I 705, reconstructed and modified to Mk. IV level, received the designation Bolingbroke Mk. II, and an additional Mk. I 717 built as a Mercury XV-powered temporary twin-

Bristol Blenheim Mk. IV L9020.

268

float seaplane became the Bolingbroke Mk. III. The Mk. IVC distinguished a single Mk. IV 9074 using a pair of 850 h.p. Wright Cyclone R1820-G3Bs, and the designation Mk. IVW was applied to a batch of fifteen Bolingbrokes using two 750 h.p. Pratt and Whitney Twin Wasp Jr. R-1830 SB4G engines.

Proposed Australian production of the Bolingbroke was covered by Specification 10/37 of 21st May, 1937, which specified compliance with 11/36

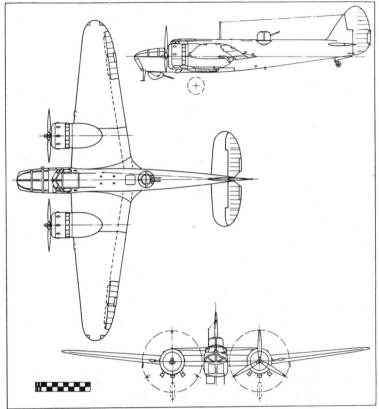

Bristol Blenheim Mk. IVL

with the exception of the use of Mercury XI engines in place of Mercury MEIIIMs and the Vickers Mk. V instead of the Browning gun; camouflage was not to be applied.

The Blenheim Mk. III designation was not in the event applied, as it had been retained for use on a short-range Type 149 variant with the lengthened nose, but installation of the extra tankage in the machines before acceptance by the R.A.F. nullified use of the term.

N6215, a Blenheim Mk. IV of No. 139 Squadron piloted by Flg. Off. A. McPherson, gained a measure of fame as the first British Service aircraft to cross the frontier of Germany in the 1939–45 War during reconnaissance of Wilhelmshaven on 3rd September, 1939.

While the evolution of the Blenheim was under way at Bristol, vastly accelerated activity in all of the major British aircraft and engine design offices was taking place in response to the heavy demands made upon them by the requirements issuing from the Air Ministry as a concomitant of the expansion of the Royal Air Force and the Fleet Air Arm.

Specification B.3/34 was promulgated to bring forth an experimental twin-engine, heavy night bomber landplane, and a tender was prepared during July, 1934, for Bristol by Frank Barnwell, offering the Type 144—a retractable undercarriage adaptation of the Type 130. It was proposed to use the original wings and front and rear fuselage but to splice in a new broader central fuselage section to take a load of up to five 550 lb. bombs. The design was based on the use either of two Pegasus IV or Perseus engines. A Vickers proposal suggested the adaptation of the Type 271 as a night bomber.

The Handley Page submission of B.3/34 was a derivation by Dr. Lachmann of his earlier H.P.51. Designated H.P.54, the new machine was of approximately the same size as J9833 but of far less angular aspect. Stringers from nose to tail faired the fuselage to a pleasant oval section, and a pair of 830 h.p. Pegasus X engines replaced the H.P.51's Tigers. Glazed gun positions were provided in the nose, dorsal and tail positions.

The prototype and first production H.P.54 K6933 made its maiden flight from Radlett on 10th October, 1936, piloted by Maj. Cordes, but the Air Ministry had already decided to order one hundred more than a year before in August, 1935, to Specification B.29/35 as an interim heavy bomber to replace the biplanes pending the arrival in service of more advanced types under development. The first examples appeared as Harrow Mk. Is with the Pegasus X, but were superseded on the production lines by the Mk. II fitted with a pair of 925 h.p. Pegasus XXs. The Harrow carried a crew of five and an internal bomb load of 3,000 lb. Its armament consisted of four Lewis guns disposed one each in the nose and amidships and two in the tail, all three turrets being power-operated. No. 214 Squadron became the initial unit to receive the graceful Harrow, its first Mk. I arriving on 13th January, 1937. Lack of production capacity precluded execution of an order for one hundred Harrows for the Fleet Air Arm.

Specification B.3/34 drew from Armstrong Whitworth the A.W.38 five-seat monoplane. All of its contemporaries possessed a goodly measure of aesthetic appeal in their lines, although basically heavy bombers, but in his new design from Coventry John Lloyd showed absolutely no concession whatever to the usual practice of establishing refined, shapely contours as a primary ally in the pursuit of aerodynamic performance. A mid-wing position was adopted in common with other monoplane bombers of the period, as such a location possessed the automatic advantage of providing a bomb-bay in the ideal position about the centre of gravity; additional accommodation for small bombs was available in the centre-section inboard of the engines.

In its overall layout the A.W.38 displayed strong evidence of its ancestor the A.W.23 and exhibited in every facet of its ponderous, graceless form an uncompromising adherence to the basic precepts governing its conception.

Handley Page Harrow prototype K6933. (*Handley Page Photo.*)

K4586, the first prototype, appeared in all-silver finish for A. C. Campbell Orde to take it on its first flight from Baginton on 17th March, 1936, and provided another instance of the haste to bring new equipment into R.A.F. service as quickly as possible; in the case of the A.W.38 an order had been placed for eighty as the Whitley in August, 1938, seven months or so prior to K4586's first take-off.

The sheer utility of line which characterized the Whitley brought handsome

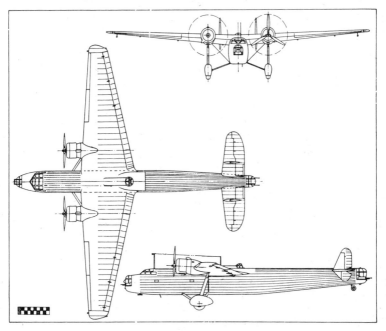

Handley Page Harrow Mk. II

advantages in speed of production, enabling No. 10 Squadron on 9th March, 1937, to introduce to the Service its first heavy bomber equipped with both a retractable undercarriage and turret armament. The all-metal, stressed-skin, monocoque fuselage construction and the use of an immense box-spar in the wings conferred on the Whitley its great virtue of outstanding strength. A pair of 795 h.p. Tiger IX engines powered K4586 and the subsequent Mk. Is. Following completion of several machines in the initial batch, lack of dihedral was found to affect stability adversely, and it was consequently introduced in the outer wing panels. Manually-operated Armstrong Whitworth turrets in nose and tail each housed one ·303 Vickers gun, and the bomb load of the Mk. I was 3,365 lb.

Development of the design proceeded to Specification B.21/35, resulting in production of the Whitley Mk. II equipped with two 920 h.p. Tiger VIII engines, the second prototype Mk. I K4587 serving as the Mk. II prototype. The Tiger VIII was retained for the Whitley Mk. IIIs developed and produced to Specification 20/36 of 4th August, 1936, K7211 being used as the prototype. The Mk. III's armament was improved by installing a Nash and Thompson power-operated turret for the single Vickers nose gun and by fitting a retractable rotating turret containing a pair of ·303 Brownings in the ventral position. This heavy, drag-producing protuberance beneath the Mk. III did not, however, justify its addition to the bomber. An increase in the dihedral of the outer wings constituted a further alteration in the Mk. III.

Major changes were apparent in the next Whitley variant—the Mk. IV— the first prototype of which was K7208, a converted Mk. I . The radial Tiger had been discarded and supplanted by two inline, pressure-water-cooled Rolls-Royce Merlin IVs developing 1,030 h.p. each. Tail armament was increased drastically to four ·303 Brownings in a power-driven Nash and Thompson turret, the nose profile was revised to incorporate an angled glazed extension for the bomb-aimer, and increased tankage further improved the overall effectiveness of the Mk. IV, which was able to attain a top speed of 245 m.p.h. at 16,250 ft. Merlin X engines of 1,145 h.p. were the power plants of the Mk. IVA. Yet another version of the Whitley was to appear, the Mk. V, which was delivered early in 1939 with Merlin X engines and a fuselage lengthened by 1 ft. 3 in. behind the tail, the extension resulting in an increase in the field of fire for the rear guns. At the same time the area of the twin rudders was increased and that of the fins reduced by discarding the curved leading edge in favour of a straight form. 1,240 h.p. Merlin XX engines were selected to power a projected Whitley Mk. VI, but the idea was still-born. The final version of the Whitley made its appearance late in 1941 when the G.R. Mk. VII with Merlin Xs was introduced into Coastal Command as a six-seat maritime reconnaissance type equipped with A.S.V. Mk. II radar for anti-submarine patrol, a rôle for which the Whitley was eminently suited by virtue of its excellent endurance.

Despite its unprepossessing appearance, the Whitley served successfully well into the war years on diverse and arduous duties, becoming a familiar and easily recognized machine with its nose-down attitude in flight, a feature

The prototype A.W.38 Whitley K4586. (*Armstrong Whitworth Photo.*)

A.W. Whitley Mk. III K8936. (*Armstrong Whitworth Photo.*)

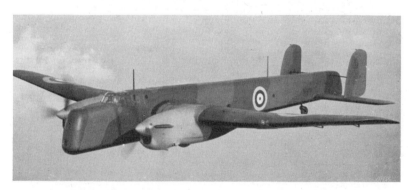

K7208, the prototype A.W. Whitley Mk. IV. (*Armstrong Whitworth Photo.*)

K9025, a production A.W. Whitley Mk. IV. (*Armstrong Whitworth Photo.*)

273

A.W. Whitley Mk. V N1352. (*Armstrong Whitworth Photo.*)

engendered by the 8·5° angle of incidence at which the wings were set to reduce the distance required for take-off and landing.

The implementation of the Expansion Programme brought drastic changes in the external finish of all new British aircraft for the Services. The silver dope used hitherto on light and medium day bombers and torpedo-bombers and the dark green applied to heavy night bombers were replaced by a system

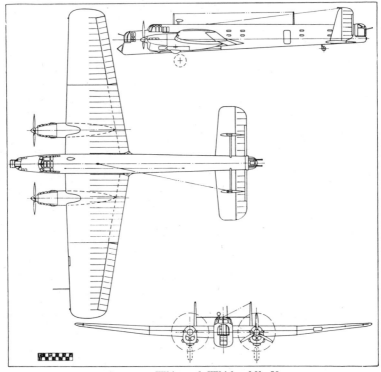

Armstrong Whitworth Whitley Mk. V

274

of camouflage in dark green and dark brown for the upper surfaces, paired with black undersides. Two schemes—one the mirror image of the other—were evolved and were applied as Scheme A to machines bearing even serial numbers and as Scheme B to their counterparts with odd numbers. The camouflage began to appear at the commencement of 1937 on new operational aircraft emerging from the factories, and a year later was applied to all front-line operational machines, eventually—after September, 1938—being ordered as the finish for all aircraft based at operational aerodromes and stations. Concurrently, national insignia, unit markings and the application of serial numbers underwent revision in many ways.

Handley Page Hampden B. Mk. I L4143. (*Handley Page Photo.*)

Specification B.9/32, calling for an experimental twin-engine day bomber, was particularly productive, as it provided the R.A.F. with both the Hampden and the Wellington. Besides Handley Page and Vickers, Bristol and Gloster prepared designs to meet the requirement.

Frank Barnwell's project for Bristol was the Type 131 monoplane of 1932 based on the use of a pair of Pegasus power plants, and Henry Folland's Gloster B.9/32 project envisaged a monoplane of 70 ft. span with a loaded weight of 12,800 lb. and driven by a pair of Perseus VI engines.

The four-seat H.P.52 represented Dr. G. V. Lachmann's third major design for Handley Page in the course of his term as chief designer during the middle 1930s and displayed strong evidence of an extension of the general precepts underlying the H.P.47. In concept one of the most original of the new generation of bombers of its era, the layout embodied the highly-tapered wings of virtually the same planform as its designer had created for the general-purpose two-seater of 1933. A second distinctive feature retained from the H.P.47 was the termination of the rear half of the fuselage in a slim tapered boom which carried the tail unit. In the case of the H.P.52 reduction of frontal resistance was pursued to the point of reducing the width of the fuse-lage to the barest minimum of 3 ft., a procedure which ultimately brought some problems in its train. The extremely slender fuselage was made relatively deep at the front so that the machine was in effect a mid-wing monoplane with the bomb-bay beneath the centre-section. This arrangement was exceptionally convenient in allowing a substantial reduction in the weight of the rear fuselage, at the same time enabling the crew to be brought together in a compact group. A further great advantage was that the abrupt reduction

275

Canadian-built Handley Page Hampden B. Mk. I AN118. (*R.C.A.F. Photo.*)

in fuselage depth at the trailing edge of the wings was ideal for the insertion of upper and lower rear-gun positions.

Dr. Lachmann's advanced ideas materialized in the H.P.52 all-green prototype K4240 which took-off from Radlett for its first flight on 22nd June, 1936, with Maj. Cordes at the controls. The designer's interest in obtaining efficiency by the application of new techniques was reflected particularly

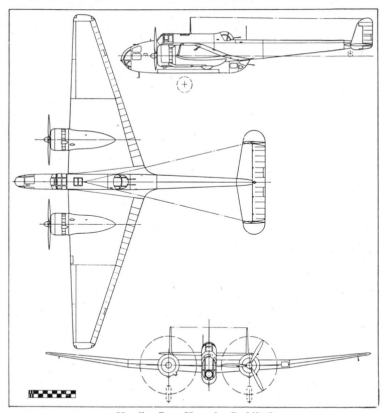

Handley Page Hampden B. Mk. I

in the form of the wings, which incorporated Handley Page slots and slotted flaps to give a speed range of 73 to 265 m.p.h. K4240 was equipped with two 820 h.p. Pegasus XX engines which were the final selection after earlier proposals to use the recalcitrant steam-cooled Goshawk and then the Perseus. The H.P.52 fully vindicated the precepts behind its conception, possessing the ability to carry a heavy load a long distance at high speed. In overall performance it came between the Wellington and the Whitley at the lower end of the scale and the Blenheim at the upper end, combining such excellent qualities that a production order for one hundred and eighty was received to Specification B.30/36 of 29th January, 1937.

Specification B.44/36, also dated 29th January, 1937, was issued simultaneously to cover production of one hundred examples by Short & Harland, the Belfast machines to be fitted with two air-cooled twenty-four cylinder inline 1,000 h.p. Napier Dagger VIII engines. L7271, the second H.P.52 prototype, made its appearance early in 1937, glittering in its highly polished metal skin and showing minor alterations in the profiles of the nose and of the ventral gun position.

Dr. Lachmann had returned during 1936 to his particular *métier*—technical research for Handley Page—relinquishing the position of chief designer for George Volkert to take it over once more. Volkert's immediate task was to adapt the H.P.52 second prototype to become the H.P.53 prototype with a pair of Dagger XIIIs, in which form Maj. Cordes took it into the air for the first time on 1st July, 1937, from Boscombe Down. L7271 was later delivered to the Queen's Island works at Belfast as the pattern for Short & Harland to produce it as the Hereford B. Mk. I.

Production of the H.P.52 was facilitated immeasurably by the continued use of the split-assembly method first instituted for the monocoque front fuselage of the Heyford and employed with great success for the Harrow contract. The system was devised by James Hamilton—an excellent production engineer—who had joined Handley Page after vacating his position at aviation manager for William Beardmore of Dalmuir to assist George Volkert with production of the eight large and complex H.P.42s. Hamilton's technique applied as to a fuselage enabled it to be constructed in two halves—split down the centre-line—with as much as possible of the interior fitting carried out before mating. The system was of particular value in the case of the slender tail boom of the Hampden with its restricted working space.

Further changes took place before the first production H.P.52, L4032, was rolled out at Radlett to make its first flight during May, 1938, subsequently being named Hampden during the next month on 24th June. In many instances the refined design of a prototype is spoiled by eventual modifications to fit it for operational service; in the case of the Hampden, however, the reverse was true. The hitherto blunt nose was replaced by a new rounded glazed assembly of far pleasanter form, and a domed cupola was fitted over the dorsal gun position in place of the previous flat-topped canopy, thereby making a more harmonious profile in conjunction with the nose and ventral gun position. Two 980 h.p. Pegasus XVIII engines were installed, turning

277

three-blade de Havilland constant-speed propellers. No. 49 Squadron, selected to introduce the Hampden into the R.A.F., received its first on 20th September, 1938. The pilot of the Hampden B. Mk. I was provided with a fixed ·303 Browning housed in the port fore-decking, and each of the three gunners' positions received a free-firing ·303 Vickers K gun, a form of armament which was, however, to prove lamentably inadequate—both in quantity and type of installation—when the Hampden was sent on raids in daylight early in the 1939–45 War. Transferred to night bombing and with armour, and with armament increased to twin Vickers K guns in dorsal and ventral positions, the Hampden proved itself a useful weapon in Bomber Command, carrying a maximum bomb load of 4,000 lb.

X3115, together with a second machine, was equipped with two 1,100 h.p. Wright Cyclone GR-1820-G105A engines as the prototype H.P.62 Hampden B. Mk. II, an arrangement which was not to attain production. Maj. Cordes conducted the Mk. II's first flight from Radlett on 3rd April, 1941. A bomb-bay of slightly greater depth characterized the torpedo-bomber Hampden T.B. Mk. I, which was adapted to accommodate the 18 in. weapon internally and was able to carry simultaneously two 500 lb. bombs in under-wing racks.

The Hereford turned out to be a disappointment owing to the temperamental nature of its Dagger power plants; there was little difference in its performance compared with that of the Hampden. No. 185 Squadron operated a flight of Herefords from August, 1939, until April, 1940, during its period as an operational training unit, and No. 35 Squadron also used it for a period while training in conjunction with No. 5 Group Pool Squadron. In many cases Herefords were subsequently modified as Hampdens.

Besides being responsible for the relatively unorthodox Hampden, Specification B.9/32 produced another outstanding twin-engine bomber of the 1939–45 War—the Vickers Wellington. R. K. Pierson's initial thoughts on the requirement for an aircraft to carry a bomb load of 1,000 lb. for 720 miles and to possess a range of 1,500 miles at its maximum weight were submitted from Weybridge during March, 1933, and suggested a twin-engine, high-wing monoplane with a fixed undercarriage and using either Mercury VIS2s or evaporatively-cooled Goshawks. In the following October, however, this layout was eschewed in favour of a revised design for a mid-wing monoplane with a retractable undercarriage and employing throughout Dr. B. N.

Handley Page Hereford L6056. (*Handley Page Photo.*)

278

Vickers Type 271 Wellington prototype K4049. (*Vickers Photo.*)

Wallis's system of geodetic construction which, by the autumn of 1933, had reached a completely practical stage of evolution for employment in the airframes of large aircraft. A pair of Goshawk Is were envisaged as the power plants for the revised bomber, and the attendant advantages to accrue from the mid-wing concept would be those of reduced root drag and the facility offered in providing a bomb-bay.

The Vickers proposal was accepted and an order placed in December, 1933, for a single prototype Type 271 to be constructed using the Goshawk engines. Work proceeded, but, by the middle of 1934, the Goshawk and its steam cooling had shown itself as too troublesome a venture to warrant further attention, despite its promised excellent power/weight ratio. The Type 271 prototype K4049 was therefore revised to take a pair of air-cooled 850 h.p. Pegasus X engines and made its début two years later. The realization of the precepts of B.9/32 by Vickers was the very antithesis of the solution adopted by Handley Page. By comparison with its sleek, incisive, stressed-skin compatriot from Cricklewood—the Hampden, amply endowed with high-lift devices—the Weybridge product was portly and matronly with its silver-doped fabric covering, beneath which could be discerned the extraordinary geodetic lattice-weave structure. When K4049 appeared at Weybridge to be taken into the air there for the first time on 15th June, 1936, piloted by Capt. J. Summers, its intended armament was lacking, and both nose- and tail-gun locations were faired over, the fuselage behind the tail terminating in an odd rounded bulge; later both nose and tail received their glazing. The H.P.52 and the Type 271 were poles apart in their approaches to the same specification, but, notwithstanding their multifarious and obvious differences, both designs were to prove later the validity of their respective concepts.

The Type 271 was successful in its trials, vindicating completely the faith which Vickers placed in the radical geodetic system by exceeding handsomely the demands of B.9/32. The machine excelled particularly in range, being capable of twice the 1,500 miles specified and able to transport double the weight of bombs twice the distance demanded. Over a distance of 2,000 miles the Type 271 could take a bomb load of 4,500 lb. in over-load conditions.

Specification 29/36 of 29th January, 1937, was formulated to cover the first production batch of one hundred and eighty of the plump new Vickers bomber, for which the firm suggested the name Crecy. This was not, however,

L4212, a Vickers Wellington B. Mk. I fitted with mass balances on the elevators. (*Vickers Photo.*)

L4213, a Vickers Wellington B. Mk. I with horn-balanced elevators. (*Vickers Photo.*)

Vickers Wellington B. Mk. IC P9238. (*Vickers Photo.*)

W5515, a Vickers Wellington B. Mk. II of No. 405 Squadron, R.C.A.F. (*R.C.A.F. Photo.*)

Vickers Wellington B. Mk. IV R1220, a converted B. Mk. IC. (*Vickers Photo.*)

Vickers Wellington G.R. Mk. VIII HX419, a converted B. Mk. I. (*Bristol Siddeley Photo.*)

Vickers Wellington G.R. Mk. VIII W5674, equipped with twin-gun front turret.
(*Bristol Siddeley Photo.*)

R3298, the Vickers Type 421 Wellington B. Mk. V prototype, a converted B. Mk. IC.
(*Vickers Photo.*)

acceptable to the Air Ministry, and the machine went into production as the Wellington Mk. I, perpetuating—as did its predecessor the Wellesley—the name of one of Britain's greatest soldiers. K4049 was lost when it crashed in April, 1937, during diving trials, but had served its original purpose well. By the time that the first production Type 285 Wellington B. Mk. I—L4212—made its first flight from Brooklands on 23rd December, 1937, the fuselage and tail surfaces had undergone considerable revision. The rear portion of the fuselage had been deepened and the previous well-rounded form of fin and rudder replaced by new surfaces of higher aspect ratio. The tailwheel had lost its spat and was now retractable, and the modification of the fuselage resulted in a two-fold increase in the bomb load. At the same time the wing span and fuselage length were increased slightly, the undercarriage fairings had been exchanged for a pair of doors hinged to each nacelle, the fuselage interior was illuminated by an expanse of side windows and the crew increased from the original four to five members. Vickers turrets were mounted at nose and tail—the rear position receiving a pair of guns—and a ventral Nash and Thompson turret was added. By the time that production of the Mk. I was reached, increased power was available in the form of the 1,000 h.p. Pegasus XVIII, which was then adopted for the Mk. I redesignated Type 290. No. 9 Squadron was the first to receive the Wellington B. Mk. I as its operational equipment in February, 1939.

Rate of output of the Wellington increased rapidly, and a new version, the Type 408 B. Mk. IA, succeeded the first model in 1939. The complement of the Mk. IA was brought up to six, and six ·303 machine-guns were disposed two each in front and rear hydraulically-operated Nash and Thompson turrets and two ventrally. Various other improvements were effected also. Still more variants were planned, including the Type 409 B. Mk. IB, which did not pass into production, and the Type 415 B. Mk. IC, of which many were built and in which the ventral position was supplanted by a pair of Vickers K guns installed to fire from each side of the fuselage. A·version of the Wellington, prepared for use by the R.N.Z.A.F. as the Type 403 B. Mk. I and a later model, the Type 412 B. Mk. IA, were delivered to No. 75 (New Zealand) Squadron for operations from Great Britain. Although the Wellington was reasonably well armed, experience early in the war of unescorted daylight raids demonstrated clearly that heavy losses were to be expected, so that, at the end of 1939, the type was taken off such work and transferred in March, 1940, to night bombing with gratifying effect.

Further variants soon appeared—the Type 298 B. Mk. II prototype L4250 with a pair of 1,145 h.p. Merlin X engines, which made its first flight on 3rd March, 1939, and the Type 299 B. Mk. III prototype L4251 with two 1,400 h.p. Hercules IIIs, the initial take-off of which came on 16th May, 1939. Both were adopted for service and passed into production during 1940 as the Type 406 B. Mk. II and the Type 417 B. Mk. III. R1220, a B. Mk. IC, was equipped with two 1,050 h.p. Pratt and Whitney R1830-S3C4-G engines and redesignated Type 410 to act as the B. Mk. IV prototype.

Specification B.23/39, later renumbered 17/40V—otherwise B.17/40, was drawn up to promote the development of a high-altitude conversion of the Wellington with the ability to fly at 40,000 ft. by housing the crew in a pressure cabin simulating conditions at 10,000 ft. The resulting Type 407 was a machine of veritable Wellsian appearance for its time, the embodiment of the pressure capsule having had a drastic effect on the front fuselage. Two proto-types—R3298 and R3299—were ordered late in 1939 and were designed around a pair of 1,650 h.p. Bristol Hercules VIII engines, the airframes

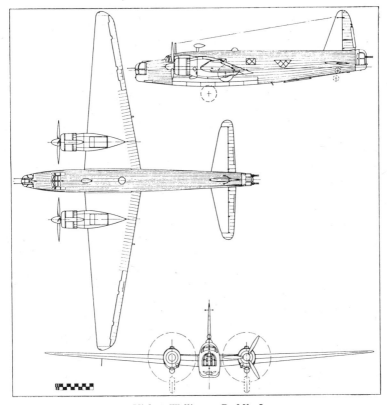

Vickers Wellington B. Mk. I

being those of two B. Mk. Is. The pressure cabin was cylindrical in section and embedded in the upper portion of the nose to give a straight top line to the fuselage and a bullet-shaped entry. The pilot was raised so that his head protruded above the fuselage to be protected by a tear-drop, clear-view, fighter-style canopy. Although he was able thereby to obtain excellent vision in the upper hemisphere, his view downwards was severely restricted. The scheduled Hercules VIIIs were slow in materializing, so Hercules III engines were substituted at first to enable R3298 to fly in September, 1940, as the Type 421 Wellington B. Mk. V. Operating at altitudes of up to 30,000 ft. in very low temperatures gave rise to some initial difficulties with freezing.

R3298 eventually received Hercules XIs complete with turbo-superchargers to become the Type 436.

The second B. Mk. V prototype, R3299, was designated Type 407, appearing at first with the intended Hercules VIIIs, but these were subsequently replaced by Hercules XIs equipped with turbo-superchargers to Type 436 standard. It was decided to construct thirty Mk. Vs, powered with Hercules VIIIs driving fully-feathering Rotol Type 6 wooden propellers, to Specification B.17/40 of 31st October, 1940, and the order was placed on 1st March, 1940, for the batch. The Specification called for a crew consisting of two pilot/navigators, and a W/T operator/air gunner. Maximum all-up weight was to be 32,000 lb. In the event, one Type 426 production B. Mk. V W5796 was completed to fly as the third and last B. Mk. V. This was the second of the scheduled B.17/40 production batch, the first—W5795—being redesigned to emerge as the Type 442 Wellington B. Mk. VI prototype fitted with two 1,600 h.p. Merlin 60 RM6SM engines. This model of the Merlin was developed specifically by Rolls-Royce at the behest of the Air Ministry in March, 1940, as a high-altitude unit to enable the projected Wellington B. Mk. VI to operate at 40,000 ft., the required power per engine being calculated as 800 h.p. at that height. A two-stage supercharger was mandatory, and the Merlin 60 so equipped was run on the bench in April, 1941.

It was decided to cancel further production of the B. Mk. V in favour of the B. Mk. VI, nineteen of the scheduled batch of Mk. Vs being finished as B. Mk. VIs. Although the B. Mk. VI reached only 38,000 ft.—some 2,000 ft. short of the stipulated height—the increase in altitude brought in its train a recurrence of the earlier freezing problems, among other difficulties. The deficiency in operational altitude was a particular embarrassment to be tackled, the ultimate solution being an increase in wing area, contrived by extending the span of W5795 by 12 ft. to constitute the Type 443. A further alteration in the Mk. VI concerned the pilot's canopy, which was modified to consist solely of a frameless Perspex dome of reduced size. In its revised form W5795 was able to attain the 40,000 ft. insisted upon, and one hundred additional B. Mk. VIs were ordered on 19th August, 1941. Plans were changed once again, however, fifty-six being cancelled. Out of the remaining forty-four, nine were produced as the Type 442, three received modified bomb-release gear as the Type 431, and twenty-four, equipped with Gee navigational fix system, became the Type 449 Mk. VIG. During 1941 Oboe—a new and extremely accurate form of radar blind bombing device—became available, and No. 109 Squadron, a unit engaged in experimental radio countermeasures operations, was selected to use a flight of Wellington B. Mk. VIs during August, 1941, for tests in preparation for Oboe's operational trials in December, 1942, and subsequent successful employment on bombing operations starting on 5th March, 1943. By the time that the high-altitude Wellington B. Mk. VI was ready for squadron service it was obsolescent as a concept and was abandoned without becoming operational.

The Wellington performed valiant duties on maritime reconnaissance and anti-submarine work with Coastal Command, Mk. ICs taking part in mine-

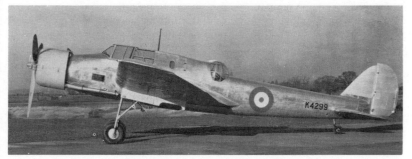

A.W.29 K4299. (*Armstrong Whitworth Photo.*)

laying and torpedo bombing, later versions appearing as the Type 429 G.R.
Mk. VIII, the Type 454, 458 and 459 G. R.Mk. XI, the Type 455 G.R. Mk.
XII, the Type 466 G.R. Mk. XIII and the Type 467 G.R. Mk. XIV. The
Type 448 B. Mk. X went into service with Bomber Command during 1943 as
a modified B. Mk. III fitted with a pair of 1,650 h.p. Hercules XVIs.

While the emphasis was on the introduction of new long-range bombers
with twin engines for the re-equipment of the R.A.F. under the Expansion
Programme, the smaller type was not omitted from the Air Ministry's requirements, and Specification P.27/32, issued in April, 1933, to produce an experimental two-seat, single-engine, day bomber to carry a 1,000 lb. bomb load at
200 m.p.h. for a distance of 1,000 miles, resulted five years later in one of its
progeny joining the Service.

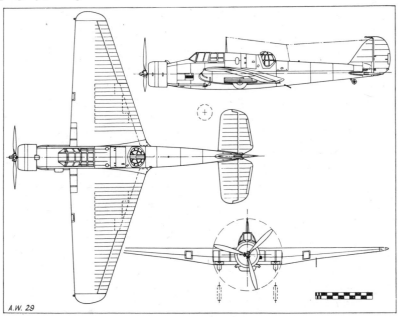

Armstrong Whitworth A.W. 29

285

Fairey Battle 953 of the S.A.A.F. (*S.A.A.F. Photo.*)

A project by Frank Barnwell, the Perseus-powered Bristol Type 136, was abandoned, and so was the Hawker P.27/32 designed by Sydney Camm and tendered during 1933.

Two other tenders, however, resulted in prototypes—the Armstrong Whitworth A.W.29 K4299 and the Fairey Battle K4303. John Lloyd's design for Armstrong Whitworth was based on the use of the supercharged 880 h.p. Tiger VIII radial engine, housed in a cowling of very broad chord and driving a de Havilland three-blade, variable-pitch propeller. The A.W.29 demon-

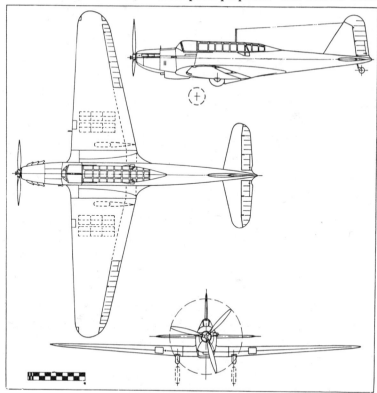

Fairey Battle Mk. I

286

strated once again its designer's current predilection for the inordinately thick wing, evolved in this case around a box girder main spar 23 in. deep and 35 in. wide at its maximum section. To the rear of this spar, fabric was used as the surface covering, and the same medium was employed to clad the tail unit. The enormously thick, tapered wings were joined to the relatively slim all-metal fuselage at the low mid-wing position, but, by virtue of the centre-section's depth, extended well above the datum line. The fairly small wheels retracted on lengthy struts rearwards into the wings, but projected slightly. The pilot's seat was in a good position above the leading edge, and his gunner, equipped with a single Lewis gun, was housed in a rotating Armstrong Whitworth cupola some distance aft at the trailing edge. Bomb aiming was carried out by the gunner from a prone fuselage position, the missiles being stowed internally in the wings with supplementary bays inside the fuselage. In designing the A.W.29, which achieved a maximum speed of 232 m.p.h. at 14,000 ft., John Lloyd made provision also for the machine to act as a torpedo-carrier, the weapon being attached to fittings under the belly. K4299's maiden flight, with Sqn. Ldr. C. K. Turner-Hughes at the controls, took place from Baginton on 6th December, 1936. A second A.W.29 was constructed, and both machines were fitted later with the Tiger IX.

The Fairey tender to P.27/32, of which the Air Ministry ordered a single prototype, was designed by M. J. O. Lobelle and exhibited all of the talented Belgian designer's characteristic refinement of line in direct contrast with the ponderous, unbeauteous aspect of the Coventry aircraft. Lobelle's *penchant* for combining the often conflicting factors of proportion, elegance and functional demands in an airframe of pleasing profile reached its zenith with the appearance of the slim and outstandingly well-formed Battle prototype K4303. The Merlin I's high power output of 1,030 h.p. and low installed frontal area were important factors influencing its choice as the sleek Fairey machine's power plant. The engine was blended cleanly into the nose of the gently-tapering, oval-section fuselage, the crew of two being housed inside a long, framed canopy which extended between the pair of cockpits set at the leading and trailing edges. The moderately-tapered, all-metal wings were set at the base of the stressed-skin fuselage, the outer panels being attached to the centre-section constructed integrally with the fuselage. Retraction of the

Belgian Fairey Battle Mk. I with extended radiator housing.
(*Musée Royal de l'Armée et d'Histoire Militaire Photo.*)

main undercarriage was to the rear, the exposed portions of the wheels being backed by metal fairings. The production Battle was given armament which consisted initially of a ·303 Browning, installed in the starboard wing just beyond the landing wheel, and a ·303 Vickers K on a Fairey high-speed mounting in the rear cockpit. Following disastrous encounters with enemy fighters during operations with the A.A.S.F. in France early in the war, an extra gun was installed in the belly at the trailing edge on a semi-free mounting to enable it to fire to the rear under remote control. The 1,000 lb. main bomb load was housed internally in four bays in the wings, but external racks under the wings accommodated a further 500 lb. of bombs. K4303's first take-off was made at Northolt by Chris Staniland on 10th March, 1936; by the time that it appeared in the New Types Park at the 1936 R.A.F. Hendon Display a new canopy had been installed, the rear portion being faired at a gentler angle into the upper decking.

The shapely Fairey was adopted as the R.A.F.'s new light bomber to take over from the outmoded Harts and Hinds, being ordered in 1935—before its maiden flight—with development taking place to Specification 23/35. In its first production version—the initial order was for one hundred and fifty-five—the Battle's maximum speed was reduced to 243 m.p.h. at 16,200 ft. from K4303's 257 m.p.h. Specification 14/36 of 27th May, 1937, was issued for a further batch of Fairey-built Battles, and Specification 32/36 of 17th August, 1936, covered those constructed by Austin Motors. No. 63 Squadron introduced the Battle Mk. I into the R.A.F., taking delivery of K7559—its first machine—on 20th March, 1937. The Battle Mk. II used the Merlin II engine, the Mk. III the Merlin III, the Mk. IV the Merlin IV and the Mk. V the Merlin V. Although basically a two-seater, arrangements were made in the design for a third crew member—a wireless operator/air gunner—to be carried. The main reason for the Battle's failure in action was that it was under-powered and obsolescent by the time that it was flown into the maelstrom over the thunderous Western Front. Apart from its use by the R.A.F., the Battle entered service in Australia, Canada, South Africa and Turkey. Eighteen—with Merlin IIIs—were built in Belgium by Avions Fairey at Gosselies for the Belgian Air Force and were altered to incorporate a radiator scoop which was extended towards the nose.

In common with its contemporaries in the R.A.F., the Hawker Audax army co-operation biplane inevitably became due for replacement. During 1933 Hawker had experimented with Hart K2434 by fitting a Dagger in place of the normal Kestrel, in which form the aircraft became known as the Dagger-Hart. When Specification 4/35 was issued to produce an Audax replacement, Hawker tendered a modification by Sydney Camm of K2434 incorporating the Dagger III, upper wings with a straight leading edge and a canted rear gun-ring. Flt. Lt. P. W. S. Bulman made the initial flight of K3719—the prototype ordered by the Air Ministry—from Brooklands on 14th February, 1936. The design was accepted for production as the Hector Mk. I with the 805 h.p. Dagger IIIMS. A ·303 Vickers Mk. V installed to port in the nose armed the pilot, the rear gunner using a Lewis on a Hawker mounting. The

Westland-built Hawker Hector Mk. I. (*Westland Photo.*)

Hector was able to carry two 112 lb. bombs beneath the lower wings. Following abandonment of plans for A. V. Roe and Company to construct the Hector, production was undertaken by Westland at Yeovil, a further refinement being the installation of a tailwheel. No. 4 Squadron in February, 1937, was the first to take the Hector into R.A.F. service.

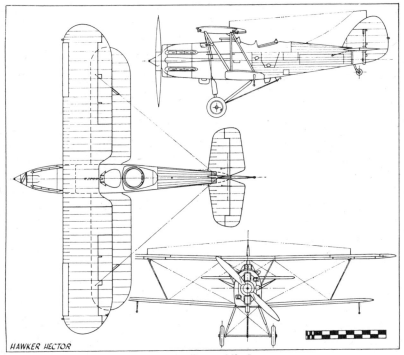

Hawker Hector Mk. I

Although the Hector had passed into production to meet the urgent needs of the Expansion Programme, it could be regarded as an interim type only, and Specification A.39/34 was drawn up for issue in April, 1935, for a new two-seat army co-operation aircraft to succeed the Hector. A Hawker project to A.39/34 was prepared by Sydney Camm, but was not built. Surprisingly, Hawker had still adhered to the biplane to meet the requirement. Roy Chadwick designed the Avro 670 as a contender to A.39/34 in October, 1935, but no progress was made towards a prototype.

The two A.39/34 prototypes which were built, however, resorted to the monoplane formula but nevertheless were vastly different in conception. Frank Barnwell's design for Bristol, the Type 148, was a low-wing monoplane of stressed-skin construction, powered by the 880 h.p. Mercury IX and equipped with a main undercarriage which retracted inwards, lying flush with the straight centre-section. The parallel-chord wings and horizontal tail surfaces were closely related in plan to those of the preceding Type 133 fighter monoplane. Defensive armament of the Type 148 comprised a pair of ·303 Browning guns installed in the port wing and a ·303 Lewis on a free mounting in the rear cockpit. When K6551, the first prototype ordered in June, 1935, was originally constructed, the rear gunner's canopy was hinged, but, when his Lewis gun was later mounted on a pillar turret, he was given a sliding hood similar to that of the pilot. Bombs were borne in under-wing racks, and aiming was from a prone position in the belly.

Capt. C. F. Uwins was the pilot for K6551's first flight from Filton on 15th October, 1937. An accident owing to failure of the undercarriage locking system was followed by reconstruction with a 905 h.p. Perseus XII engine, the rebuilt Type 148 being assessed in competition with K6552, the Type 148B using the 1,050 h.p. Bristol Taurus II, which had taken-off for the first time during May, 1938.

Westland's prototype to A.39/34 was designed by Arthur Davenport under W. E. W. Petter's technical direction and, in its service form as the Lysander, proved to be one of the most original and distinctive types of aircraft to be added to the strength of the R.A.F. Petter and Davenport rejected the biplane entirely and evolved a high-wing cabin monoplane, of which two prototypes—K6127 and K6128—were ordered in June, 1935. The 890 h.p. Mercury XII was selected to power the machine, the airframe of which was metal covered with fabric. In keeping with its decreed rôle, strong emphasis was laid upon slow-speed handling qualities, and the graceful wings were equipped with full-span Handley Page leading-edge slots and with slotted flaps of generous area, inter-connected with the root slots.

Proposals considered originally included an undercarriage retracting into stub wings, but, finally, fixed internally-sprung main wheels were shrouded by prominent spats and carried on a sturdy cantilever unit, the two legs of which were formed from a rectangular-section light alloy extrusion. Each spat housed a single ·303 Browning gun fired by the pilot; a Vickers K gun armed the rear cockpit. A good view for the crew was mandatory in the requirement, and generous glazing of the cabin was provided to ensure it.

K6127, the prototype Westland Lysander. (*Westland Photo.*)

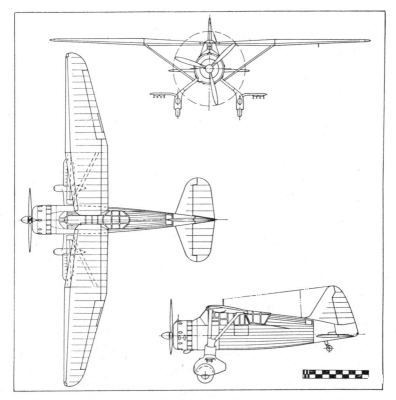

Westland Lysander Mk. I

For bombing, stub wings—equipped with racks to take six bombs each—were attached to the spats.

Work on the Lysander proceeded so rapidly that K6127 was completed in a year from the date of ordering, Harald Penrose taking the silver-doped monoplane on its first flight on 15th June, 1936, from Yeovil. K6128's maiden flight was made by Penrose on 30th October, 1937, also at Yeovil. Compared with the Bristol Type 148's speed range of 62 to 255 m.p.h. without slots, that of the Lysander was 55 to 229 m.p.h. The decision was made to order the Westland product, and Specification A.36/36 of 27th January, 1937, was drawn up to cover production. No. 16 Squadron introduced the Lysander Mk. I to the R.A.F. towards the close of 1938. Subsequent main versions of the Lysander were the Mk. II with the 905 h.p. Perseus XII, the Mk. III using the 870 h.p. Mercury XX or XXX and the Mk. IIIA with the 870 h.p. Mercury XXX, the Mk. IIIA differing also in carrying two Brownings in the rear cockpit.

An obscure—and faintly bizarre—requirement which was not proceeded with was Specification B.4/36, which outlined a scheme for a catapulted bomber. A project was prepared by Short Brothers for adaptation of the Stirling to B.4/36.

Another 1936 requirement—Specification M.7/36 of 8th September, 1936 —called for a new F.A.A. torpedo-spotter-reconnaissance aircraft to transport an 18 in. Mk. XIIA torpedo. Points to be borne in mind particularly were comfort of the crew by provision of heated and sound-proofed cockpits, the fitting of dual controls, a power-driven turret for the gunner to enable easy operation of the guns at any speed, installation of full observation and navigation facilities, a sling to hook on to a ship's crane while taxying on water, metal-covered leading edges to wings and tailplane if fabric covering were used, fireproof cockpit padding, a British engine, variable-pitch propeller and ease of manufacture in quantity. An appendix to M.7/36 stipulated either one or two engines, 10,000 lb. maximum A.U.W. on wheels or floats, minimum cruising speed 183 kt. at 6,000 ft., maximum stalling speed 58 kt., service ceiling of over 20,000 ft., and a take-off run of 200 ft. against a wind of 20 kt. Three crew members were to constitute the number for reconnaissance and two as a torpedo-bomber. The pilot was to be provided with a fixed gun and 400 rounds, the gunner's turret amidships to carry two guns with 1,000 rounds

1589, a Westland Lysander of the R.C.A.F. (*R.C.A.F. Photo.*)

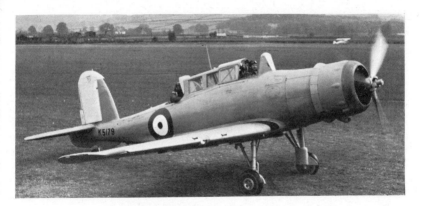

The second Blackburn Skua prototype K5179. (*Blackburn Photo.*)

each. For torpedo attack a good view was mandatory for the pilot, and limiting sizes were span 50 ft. open and 18 ft. folded, length 37 ft. on wheels or 44 ft. on floats, and height 14 ft. 9 in. Fairey prepared an initial project layout to M.7/36 for the Albacore, but the requirement was later abandoned.

Fairey interest was kindled also by Specification O.8/36 of 10th July, 1936, for a dive bomber reconnaissance aircraft. An appendix to O.8/36 called for a production ship plane to operate mainly from carriers but able also to fly from sheltered waters on floats only as a three-seat spotter reconnaissance machine. As a shipboard dive bomber a crew of two was stipulated, armament to be one front gun and two to the rear in a power-operated turret. The engine was to be an air-cooled unit of about 1,000 h.p., the machine's weight in either form to be 8,500 lb. Maximum measurements were to be span 46 ft. or up to 50 ft. absolute limit open and 18 ft. folded, length 37 ft. on wheels or 44 ft. on floats, and height 14 ft. 9 in.

Yet another requirement which drew a project from Fairey—and also from Short—was Specification S.9/36 of 9th February, 1937, for a three-seat spotter fighter ship plane or floatplane for operation from carriers. One or two engines could be fitted, but the aircraft was to be devoid of fixed forwards-firing armament. Four movable guns, however, were to be fired by the gunner from the fuselage, 1,000 r.p.g. to be provided or, if possible, 1,500 r.p.g. As a bomber the machine was to operate as a dive bomber only, carrying two 250 lb. S.A.P. or B. or four 100 lb. A.S. bombs. Maximum measurements of the design were to be span 50 ft. open and 18 ft. folded, length 44 ft. on floats, and height 14 ft. 9 in.

Although S.9/36 was not pursued, the Fleet Air Arm eventually gained its dive bomber—and, incidentally, its first operational monoplane—as a result of Specification O.27/34, which was issued to produce an experimental two-seat fighter dive bomber. Layouts tendered included the Avro 666 of October, 1934, using a Tiger engine, the Boulton Paul O.27/34, the Hawker O.27/34 and the Vickers Type 280, together with a Blackburn project designed by G. E. Petty.

293

The Blackburn design—the Skua—was subsequently ordered as two proto-types, K5178 and K5179, in April, 1935, K5178 making its first flight in 1937. The Mercury IX was fitted to the pair of prototypes, but the developed production Skuas—ordered to Specification 25/36 of 24th October, 1936—were equipped with the 905 h.p. Perseus XII. As a dive bomber the Skua attacked with a 500 lb. bomb stowed beneath the fuselage and swung clear of the propeller by a hinged crutch.

The expansion of the R.A.F.'s bomber force was not scheduled to be confined to the types with either one or two engines. The Air Staff took into account the possibility of the need for a larger machine capable of lifting a far heavier load and of transporting it a substantial distance.

Under the signature of Maj. John S. Buchanan, Deputy Director of Technical Development, Air Ministry Specification B.12/36 of 15th July, 1936, was promulgated to bring forth a high-performance heavy bomber for use in any part of the world and able to resist attacks from all directions. The machine was to have four engines, but the span was not to exceed 100 ft. Performance stipulated included a speed of not less than 230 m.p.h. at 15,000 ft. on two-thirds maximum power. At the same height the minimum range was to be 1,500 miles on two-thirds power with normal load. Maximum range called for was not less than 3,000 miles, coupled with a minimum 28,000 ft. service ceiling with 2,000 lb. bomb load. A good view was insisted upon for the crew of six—two pilots, one observer, two air gunners and a wireless operator. Two guns were to arm a power-operated turret in the nose, four were to be installed in a similar turret in the tail and a pair of guns were required amidships in a retractable ventral turret. The maximum bomb load desired was 14,000 lb.

B.12/36 was tangible evidence that the R.A.F. was at last on the way to being equipped with its first new heavy, four-engine bomber since the short life-span of the V/1500 nearly twenty years previous. The prize was sub-stantial, and response from the industry came in the form of proposals from Armstrong Whitworth, Avro, Bristol, Handley Page, Hawker, Short, Super-marine and Vickers.

Frank Barnwell's ideas for Bristol were tendered during 1937 as a mono-plane based on the use of four Bristol Hercules engines.

B.12/36 projects were prepared by both R. K. Pierson of Vickers and R. J. Mitchell of Supermarine. Destined to be Mitchell's last design prior to his death in 1937, the bomber was a dramatically different project from that of his superlative Spitfire and provided ample evidence of its creator's diversity of talent and of his innate genius. Three different layouts were prepared by Supermarine—the Type 316 using Daggers, the Type 317 with Hercules and the Type 318 equipped with Merlins—the basic airframe being that of a four-engine, mid-wing monoplane of 93 ft. span, featuring low aspect ratio wings with a leading edge tapering rearwards to a straight trailing edge and housing the major proportion of the bomb load inside the mainplanes. Mitchell's design was the favoured of the pair prepared at Weybridge and Woolston, and single prototypes—L6889 and L6890—were ordered of the

Short Stirling B. Mk. I N3641 without dorsal turret. (*R.N.Z.A.F. Photo.*)

Types 317 and 318. Neither, however, was destined to emerge from the works at Southampton, as both were destroyed by enemy bombing during 1940 when approaching completion.

Arthur Gouge's S.29 design for Short Brothers was more fortunate, as swifter progress was made in its genesis, so that L7600, the first prototype Stirling, was completed before the war for John Lankester Parker to take it on its initial flight at Rochester on 14th May, 1939. Before L7600 made its début its basic form had been subjected to proving trials conducted with the S.31 M4, a half-scale, two-seat flying model of the S.29, powered by four 90

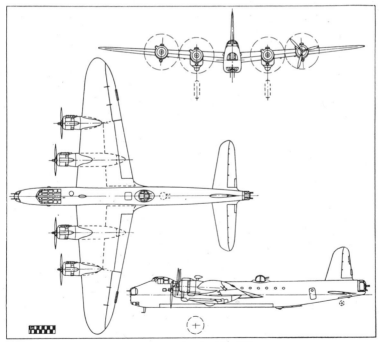

Short Stirling B. Mk. III

295

Short Stirling B. Mk. III BF509. (*Short Photo.*)

Short Stirling B. Mk. IV PK237, the 1,000th Stirling constructed by Short & Harland.
(*Short Photo.*)

h.p. Pobjoy Niagara III radials. Lankester Parker flew the all-silver M4 during 1938, and in 1939 new engines, 115 h.p. Niagara IVs, were fitted, camouflage being applied to the machine on the outbreak of war.

To keep within the specification's limit of 100 ft. span—dictated by the maximum width of hangar doors—Gouge was compelled to evolve low aspect ratio wings of 99 ft. 1 in. span to endow the Stirling with sufficient area to meet its commitments as a bomber. High-altitude performance was subsequently to suffer thereby.

L7600's first landing was marred by the collapse of the undercarriage, and L7605—the second prototype—was not ready for its maiden flight until after the outbreak of hostilities. Both prototypes were equipped with four 1,375 h.p. Hercules II engines, but production seven-seat B. Mk. Is carried 1,595 h.p. Hercules XIs. Apart from its lack of an adequate service ceiling, the Stirling was found later to be at a disadvantage in being unable to accept bombs of greater than 4,000 lb. each, owing to division of the fuselage's lengthy bomb-bay into separate compartments. Additional bombs were housed in the wings inboard of the engines to give a total capacity of 14,000 lb. Distinctive features of the Stirling were the length of its fuselage and also its height above the ground on its tall and complex undercarriage, a massive pair of units dictated by the decision to set the wings at mid-depth in the fuselage. The armament of the prototype and first few production Stirlings consisted of ·303 Brownings—two in the nose, four in the tail and two in a retractable ventral turret.

Following production of a number of the B. Mk. I Ser. I, a Frazer Nash dorsal turret with a pair of Brownings was added. This armament was augmented later in the B. Mk. I Ser. II by two side-mounted, free-firing ·303 Brownings. August, 1940, saw No. 7 Squadron taking delivery of its B. Mk. Is to become the first operational Stirling squadron and, at the same time, the first in the R.A.F. to be equipped with four-engine, heavy bomber monoplanes.

The Stirling B. Mk. II, of which two prototypes—N3657 and N3711—and three production examples were built, was equipped with 1,600 h.p. Wright R-2600-A5B Cyclone 14s as an insurance against shortage of the Hercules.

The last bomber variant of the Stirling was the B. Mk. III using four 1,650 h.p. Hercules VIs or XVIs, the two prototypes being converted Mk. Is BK648 and BK649.

Specification P.4/34 of 12th November, 1934, contained details of a very different machine from the massive Stirling, going to the other end of the scale for an experimental two-seat, light day bomber. Prototypes appeared from Fairey and Hawker—both using a single Merlin but differing considerably in their appearance.

The Fairey P.4/34 exhibited all of the gifted Marcel Lobelle's customary sleekness of line, being one of the most aesthetically appealing of its particular class ever designed. Evolved during the same period as the Battle, it was not surprising that the P.4/34—although smaller—should follow the same basic form. Two prototypes—K5099 and K7555—appeared in 1936 and 1937 respectively; Flt. Lt. C. S. Staniland took K5099 on its maiden flight on 13th January, 1937, K7555 flying a few weeks later on 19th April, 1937. All-metal construction was used and the main undercarriage was completely retractable,

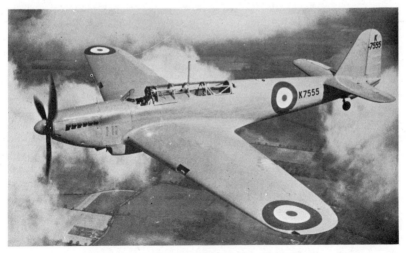

K7555, the second Fairey P.4/34 prototype. (*Fairey Photo.*)

Hawker Henley prototype K5115. (*Hawker Photo.*)

folding inwards. K5099 was equipped with the 1,030 h.p. Merlin I, but K7555 received the 1,030 h.p. Merlin II. Fairey-Youngman flaps were installed experimentally in the second P.4/34, the top speed attained being 284 m.p.h. The glazed canopy covering the tandem cockpits was set low on the slim fuselage and continued into the rear-decking in an unbroken line. The design was stressed to act as a dive bomber and carried its 500 lb. bomb load on external racks. Although the P.4/34 was not able to receive a production order in its intended rôle, the effort expended on its conception was not wasted, as its high performance was instrumental in its successful adaptation as the Fleet Air Arm's Fulmar two-seat fighter armed with eight guns.

The Fairey P.4/34's competitor to the same requirement, the Hawker P.4/34 K5115, made its initial flight from Brooklands on 10th March, 1937, Sydney Camm's design being rather different in its approach to the problems of producing an advanced day bomber of high performance. Fairey aircraft had always tended to be slimmer in profile than most of their rivals and—by comparison—K5115 exhibited a plumper appearance in its compact elevation. Whereas the Fairey contender was a low-wing monoplane, the Hawker machine's mainplanes were set at the low mid-wing position in the fabric-covered fuselage. To facilitate quantity production, the Hawker design utilized the fabric-covered outer wing panels of the Hurricane. The engine chosen was the Merlin F. The main bomb load of 500 lb. was to be stowed internally in the fuselage, a factor behind the final choice of wing location. External racks beneath the wings could carry an additional eight 25 lb. bombs. A Vickers Mk. V gun in one wing armed the pilot, and a Lewis was provided for the rear gunner. Retraction of the main undercarriage units was inwards.

The name Henley was applied to the Hawker P.4/34, and metal-covered wings replaced the fabric surfaces of K5115 during mid-1937. The Merlin F was supplanted by the 1,030 h.p. Merlin I during the same summer. Despite an excellent showing in trials, Air Ministry ideas concerning the use of the light day bomber envisaged by P.4/34 eventually changed, and the requirement was abandoned. As the Henley T.T. Mk. III, the Hawker design was subsequently produced by Gloster as a target tower to Specification 42/36 of 23rd December, 1936. The Henley Mk. II K7554, the second prototype, was flown by Flt. Lt. P. G. Lucas at Brooklands initially on 26th May, 1938, serving with a Merlin II as the model for the target-towing version.

To back the endeavours being made to build up R.A.F. bomber strength after years of shameful neglect, Specification P.13/36 of 8th September, 1936, was drawn up to provide a twin-engine medium bomber landplane with a minimum crew of four, comprising two pilots, one W/T operator and one air gunner. A power-operated turret in the nose was to mount two guns, and four guns were to be installed in a similar tail turret. The machine was required to accommodate a maximum bomb load of 8,000 lb., and provision was to be made for the alternative internal stowage of two torpedoes 18 ft. 2·5 in. long.

P.13/36 brought responses from Avro, Handley Page and Hawker. Eventually, only the Avro proposal was constructed to the basic requirements of P.13/36, but to the Specification goes the credit for the indirect conception later of two of the most outstanding of four-engine British bombers—the Halifax and the Lancaster.

The Hawker P.13/36 project drafted by Sydney Camm and tendered on 1st January, 1937, envisaged a low mid-wing monoplane powered by a pair of Vultures mounted in long nacelles which housed the retractable undercarriage. Gun turrets were to be installed at nose and tail, and twin fins and rudders formed the vertical tail surfaces.

At Cricklewood George Volkert prepared the H.P.56 as the Handley Page design to P.13/36, evolving the monoplane—as a development of the H.P.55 to B.1/35—around two twenty-four-cylinder, liquid-cooled 1,760 h.p. Rolls-Royce Vultures, a type of engine which was afflicted unfortunately with recurring troubles in development and proved to be an unexpected disappointment. The Air Ministry ordered two prototype H.P.56s—L7244 and L7245 —in April, 1937, but the likelihood of reduction of large-scale production of the scheduled engine, as a result of the Vulture's vicissitudes, brought the abandonment of the H.P.56 by Handley Page in 1937.

Notwithstanding, the ostensibly powerful Vulture I engine went on to inflict its recalcitrance on another P.13/36 bomber for which it had been selected—the Avro 679 Manchester designed by Roy Chadwick. Much was expected of the Manchester, and could well have been achieved but for the unreliability and eventual lack of power shown by its engines. On 8th September, 1936, two prototypes—L7246 and L7247—were ordered, L7246 making its first flight on 25th July, 1939, from Ringway with Capt. H. A. Brown at the controls. The design had evolved as a mid-wing monoplane to carry a crew of seven and a bomb load of 10,350 lb. The engines were mounted on a rectangular centre-section to which were attached tapered outer

Avro Manchester B. Mk. I L7515. (*Avro Photo.*)

wing panels; the tailplane terminated in twin fins and rudders. L7246 was without armament, but was fitted with a third—central—fin following initial tests. Trials were conducted with L7246 at R.A.E. Farnborough in conjunction with catapulted take-off and arrested landing apparatus, ideas subsequently discarded. A crash at A. & A.E.E. Boscombe Down brought L7246's career to an end, but L7247 took to the air at Ringway on 26th May, 1940, complete with the centre fin and armament consisting of a pair of ·303 Browning guns in each of its three turrets, disposed at the nose, ventrally and in the tail. A dorsal turret was eventually fitted in place of the ventral installation, and the wing span was increased by 9 ft. 11 in. to 90 ft. 1 in.

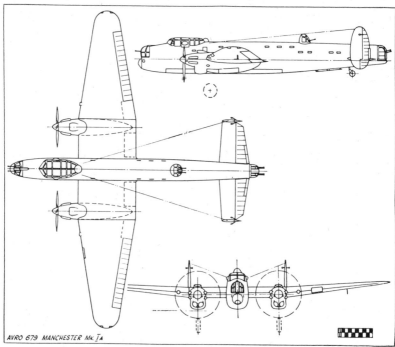

AVRO 679 MANCHESTER Mk IA

Avro Manchester B. Mk. IA

300

Production for the R.A.F. had been decided upon a considerable time previously to Specification 19/37 for the Manchester B. Mk. I/PI. No. 207 Squadron introduced the first Manchesters into service in November, 1940, its B. Mk. Is retaining the third fin; the B. Mk. IA, however, discarded the centre fin in favour of main fins and rudders of increased area mounted on an extended tailplane. The B. Mk. IA's Vultures were able to deliver 1,845 h.p., and tail armament was raised to four Brownings. The Vulture's shortcomings had been only too apparent at an early stage, and alternative projects were studied for the Manchester B. Mk. II to use either a pair of 2,520 h.p. Bristol Centaurus or 2,100 h.p. Napier Sabre I power plants. In the event, another—and eminently satisfactory—solution was adopted, but the Manchester's period in service with Bomber Command was necessarily brief.

The hurried era of feverish rearmament prior to the outbreak of the 1939–45 War had widespread repercussions, and Airspeed Ltd., a company which had specialized hitherto in wooden civil aircraft of small to medium size, were encouraged to sound the possibilities in military construction. Following the short production run of Convertible Envoys, projects were investigated for the A.S.7 Military Envoy, the A.S.7J Military Envoy with Cheetah VIs and the A.S.7K Military Envoy using Wolseley Scorpio IIs. An original project which was discussed by Airspeed was for a four-engine day and night bomber, designated A.S.15, but no progress was made with the idea.

Two specifications which were prepared but on which no action was taken were B.25/37 for a heavy bomber and P.26/37 for a high-altitude medium bomber.

Among the last of Capt. F. S. Barnwell's projects for Bristol before his death on 2nd August, 1938, was that of the Type 155 medium day bomber. The design was a development of the Type 152—which became the Beaufort—and was for a mid-wing monoplane equipped with a pair of Bristol Taurus engines and—then a comparative novelty for a British aircraft—a tricycle undercarriage. The Type 155 was to be heavily armed with two hydraulically-driven turrets—one dorsal and one ventral—each with two 20 mm. cannon. After some progress had been made with the design, B.17/38 was issued for the project, decreeing the use of composite construction in the aircraft. Bristol thereupon abandoned the Type 155 in favour of Armstrong Whitworth.

Specification S.30/37 issued on 31st January, 1938, laid down requirements for a twin-engine, torpedo-bomber reconnaissance aircraft for the Fleet Air Arm. Stress was laid upon the importance of the pilot's comfort, and dual controls were to be provided. The pilot was to have a blind-flying hood, a padded headrest and armrests, and his seat was to possess 4 in. vertical and 6 in. horizontal movement. The gunner's field of fire and provision for the observer were to be as for Specification S.24/37. Three months would be allowed for preparation of a mock-up of the proposed design. The type of engine was to be 100 hr. type-tested British—an air-cooled unit being preferred—and satisfactory operation in arctic and tropical conditions would be required. A variable-pitch propeller was specified, together with stops on the controls and night-flying equipment. Easy loading of torpedo and bombs was required, and arrester gear was to be installed. The flotation gear fitted had to support the aircraft for over one hour, and the design was to incorporate alternative wheel and float undercarriage. Deck landing was to be possible with one engine stopped.

An appendix to S.30/37 stipulated a land undercarriage with three wheels, and a preference was expressed for the design to be based on Specification S.24/37 to carry out reconnaissance spotting, level and dive bombing and torpedo attacks. If possible, as a floatplane the machine should be able to bomb and to launch torpedo attacks. As a bomber ship plane the A.U.W. was not to exceed 10,500 lb.; as a floatplane 11,500 lb. was to be the A.U.W. The maximum military load was to be carried within the stipulated A.U.W. Maximum sizes were to be span 50 ft. extended and 18 ft. folded, length 40 ft. as a ship plane and 44 ft. on floats and height 14 ft. The highest possible cruising speed was demanded—a minimum of 185 kt. at normal reconnaissance load—and 5,000 ft. height must be maintained on one engine with full load as a ship plane. On wheels the maximum stalling speed required was 56 kt. with full reconnaissance load. Reconnaissance range was stipulated as 6 hr. at 2,000 ft. at not less than 120 kt. plus 15 min. at maximum take-off power at sea level. As a torpedo-bomber the range was to be 600 n.m. at 6,000 ft. at not less than 120 kt. plus 15 min. at maximum take-off power at sea level. A pilot, observer and air gunner were to be carried for reconnaissance, but two only were needed for torpedo-bombing. One fixed gun with 400 r.p.g. was to be provided for the pilot; the gunner's single machine-gun was to have 1,000 r.p.g. The offensive load was to consist of one 1,500 lb. torpedo or six 100 lb. A.S. or six 250 lb. S.A.P. G.P. or six 250 lb. B or three 500 lb. S.A.P. or G.P. bombs. The Short S.30/37 and General Aircraft Ltd. GAL. 39A and 39B projects were prepared to meet S.30/37, but none was built. The GAL.39A and 39B were devised in 1938 as high-wing monoplanes, each with two 500 h.p. Bristol Aquilas; variable-area wings were proposed for the 39B.

Specification 10/36 of 30th June, 1936, however, did result in production being attained. The requirement represented the amalgamation of Specifications M.15/35 for an experimental shore-based torpedo-bomber and G.24/35 for an experimental general-purpose reconnaissance landplane, to both of which the twin-engine Avro 672 with 56 ft. 3 in. span and the Avro 675 of May, 1936, with Armstrong Siddeley Terriers, were designed. 10/36 stipulated that the combination of the pair of previous specifications was to be without detriment to either, the resulting aircraft to carry a crew of four, consisting of two pilots, one W/T operator and one air gunner. A single fixed gun was to be installed for the pilot, two guns being provided in the rear turret. As an alternative to a torpedo, the 10/36 machine was to accommodate a 2,000 lb. A.P. bomb.

Of the pair of aircraft ordered into production to 10/36, one was to exhibit such shortcomings that it was withdrawn after only a brief spell on operations, but the other was to prove very successful. The unexpected and unhappy failure was the Botha G.R. Mk. I designed for Blackburn by G. E. Petty and ordered in December, 1936, over two years before the pair of

Blackburn Botha G.R. Mk. I L6264. (*Blackburn Photo.*)

prototypes—L6104 and L6105—made their maiden flights in the spring of 1939. In appearance the Botha was a clean and quite attractive high-wing monoplane of stressed-skin construction with a complement of four. Alternative engines fitted were two 880 h.p. Perseus Xs or 930 h.p. Perseus XAs, and the Botha was armed with a single fixed ·303 gun for the pilot and a pair of ·303 guns in a power-driven dorsal turret. The high-wing layout facilitated housing of the torpedo internally without making it necessary to deepen the fuselage inordinately.

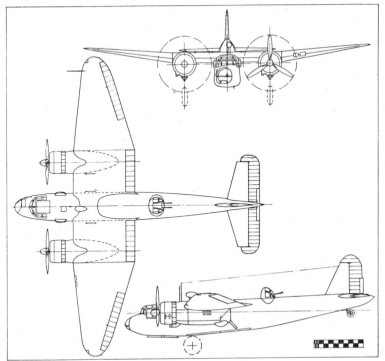

Blackburn Botha G.R. Mk. I

Bristol Beaufort G.R. Mk. I N1007. (*R.C.A.F. Photo.*)

M.A.E.E. Helensburgh Report H/A/295 of 16th July, 1942, dealt with flotation and drop tests conducted with a Botha at the Blackburn Clyde factory at Dumbarton to investigate the machine's strength under drop conditions. The airframe had been modified after static tests at Brough, and trials were made at a loaded weight of about 14,000 lb. It took 7 min. to completely flood the undamaged fuselage, the aircraft continuing to float nose down on its buoyancy compartments in the outer wings and tail without sign of sinking. The drop test was made on three points from 2 ft. 6 in. height—the same height as that of a previous test carried out on a Hudson—the Botha breaking its back on impact at the frame below the wings' leading edge. Accelerations recorded were 4G at the tail and 5G at the centre-section. It was concluded that the Botha needed strengthening at this frame before it could be regarded as strong enough for ditching. The drop disclosed that the bomb-bay doors were satisfactory and should assist in protecting the rear buoyancy compartment from damage. Damage was caused neither to the modified bomb-aimer's window nor to the stiffened Novellon nosepiece. During the flotation test the machine was lowered gently and allowed to sink freely, observers inside the fuselage noting its attitude and the influx of the water. The airframe employed in the trials consisted of a new fuselage and main structural and outer buoyant portions of the wings. Omitted were the leading edge of the wings and of the centre-section, the roof fairing from the

Australian Bristol Beaufort A9-66 incorporating modified fin and rudder. (*R.A.A.F. Photo.*)

cabin to the wings, the wingtips, ailerons, trailing edge, flaps, rudder and elevators. Concrete slabs replaced the engines and turret, 226 gall. of water ballast occupied the main fuel tanks, the oil tanks also were filled with water, and 50 lb. of ballast was stowed in the rear fuselage.

Additional production of the Botha by Boulton Paul was planned to Specification 39/36, and Specification 45/36 was drawn up for further production by Blackburn, but neither project was proceeded with. No. 608 Squadron

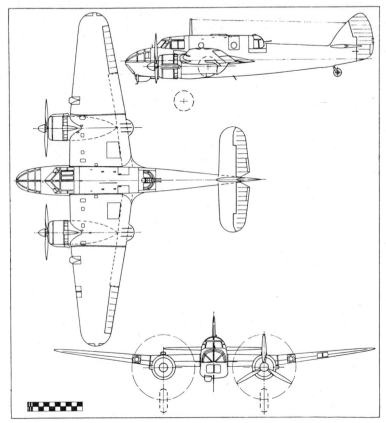

Bristol Beaufort G.R. Mk. I

in October, 1939, became the first to use the Botha, but its lack of power and other shortcomings for its prescribed rôle dictated its withdrawal to use for patrol work and, eventually, to employment as a trainer. In company with the Gloster F.9/37 the prototype Botha was one of the two aircraft, then classed as secret, which were flown at high speed past M.P.s assembled at Northolt on 23rd May, 1939.

Far more successful than its contemporary—the Botha—was the Bristol design to 10/36, the Beaufort, which Capt. Barnwell had prepared as the Type 152 in April, 1936. Modifications incorporated following submission

A.W. Albemarle V1599, built by A. W. Hawkesley. (*Armstrong Whitworth Photo.*)

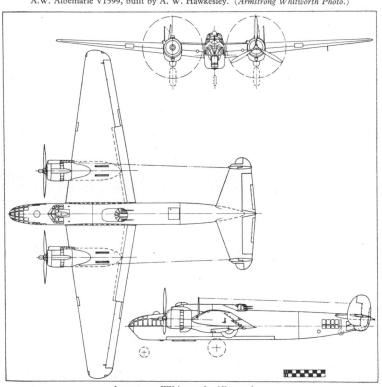

Armstrong Whitworth Albemarle

306

of the design to the Air Ministry included provision for a crew of four, an increase in the depth of the fuselage about the crew stations and semi-exposure of the torpedo in the belly. A production order was placed in September, 1936, over two years before Capt. Cyril Uwins took the prototype L4441 into the air at Filton for the first time on 15th October, 1938. The Beaufort was a compact mid-wing monoplane of hefty appearance, powered—in the proto-type—by a pair of Taurus engines in place of the Perseus units proposed originally, which, if used, would have resulted in a lower performance. Recurrent minor troubles delayed introduction to the R.A.F. until December, 1939, when No. 22 Squadron received the first Beaufort G.R. Mk. Is. The Beaufort's offensive capacity consisted of a 1,500 lb. bomb load or a single 1,605 lb. 18 in. torpedo. The G.R. Mk. I received the 1,130 h.p. Taurus VI, XII or XVI and the G.R. Mk. II—the prototype of which was a converted Mk. I N1110—the 1,200 h.p. Pratt and Whitney Twin Wasp S3C4G. A pair of Merlin XXs were proposed for the G.R. Mk. III, but the project lapsed.

Several versions of the Beaufort were constructed in Australia using Twin Wasps. The Beaufort fully justified its production by taking part in numerous successful actions against the enemy until superseded in operational service during 1943.

Specification P.9/38 was issued to cover a twin-engine medium bomber project by John Lloyd at Armstrong Whitworth, which was discontinued in favour of the requirements outlined in Specifications B.17/38 and B.18/38. B.17/38 of 12th September, 1938, was drawn up for a reconnaissance bomber for rapid production by Bristol—the Type 155—and was amended on 9th November, 1938, in respect of a general reconnaissance bomber. The design was to be based on the exploitation—in a national emergency—of labour and materials to ensure quick and cheap production by unskilled and semi-skilled labour. Materials to be investigated included wood and metal, synthetic and compressed wood and laminated materials. The aircraft was to have a minimum speed at 5,000 ft. of 250 m.p.h. at maximum economic cruising power. The crew was to number five—two pilots, one W/T operator and two air gunners—and a maximum bomb load of 4,000 lb. was demanded. Two Browning guns were to be carried in the upper turret and four in the lower.

Adaptation of the Bristol Type 155 design was carried out by John Lloyd on the transfer of the project from Bristol to Coventry, Specification B.18/38 of 9th November, 1938, being issued to cover the machine under its new designation Armstrong Whitworth A.W.41, ultimately to become the Albe-marle. Fitted with two 1,590 h.p. Hercules XIs, P1360—the first prototype—made its initial flight in 1939, but eventually crashed. The second A.W.41—P1361—took-off for the first time on 20th March, 1940, but, although the first production Albemarles were constructed as bombers, the type was not employed as such and was adapted for use as a glider tug and as a special transport.

To produce a successor to the Wellington, Specification B.1/35 was issued for an experimental heavy bomber, drawing tenders from Airspeed, Armstrong

307

Vickers Warwick G.R. Mk. V PN782. (*S.A.A.F. Photo.*)

Whitworth, Handley Page and Vickers. The Airspeed A.S.29, designed by Nevil Shute Norway and Alfred Hessell Tiltman, was to have been powered by four Bristol Aquila radials or four Rolls-Royce Goshawk inline engines.

John Lloyd's proposal for Armstrong Whitworth was for a development of the Whitley equipped with a pair of three-row radial Armstrong Siddeley Deerhound engines as the A.W.39. Although the Air Ministry did not order a prototype, the company converted K7243, a Whitley Mk. II, to test the new units. Difficulty was experienced with cooling the rearmost row of cylinders

Vickers Warwick L9704 testing nacelle armament installation scheduled for Vickers Windsor. (*Vickers Photo.*)

308

to the detriment of the Deerhound's development, and K7243 subsequently crashed. A second Armstrong Whitworth project was prepared to B.1/35 and was allocated the serial K8180.

K8179 was allotted to the H.P.55, George Volkert's B.1/35 design for Handley Page, evolved around two Hercules HE1SMs, Merlin or Vulture engines, but, again, the design was still-born.

Slightly better luck, however, attended R. K. Pierson's design for Vickers which eventually went into service, but not in its intended rôle as a long-range bomber. The machine followed the general lines of the Wellington and retained the geodetic system of construction. A pair of the unlucky Vultures constituted the power plants of K8178, the first prototype Warwick, which made its initial flight on 13th August, 1939. Lack of performance with K8178 was responsible for two Centaurus engines being fitted to L9704, the second prototype, which was taken on its maiden flight in April, 1940. The Warwick was ordered for the R.A.F. in December, 1940, but delays in meeting the commitment rendered the design obsolete as a bomber by the time production was under way in July, 1942.

Shortage of Centaurus engines resulted in 1,850 h.p. Pratt and Whitney Double Wasps being installed in the B. Mk. I, and in January, 1943, the decision was taken to adapt the Warwick for air-sea rescue work. Carrying a crew of six, the B. Mk. I was armed with nose and dorsal turrets housing two ·303 guns each and a tail turret with four ·303s. The Warwick G.R. Mk. V used a pair of 2,520 h.p. Centaurus VIIs and came into service during 1945, equipped to fly on anti-submarine patrol. Its bomb load was 2,000 lb. and armament comprised one ·5 nose gun, two ·5 guns firing one from each side of the fuselage and four ·303 or ·5 tail guns.

The abandonment by Handley Page of its H.P.56 project to Specification P.13/36—owing to the trouble encountered during development of the Vulture—was followed by an immediate revision of the design by George Volkert to incorporate four Merlins as the H.P.57. This decision was instrumental in producing the most celebrated Handley Page bomber of all, the Halifax, a magnificent machine destined to play a very significant part in the overthrow of the Axis Powers during the 1939–45 War.

In redesigning the original H.P.56 to take four engines, Volkert was compelled to increase the size of the aircraft considerably, the weight rising by 50%. War had broken out by the time that L7244, the first prototype of two ordered on 3rd September, 1937, was ready for Maj. Cordes to conduct its initial flight on 25th October, 1939, from Bicester—chosen in case Radlett were bombed should the existence there of the new aircraft become known to the Germans. L7245, the second prototype, followed into the air on 17th August, 1940, again with Maj. Cordes at the controls. The name Halifax was bestowed on the great bomber which became the second of the R.A.F.'s new generation of four-engine bombers to enter service, No. 35 Squadron taking the initial aircraft on 23rd November, 1940.

The production Halifax B. Mk. I Ser. I—to Specification 32/37—was fitted with 1,280 h.p. Merlin Xs, which gave it a maximum speed of 265 m.p.h.

L7245, the second prototype Handley Page Halifax B. Mk. I. (*Hanaley Page Photo.*)

Handley Page Halifax B. Mk. II W7710 LQ-R 'Ruhr Valley Express' of No. 405 Squadron, R.C.A.F. (*R.C.A.F. Photo.*)

Handley Page Halifax B. Mk. II Ser. I of No. 35 Squadron. (*Handley Page Photo.*)

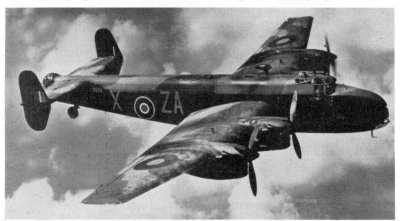

BB324, a Handley Page Halifax B. Mk. II Ser. I (Spec.) of No. 10 Squadron, without dorsal turret and flying on two engines. (*Handley Page Photo.*)

The design of the B. Mk. I was that of an orthodox mid-wing monoplane with twin fins and rudders set at the ends of the tailplane and with gun turrets at nose and tail. The Halifax was naturally subjected to intensive development and appeared in many forms, including the B. Mk. I Ser. II and Ser. III, and the B. Mk. II Ser. I, Ser. I (Special) and Ser. IA. The B. Mk. II Ser. I introduced a two-gun dorsal turret and 1,390 h.p. Merlin XXs. The maiden flight of the H.P.59 Halifax B. Mk. II was carried out on 29th March, 1941, from Radlett by Maj. Cordes. The B. Mk. II Ser. I (Special) discarded the front and dorsal turrets and also the exhaust muffs. The Mk. II Ser. IA displayed a revised and lengthened nose of Perspex, a dorsal turret and 1,390 h.p. Merlin XXII engines; later Ser. IAs carried new style large rectangular fins. A major revision was made in the B. Mk. III, which changed to 1,615 h.p. Hercules XVI radials for power, among other alterations which

Handley Page Halifax B. Mk. III LV857. (*Handley Page Photo.*)

later included an extension of the wing span to 104 ft. 2 in. The H.P.61 B. Mk., V, VI and VII were other bomber versions of the powerful Halifax, the Mk. VI to Specification B.27/43 using 1,800 h.p. Hercules 100s and the Mk. VII Hercules XVIs. The H.P.69, a Halifax with turbo-supercharged Hercules, was not proceeded with, nor was the H.P.58 Halifax project.

Maj. Cordes left Handley Page on 31st July, 1941, and Flt. Lt. J. R. Talbot undertook the first flights of the H.P.61 Halifax B. Mk. III in 1942, the Halifax B. Mk. VI on 10th October, 1944, and the Halifax B. Mk. VII, all taking place at Radlett.

Specification B. 17/37 was issued to meet a requirement for a dive bomber, but was subsequently cancelled in favour of Specification B.19/38 for a twin-engine bomber landplane.

B.19/38 in turn was renumbered Specification B.1/39, dated 6th March, 1939, calling for a bomber landplane for use in all parts of the world and to replace all medium and heavy bomber types. Four engines were specified, the wing covering was not to be fabric, and the maximum gross weight was to be 50,000 lb. A minimum speed of 280 m.p.h. at 15,000 ft. at maximum economical cruising power and a minimum range of 2,500 miles at 15,000 ft.

311

Handley Page Halifax B. Mk. VI. (*Handley Page Photo.*)

with 9,000 lb. bomb load were required. The machine had to be able to accommodate a bomb load of 10,000 lb. and was to be armed with 20 mm. Hispano guns installed as four each in dorsal and ventral turrets. Maximum turret weight each was to be 1,460 lb., and each turret was not to exceed 10 ft.

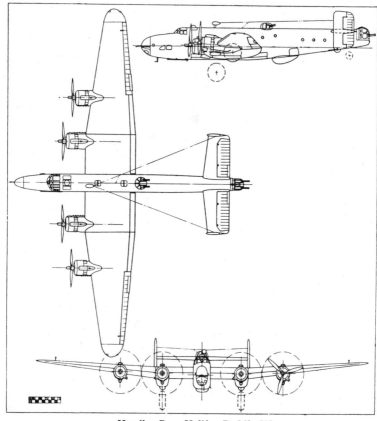

Handley Page Halifax B. Mk. VI

312

diameter and 6 ft. depth. The intention was to evolve an ideal standard bomber.

At Bristol L. G. Frise had prepared both the Type 157—to carry a crew of three, a dorsal turret and to use a pair of Hercules—and the Type 159 to B.1/39, the Type 159 being a seven-seat low-wing monoplane of 114 ft. span fitted with four 1,550 h.p. Hercules VIIs, but able to accommodate alternative engines. The Type 159 advanced as far as a full-size mock-up and a structural test section, but the promising project was cancelled in mid-1940.

Two Vickers projects to B.1/39 were the Types 405 and 415 prepared by R. K. Pierson to utilize geodetic structure with high aspect ratio, elliptical wings, but neither received a prototype order, and the same fate befell the Armstrong Whitworth A. W. 48, the Avro 680, 681 and 682, and a project by Short Brothers, the S.34.

The Handley Page tender to B.1/39 was the H.P.60A, a development by George Volkert of the Halifax and provisionally designated Halifax Mk. IV. The machine would have had Merlin 65s and a larger bomb-bay, the intention being to prove the design by building a Niagara-powered small-scale version. The Air Ministry's provisional plans to order two prototypes each applied both to the Bristol and Handley Page designs, but neither reached the stage of prototype construction.

It was intended that, with the issue of Specification S.41/36 of 11th February, 1937, detailing the requirement for a torpedo-spotter dive bomber reconnaissance aircraft, a replacement for the Swordfish would emerge. Fairey had prepared such a design layout to Specification M.7/36, and Marcel Lobelle proceeded to develop it into the Albacore to meet S.41/36. The machine appeared as a three-seat, 50 ft. span, single-bay biplane to make its first flight from the Great West Aerodrome on 12th December, 1938, in the hands of Chris Staniland. The first prototype was L7074—Fairey airframe F3274—fitted with the 1,065 h.p. Taurus II engine. Enclosed, heated accommodation was provided for the crew in a metal monocoque fuselage, and other refinements were part of the design. The engine of the production Albacore was the 1,130 h.p. Taurus XII.

M.A.E.E. Helensburgh Report H/154 Pt. 1 of 28th March, 1940, dealt with handling trials of L7074, on twin floats and equipped with a Taurus IM(a), to determine its suitability for use by a Service unit and for catapult trials. The tests were carried out at the Fairey Hamble works during March, 1940, at A.U.W.s of 10,817 lb. and 11,317 lb. The water rudders were operated by H.P. hydraulic control or by a mechanical system if there were hydraulic failure. These water rudders were very effective in winds of up to 15 m.p.h.; there was practically no load on the rudder bar and turning was easy. The floats were extremely dirty, through water building up against their bows, and in taxying at 15 kt. the water washed over the floats in front of the foremost struts. There was a slight swing on take-off, and the machine eased off the water at about 62 kt. I.A.S. At the lighter loaded weight take-off time was about 26 sec. and about 29 sec. with the heavier load. A slight porpoising tendency was noticed, and water from the floats was thrown up at the propeller

Fairey Albacore. (*Fairey Photo.*)

on take-off, causing considerable buffeting of the propeller even in slightly choppy water. Air handling was generally acceptable for Service use, but the controls were not evenly harmonized, and the rudder was very heavy for an inexperienced pilot. The downwards slope of the decking from the pilot's position tended to encourage landing on the heels of the floats, as the impression was obtained that the aircraft was level when it was in reality tail down. The floatplane Albacore was assessed as suitable for operation in sheltered

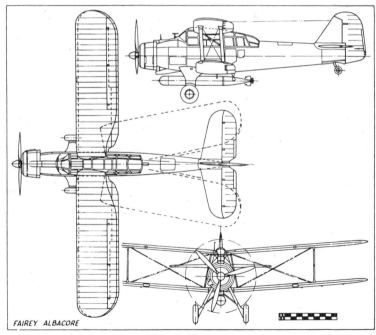

FAIREY ALBACORE

Fairey Albacore

314

N1005, a Bristol Beaufort G.R. Mk. I. (*R.C.A.F. Photo.*)

W5065, a Blackburn Botha G.R. Mk. I. (*Blackburn Photo.*)

waters and passed as suitable to undergo catapult trials, but the extreme dirtiness of the floats was considered a serious handicap to its Service use.

The rearmament period of some five years before the final outbreak of the 1939–45 War witnessed rapid strides being made in every aspect of the design of British military and naval aircraft, the specifications formulated during those tense years resulting ultimately in the development, standardization and production of those bombing and torpedo-carrying aircraft which were to serve with such distinction.

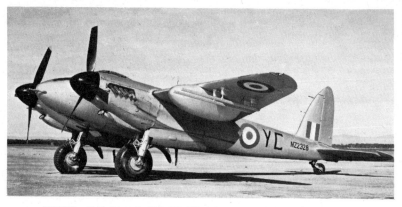

NZ2328, a D.H. Mosquito F.B. Mk. VI of the R.N.Z.A.F. *(R.N.Z.A.F. Photo.)*

CHAPTER SEVEN

HARBINGERS OF HELL

Vastly different circumstances ordained that development of the bomber and the torpedo-carrier should follow a path that was in marked contrast with that taken a quarter of a century earlier when North-West Europe became engulfed in the hitherto unimagined holocaust of the 1914–18 War.

When, for the second time in the twentieth century, German forces stepped across the frontiers of the Fatherland, in the main the British bombing and torpedo-bombing aircraft with which the war against the Axis Powers was to be promoted initially were already in squadron service or had flown in prototype form. The dire necessity of forcing development in every conceivable direction at the greatest possible rate to achieve and maintain superiority in performance over the enemy was instrumental in stimulating a continual flow of new requirements from the Air Ministry.

The Albacore had been produced as the intended successor of the Swordfish as a carrier-borne torpedo-bomber, but events subsequently conspired to relegate the later biplane to a supplementary rôle in supporting the Swordfish in attacks against Axis shipping. Nevertheless, such an anomalous position was not foreseen when consideration was given to providing ultimately a successor to the Albacore, and Specification S.24/37 of 6th January, 1938, was formulated to inspire such a design. In the event, the Swordfish remained on active service alongside its two successors from Fairey for the duration of the War. The new requirement asked for a torpedo-bomber reconnaissance aircraft for the Fleet Air Arm in which great importance was attached to comfort of the pilot's cockpit. The seat armrests were to possess 4 in. vertical and 6 in. horizontal adjustment, and a padded headrest and a windscreen wiper were to be included. Dual controls and a blind-flying hood or shutters were also required, together with a good shield and protection for the gunner during launching. The field of view from the gunner's seat was to be greater than the field of fire for his guns, and full navigation facilities, a belt and W/T key were to be provided for the observer. The mock-up of the proposed aircraft was to be ready in three months from the date of order. The engine was to be British, to have passed the 100 hr. type test and an air-cooled unit would be preferred. A cartridge starter and hand-turning gear were to be incorporated, together with a variable-pitch propeller or its equivalent in the first aircraft. Adjustable control surface stops were required on the prototype, and they were to avoid jamming the airframe. Full night flying equipment was to be included, and the machine had to be able to carry a 1,500 lb. torpedo equipped with air rudders, electrical release of the weapon being in the hands of the pilot, who was to have an illuminated torpedo sight. The arrester gear controls were also to be in the pilot's compartment. The aircraft was to be designed for catapulting as a ship plane and as a floatplane, embodying flotation gear to enable the machine to float for at least one hour.

Out of six S.24/37 proposals, two were eventually built as prototypes, and one ultimately went into production. The unbuilt layouts consisted of the Blackburn B.29 by George Petty, the Supermarine Type 380 conceived by Joseph Smith, the Westland P.11 drawn up by Arthur Davenport and W. E. W. Petter, and Sydney Camm's Hawker S.24/37. The Hawker entrant was quite an elegant shoulder-wing, cantilever monoplane with a single Taurus radial as its power plant. Alternative undercarriages consisted of a pair of fixed divided units with spats and of twin floats. The wings were fairly sharply tapered and surmounted in the centre-section by the crew's glazed canopy extending from leading to trailing edges.

Two prototypes—R1810 and R1815—were completed of an alternative Supermarine S.24/37 design, the Type 322, which found itself called Dumbo, an appellation attributable in all probability to its most unusual feature— variable-incidence wings. A contributory factor to its nickname may well have been the Type 322's singularly squat, unprepossessing appearance, occasioned by its deep, humped fuselage, abbreviated nose and short, arched, fixed undercarriage. Variation of incidence was Smith's proposed solution to the problem of increasing the angle of descent and reducing the landing speed and run of a carrier-borne torpedo aircraft of clean design. In addition to conferring desirable low-speed characteristics during the landing phase, the property of increasing incidence was of equal benefit in reducing the run at take-off. One point particularly in the design's favour was the excellence of the view forwards over the nose.

Different versions of the Merlin were fitted to the pair of prototypes— R1810 receiving the 1,300 h.p. Merlin 30 driving a three-blade propeller and R1815 the 1,600 h.p. Mk. 32 with a four-blade propeller. The first Type 322 —R1810—made its maiden flight during February, 1943, the delay in completion of the machine being attributable to Spitfire production commitments. Incorporation of Handley Page slots and interconnected flaps in variable-incidence, folding wings possessing qualities of very high lift—a coefficient

Fairey Barracuda T.B. Mk. II built by Westland. (*Westland Photo.*)

of 3·9 being attained—resulted in an engine-on stalling speed for R1815 of about 58 m.p.h., combined with very good control at low speeds. Composite construction was a feature of both aircraft, R1810 having a plywood skin and R1815 a covering of Alclad; the fin and rudder of R1815 were also of greater area than those of R1810. The choice of variable incidence for the wings precluded their use as housings for a retractable undercarriage and resulted in the use of a fixed unit.

The wings of the Type 322 were arranged to pivot about the front spar, a pair of screw jacks operating through a chain drive—either electrically or manually—against the rear spar to bring about the change in incidence. This was variable from 2°, at which the flap setting was neutral, to 15°, at which the

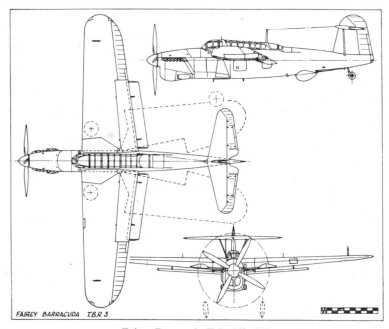

Fairey Barracuda T.R. Mk. III

flaps dropped to 60°. Both Type 322s recorded promising results in their trials, but the excessive delay in their completion—scheduled originally for the spring of 1941—militated against eventual production.

Specification S.24/37's demands were satisfied ultimately by the distinctive Fairey Type 100 Barracuda designed by M. J. O. Lobelle and following also the high-wing monoplane concept. Criticized adversely by many on aesthetic grounds owing to its relatively cluttered and gawky appearance when on the ground, the machine may have lacked the phenomenal cleanliness of line with which its recent antecedent low-wing monoplanes from Fairey were endowed, but, none the less, the sight of a full squadron of Barracudas peeling off to dive in line astern, following each other down like a galaxy of graceful sailplanes floating earthwards, was a spectacle unlikely to be forgotten by anyone fortunate enough to witness it.

The twenty-four-cylinder × 1,200 h.p. Rolls-Royce Exe engine was selected in the first instance as the power plant for the Barracuda, the unit being tested during 1938 in Battle K9222. Development of the sleeve-valve, pressure-air-cooled Exe was ultimately brought to a halt, and the 1,300 h.p. Merlin 30 took its place in the design, the first prototype P1767—Fairey airframe F4468—flying initially on 7th December, 1940, from the Great West Aerodrome, piloted by Chris Staniland. The 49 ft. 2 in. span machine seated three—the pilot, observer/navigator and wireless operator/air gunner—in an enclosure surmounting the slim fuselage from leading to trailing edges above the tapered cantilever wings set at shoulder level. P1767's tailplane was set at the junction of the fin and fuselage, but buffeting troubles caused it to be raised on subsequent examples to a position towards the top of the fin, where it was supported by struts. One of the Barracuda's most notable features was the remarkable form of undercarriage evolved as a pair of split units to accommodate the 18 in. external torpedo, to give sufficiently wide track and to retract flush with the underside of the stressed-skin wings. The trailing edge inboard of the ailerons was adorned by a pair of large hydraulically-operated Fairey-Youngman flaps which, apart from their normal function, could be set at a negative angle of 30° to operate as dive brakes. Fittings beneath the wings enabled the Barracuda to carry bombs, a mine or depth charges; defensive armament consisted of two Vickers K guns in the rear compartment. As the Fleet Air Arm's first carrier-based monoplane torpedo-bomber, the Barracuda T.B. Mk. I joined the Navy on 10th January, 1943, when No. 827 Squadron became the initial operational unit after relinquishing its Albacores.

P1767 and P1770—the second prototype—appeared in 1941 incorporating the elevated horizontal tail surfaces, and continuing development produced the Barracuda T.B. Mk. II—P1767, again the prototype, flying on 17th August, 1942—with the increased power of the 1,640 h.p. Merlin 32 with a four-blade propeller, together with the inclusion of A.S.V. Mk. IIN radar. During 1943 the Barracuda T.R. Mk. III appeared, still with the Merlin 32 engine, but equipped with A.S.V. Mk. X for anti-submarine work, the radar scanner being housed in a fairing beneath the rear fuselage. DP855, a T.B.

Mk. II, was modified as the prototype T.R. Mk. III to make its maiden flight in 1943. Relatively little use was made of the Barracuda as a torpedo-carrier during the war, but the type was spectacularly successful in the rôle of dive bomber and, equipped with R.A.T.O.G., was very useful on anti-submarine patrols from small escort carriers.

Additional evolution of the Barracuda was undertaken by fitting the 1,850 h.p. Griffon VII engine, a trial installation taking place in P9976—a modified T.B. Mk. II—which flew thus on 16th November, 1944, from Ringway; production of this development was proposed as the T.R. Mk. IV. P9976 underwent still further revision in 1944 to become a two-seater with the 1,850 h.p. Griffon VIII and increased wing area. The eventual production Barracuda T.R. Mk. V of 1945 received another boost in power with the installation of the 2,020 h.p. Griffon 37, being equipped also with wings incorporating square tips and an increase in span to 53 ft. 0·5 in. Strengthening of the airframe was incorporated, together with modifications to the electrical system. The machine's radar was installed beneath the port wing's leading edge in a housing which could be removed rapidly as a complete unit. A wing-mounted ·5 Browning gun, firing forwards, constituted the T.R. Mk. V's sole armament. The first T.R. Mk. Vs, converted from early models, kept the original fin and rudder; initial production T.R. Mk. Vs embodied a dorsal fin, while final production T.R. Mk. Vs received a new rudder of increased height terminating in a pointed tip. External racks carried a maximum bomb load of 2,000 lb. This final version of the Barracuda attained a maximum speed of 253 m.p.h. at 10,000 ft., but relatively little employment remained for it by the time it entered service in 1946, the Fleet Air Arm using the type for training instead of issuing it to operational squadrons.

The parlous position in which the United Kingdom was placed during the summer of 1940 engendered numerous—and often fantastic—improvisations to deal with the anticipated German invasion of Britain's shores. The popular de Havilland D.H.82A Tiger Moth two-seat trainer was the least warlike and most inoffensive of aircraft, but found itself by chance included among the bizarre schemes devised to boost the R.A.F.'s retaliatory power when the company put forward a proposal for converting the tiny biplane into a bomber by equipping it with eight under-fuselage racks beneath the rear cockpit, each able to carry a 20 lb. or 25 lb. bomb. The racks were those devised eight years before for the military Dragons supplied to Iraq. The intention was that the Tiger Moth bombers should be flown solo to attack invading troops as they landed on the beaches. Trials were conducted at Hatfield by Maj. Hereward de Havilland and at A. & A.E.E. Boscombe Down with the conversion from July, 1940, the machine earning a perfectly satis-factory report. As an alternative, the Tiger Moth's bomb-racks could be installed four on each side beneath the lower wings, thus obviating trimming difficulties. Tests were carried out also from Hatfield by Maj. de Havilland with a Tiger Moth carrying a single bomb weighing 240 lb. with which the machine managed to reach a height of 7,000 ft.

Percival Aircraft Ltd. had indulged, too, in schemes for modification of

LS479, a Fairey Barracuda T.R. Mk. V with original form of tail unit. (*Fairey Photo.*)

civil machines as light bombers, during 1935 the company's projects including the proposed conversion for China of the Vega Gull as the P.10A* with the 205 h.p. D.H. Gipsy Six II to carry sixteen 20 lb. bombs, the P.13 derivative of the Vega Gull with open tandem cockpits and the 200 h.p. D.H. Gipsy Six I and the P.13A version of the Vega Gull to use the 205 h.p. D.H. Gipsy Six II driving a variable-pitch propeller—both the P.13 and the P.13A being designed for Iraq. When, in mid-1940, the threat of invasion was at its zenith

* These Percival designations were allocated retrospectively.

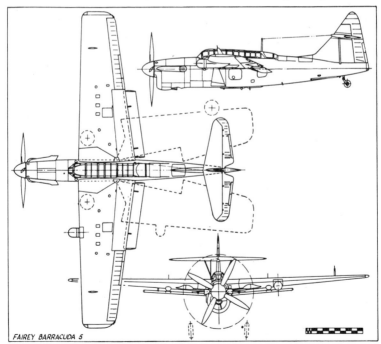

Fairey Barracuda T.R. Mk. V

321

the Percival chief designer prepared the P.29 light bomber version of the Proctor for anti-invasion defence. P5998, the Proctor prototype fitted with the 208 h.p. D.H. Gipsy Queen II engine, was converted and flown in its bomber form in the summer of 1940, but the project was subsequently abandoned.

The name of de Havilland came prominently to the forefront of bomber development during and immediately after the 1914–18 War with the introduction of the D.H.4, D.H.9, D.H.9A and the D.H.10. A lull then ensued and, apart from the design and construction of various prototypes during the next two decades, the firm concentrated on the civil market with notable success and played virtually no part in British bomber evolution. The inspiration of Capt. Geoffrey de Havilland and his fellow directors, however, was—at a single stroke—to bring about a totally unexpected, dramatic and startling addition to the types of bomber available to the Royal Air Force for the conduct of its wartime operations. The aircraft concerned—the two-seat de Havilland D.H.98 Mosquito—was a design of brilliant conception, destined to establish itself as one of the most successful of all aeroplanes and, indisputably, the most outstanding machine of its particular class ever to take to the air.

The steadily worsening political position in Europe during the late 1930s and the inevitability of war, as the ultimate outcome of Germany's repeated territorial aggression, became obvious to the chairman and the directors of the de Havilland Aircraft Company at Hatfield. In the midst of its concentration on production of civil aircraft for the thriving private and commercial market the concern began to consider the ways in which, apart from the supply of training and communications aircraft to the R.A.F. and the F.A.A., it might be of assistance in implementing the Services' offensive power. De Havilland had specialized in wooden construction for aircraft, with the emphasis, in two types in particular—the D.H.88 Comet and the D.H.91 Albatross, on strength combined with efficiency and excellent performance. Even in a well-established period during which all-metal construction for operational aircraft had been insisted upon by the Air Ministry for a decade, the company was prepared to suggest that an exception to the all-metal dictum should be considered. De Havilland—with nearly a quarter of a century's experience in designing and constructing numerous wooden aircraft of outstanding and unqualified success—could advance several cogent reasons in support of the contention that there was once again a place for an all-wood, high-speed, light bomber in the inventory of the Royal Air Force. Judicious use of wood would automatically bring in its train several advantages, not least among them being—if matched with adequate power—a very high operating speed.

Initial thoughts during mid-1938 centred on various adaptations of the current Albatross airliner, designed by A. E. Hagg and unquestionably one of the most elegant and refined aeroplanes ever to be seen in the sky, the suggestion being that it could carry a bomb load of 6,000 lb. as far as Berlin at a fuel consumption of 1 gall. for 2·5 miles. Second thoughts resulted in a far more original approach—the use of a pair of powerful Merlins in an airframe of reduced size able to carry a crew of two and an adequate bomb load, but consequently so fast that the radical proposal could be made that defensive armament could be discarded. Dispensing with guns brought the benefits of increased performance and load capacity.

During October, 1938, the Air Ministry was apprised of the scheme for the new bomber as a Private Venture, but no progress was made either then or in the course of the ensuing twelve months. The advent of war in September, 1939, brought a renewed approach to the Air Ministry by the firm and, this time, some positive response was received, especially from Air Marshal Sir Wilfred Freeman, Air Council Member for Research, Development and Production. Eventually, on 29th December, 1939, agreement was reached that de Havilland should proceed with detail design of an all-wood, two-seat, light bomber able to transport a bomb load of 1,000 lb. with a performance equal to that of a fighter and possessing a range of 1,500 miles. Additional substance was given to the project eight weeks later when Specification 1/40/D.H. of 1st March, 1940—otherwise B.1/40—was issued in respect of a de Havilland light reconnaissance bomber, fifty of which were ordered.

Even so, despite unqualified conviction at de Havilland that the entire concept was undoubtedly correct and destined to be of the utmost value as a weapon, on the whole the Air Ministry still possessed unfounded qualms about the venture, so that, when—after the Dunkirk catastrophe—it was necessary to review the range of aircraft scheduled for—or already in—production, the D.H.98 was deleted from the list. This daunting decision brought forth representations from de Havilland which were sufficiently telling for the programme to be reinstated during July, 1940, after a break of but a few weeks. Once again official doubts arose about the advisability of embarking upon the introduction of an unarmed bomber, and instructions were issued that only twenty of the batch of fifty were to be completed as bombers, the rest to be fighters.

Design work under R. E. Bishop proceeded at such a fast rate that on 25th November, 1940, in the very short period of four days under eleven months since the start of detail design, E-0234—the all-yellow bomber version first prototype—was able to take to flight for the first time from Hatfield piloted by Geoffrey de Havilland, Jr. The Mosquito was an immediate success and, after its second flight, E-0234 became W4050. For the next eleven weeks what was now the world's fastest military aircraft underwent its constructor's trials until delivery to A. & A.E.E. Boscombe Down on 19th February, 1941, for official assessment. The inception of the Mosquito afforded a direct comparison with that of its renowned ancestor the D.H.4, both of them being wooden, two-seat, bombers capable of outpacing contemporary hostile fighters. In the Mosquito's case, however, events were to conspire to enable it to establish a reputation of immeasurably greater lustre than that of its antecedent.

Beauty of form had progressively asserted itself as a de Havilland hallmark and had entered a new phase of outstanding purity of line with the Comet of 1934. A notable fact was that this propensity for elegance was perpetuated

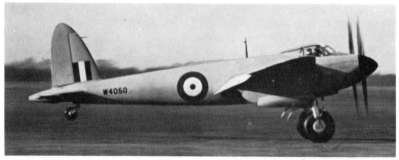

Geoffrey de Havilland, Jr., testing the prototype de Havilland Mosquito W4050. (*de Havilland Photo.*)

D.H. Mosquito B. Mk. IV DK338. (*R.C.A.F. Photo.*)

by successive chief designers, with the Mosquito exhibiting superlative over-all form unapproached by any other warplane in its category. The finely-shaped oval fuselage, fabricated as a monocoque in two halves from balsa wood sandwiched between two layers of plywood, was carried by sharply-tapered wings set at shoulder level. K4050's pair of 1,460 h.p. Merlin 21s were installed in line with the nose on the underside of the wings and shrouded in slim nacelles, the rear portions of which housed the main undercarriage units. The crew of two were seated abreast at the leading edge and flanked by the pair of horizontal radiator intakes located on each side in the wing roots.

Operational plans for the use of such a phenomenal product as the Mosquito were pressed ahead with utmost speed. W4072, the prototype Mosquito B. Mk. IV, made its first flight on 8th September, 1941, and the B. Mk. IV Ser. II joined No. 105 Squadron on 15th November, 1941, the unit becoming operational during May, 1942. The intended load of the B. Mk. IV was to consist of four 250 lb. bombs, but modification of 500 lb. missiles made it possible to accommodate four of the larger bombs, thereby doubling the machine's destructive power when it entered the R.A.F. Only ten of the B. Mk. IV Ser. I Mosquitoes with Merlin 21 or 23 engines were built and were followed by the B. Mk. IV Ser. II with Merlin 21, 23 or 25 engines in nacelles extending behind the wings. Once on active service against the enemy, the magnificent Mosquito justified fully de Havilland faith in the concept and confounded completely the short-sighted, faint-hearted critics who had opposed its production.

Modifications to increase the bomber version's offensive capacity and performance followed at a fast rate, it being found possible to house far larger bombs by revision of the bomb-bay and to improve range by installing drop-tanks. With the larger bomb-bay a single 4,000 lb. bomb could be carried. Only one B. Mk. V was built, the machine receiving strengthened wings to enable them to carry two 500 lb. bombs externally. Production of the B. Mk. IV was undertaken in Canada as the B. Mk. VII, the engines used being 1,300 h.p. Packard-built Merlin 31s. KB300, the first of this model, made its initial flight from Toronto on 24th September, 1942, with Geoffrey de Havilland, Jr., at the controls. The B. Mk. IX was produced as a high-altitude bomber with a pair of 1,680 h.p. Merlin 72 engines, DZ540—a converted B. Mk. IV—serving as the prototype. The B. Mk. IX attained a ceiling of over 36,000 ft., achieved by increasing the wing area from 435 sq. ft. to 454 sq. ft. At the same time the fuselage was lengthened to 44 ft. 6 in. The B. Mk. IX was used to particular effect loaded with the 4,000 lb. bomb and equipped with Oboe. Before revision of the Mosquito to drop the 4,000 lb. missile, only the heavy bombers, with their slower speeds, could deliver it. Use of the Mosquito meant that the heavy bomb could be transported at far

D.H. Mosquito B. Mk. XVI RV324. (*Dowty Photo.*)

D.H. Mosquito B. Mk. 35. (*de Havilland Photo.*)

325

D.H. Mosquito F.B. Mk. 40 A52–62 of the R.A.A.F. (*R.A.A.F. Photo.*)

higher speed, with consequent reduction in risk of interception. The B. Mk. XVI was developed from the B. Mk. IX and was equipped with a pressure cabin to enable it to operate at an altitude of 40,000 ft. The prototype B. Mk. XVI, MP469, flew for the first time during November, 1943, the intention being that the bomb load should be 3,000 lb. This was, however,

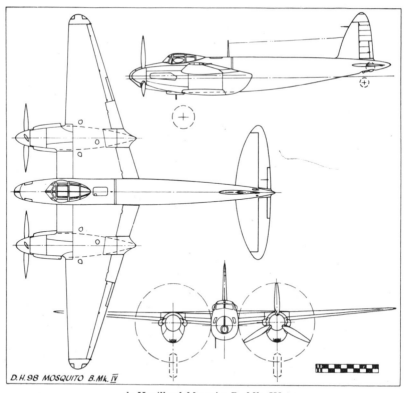

D.H.98 MOSQUITO B.Mk. IV

de Havilland Mosquito B. Mk. IV

increased in all production B. Mk. XVIs by enlarging the bomb-bay to take the 4,000 lb. bomb, together with attachment points for a pair of 50 gall. tanks beneath the wings. Power plants of the B. Mk. XVI were a pair of 1,680 h.p. Merlins 72 and 76 or 1,710 h.p. Merlins 73 and 77. The final Mosquito bomber variant was the B. Mk. 35, which took to the air initially on 12th March, 1945, as an improved B. Mk. XVI equipped with a pair of 1,690 h.p. Merlins 113 and 114, which gave it a top speed of 422 m.p.h. at 30,000 ft.

A. & A.E.E. Boscombe Down Report 767C/Pt. 1 of 5th November, 1941, recorded take-off tests conducted with Mosquito B. Mk. IV Ser. I W4057, fitted with Merlin 21s. The only variation from standard at the time of the trials was that the machine was equipped with a Dowty oleo-pneumatic leg for the tailwheel. With 25° flap the take-off run was 445 yd. and take-off speed 98 m.p.h. At a height of 50 ft. the speed had increased to 108 m.p.h. On landing the tailwheel was found to be bottoming and was seen to shimmy violently immediately after touching down. The tests were therefore discontinued, and the tailwheel leg later replaced by a Dowty all-oil type.

The Mosquito was an example of inspired British design and engineering and was without peer in its particular class. Flown with consummate skill and courage on many daring exploits, it made a profound contribution to the R.A.F.'s prowess during the 1939–45 War.

In the course of 1939, Specification B.27/39 was prepared in respect of a proposed Blackburn high-speed, light bomber, but was subsequently renumbered as Specification B.3/40 of 10th July, 1940, to cover a high-speed, light reconnaissance bomber by Blackburn. The crew required comprised a pilot and an air observer, and the machine was to be designed for rapid manufacture with consideration given to the use of a wooden airframe. Griffon engines were stipulated, together with the installation of three F.24 cameras. Maximum weight was to be 20,000 lb., and performance called for included—at 18,000 ft.—a maximum speed of at least 400 m.p.h. and a minimum cruising speed of 345 m.p.h. and a range of 1,250 miles at the same altitude.

B.3/40 remained on paper only, and the same fate befell three other requirements of 1940—Specifications B.7/40, B.20/40 and E.28/40. B.7/40 was a derivation of B.11/39 for a high-performance light bomber. In its B.7/40 form of 22nd May, 1940, the requirement demanded a high-speed, light bomber to undertake short-range bombing. Preference was expressed for an air-cooled type of engine, and the design had to possess a simple structure in the interest of quantity production. The complement was to consist of a pilot, an air observer, a W/T operator/air gunner and an air gunner. Maximum all-up weight was to be 20,000 lb., and the armament required was to be composed of four fixed ·303 guns for the pilot, a centre turret with two ·5 guns and a ventral position housing another pair of ·5 guns. The machine's bomb load of 1,000 lb. was to be carried internally. Performance requirements included a maximum speed of at least 300 m.p.h. at 5,000 ft. and 800 miles range at maximum economical cruising speed. Two projects were prepared to

B.7/40—a revised Armstrong Whitworth A.W.48 by John Lloyd and the Hawker P.1001, Sydney Camm's development of the Henley.

Camm devised yet another variant of the Henley in 1940 as the Hawker P.1006, which was tendered to Specification B.20/40 requiring an aircraft capable of close-support bombing and tactical reconnaissance.

Specification E.28/40 of 17th February, 1941, was a revision of Specification S.15/39, which had called for a torpedo-bomber reconnaissance aircraft. In its new form E.28/40 covered a design for an experimental naval research aircraft for the Fleet Air Arm, based on the liquid-cooled Sabre engine, as a potential Barracuda replacement. On 16th August, 1941, the power-plant stipulation was amended to a Centaurus. The resulting machine was to be capable of reconnaissance, torpedo-bombing and level and dive bombing, operating in all parts of the world. Overall dimensions were not to exceed span 52 ft. 6 in. extended and 18 ft. folded, length 44 ft. and height 13 ft. 6 in. 20,000 lb. was set as the maximum all-up weight, and the crew of three stipulated as pilot, observer and W/T operator/air gunner. Cruising speed was to be 200 kt. at 10,000 ft. with torpedo and 120 kt. at the same altitude for reconnaissance.

The Folland E.28/40 prototype, designed by H. E. Preston and allotted the serial DX160, was partly completed before work on it was discontinued in 1943. The FO.116 was a shoulder-wing, cantilever monoplane with tapered mainplanes bearing four prominent external guides for the area-increasing flaps. The crew were housed in a glazed canopy which terminated at the rear in a dorsal turret set mid-way along the fuselage. Unusual features of the Folland design were the incorporation of variable incidence in the wings—which could range from 4° to 15°—and the use of a fixed undercarriage, made obligatory by the ability to alter the incidence setting of the wings.

The main stream of British bomber evolution has followed a fairly logical sequence composed of steady, progressive steps which were discussed reasonably well ahead in most cases, even though their execution in peacetime may often have been extremely tardy. Nevertheless, exceptions to this practice have occurred, and a notable example is that which eventually provided the most successful and illustrious British heavy bomber of the 1939–45 War—the Avro Lancaster. If the Manchester had not suffered from the failings of its twin Vultures its four-engine immediate descendant might well never have been designed. In the event, however, it became a fortuitous failure in producing for Bomber Command an indispensable weapon of great power with which to break Axis strength.

The birth of the immortal Lancaster was achieved virtually at a single stroke by removing the two Vultures and substituting in their place four of the well-established, reliable and already battle-proven Merlin power plants. This fateful decision was taken in the summer of 1940 as the second of the two alternative projects for fitting the Manchester with new engines. The first proposal considered envisaged the Manchester B. Mk. II with a pair of Centaurus or Sabre units; the second—and that ultimately adopted—was for the use of four 1,145 h.p. Merlin Xs under the designation Manchester

Avro Lancaster B. Mk. I NG347 QB-P 'Piccadilly Princess' of No. 424 Squadron, R.C.A.F., constructed by Armstrong Whitworth. (*R.C.A.F. Photo.*)

B. Mk. III. The major modification which Roy Chadwick made to BT308—which became the 683 Lancaster B. Mk. I prototype—lay in the provision of a fresh centre-section to accommodate the new quadruple engines.

The new machine made a successful maiden flight from Ringway on 9th January, 1941, with Capt. H. A. Brown at the controls. Initially BT308 retained the Manchester B. Mk. I style of tail unit embodying the central fin; this empennage was modified later to match that of the Manchester B. Mk. IA with twin fins and rudders only of increased size. Manufacturer's trials were eminently satisfactory, resulting in delivery to A. & A.E.E. Boscombe Down in under three weeks for official assessment to start on 27th January, 1941, on the strength of which immediate production of the Lancaster was instituted. The first B. Mk. Is to leave the lines were modified Manchester airframes until L7527, equipped with 1,480 h.p. Merlin XXs and the first of the full production seven-seat Lancaster B. Mk. Is, took-off from Woodford for the first time on 31st October, 1941.

As the flow of Lancasters increased, continued development by Rolls-Royce brought installation of 1,480 h.p. Merlin 22s and 1,640 h.p. Merlin 24s. The machine was armed with ·303 guns—two each in nose, dorsal and ventral turrets and four in the tail turrets. Little use was made of the ventral guns, and the standard number installed became eight ·303s in three Frazer-Nash hydraulically-operated turrets. From December, 1941, No. 44 Squadron became the first to operate the Lancaster, having received the prototype BT308 for Service Trials during September, 1941.

A switch to radial engines was made with the installation of 1,650 h.p. Hercules VIs in the B. Mk. II, the prototype of which was DT810; three hundred B. Mk. IIs were constructed by Armstrong Whitworth. Further production ensued of the Lancaster B. Mk. III—prototype W4114—equipped with Packard-built 1,300 h.p. Merlin 28s, 1,480 h.p. Merlin 38s or 1,640 h.p. Merlin 224s. Together, the B. Mk. I and the B. Mk. III became the principal Lancaster production models. The Lancaster B. Mk. IV and B. Mk. V were scheduled as major developments to Specification B.14/43; the production order to this requirement was eventually cancelled as a modification of the Lancaster, and the specification transferred to cover the proposals as the Avro Lincoln. Two B. Mk. Is and seven B. Mk. IIIs were converted into Lancaster B. Mk. VIs, scheduled for service with 1,750 h.p.

Merlin 85s or 102s enclosed in new annular cowlings, but further production was abandoned. Four 1,620 h.p. Merlin 24s equipped the Lancaster B. Mk. VII, which appeared with revised armament in the form of a pair of ·5 Brownings in a Martin dorsal turret. NN801 was the prototype B. Mk. VII.

The demand for the Lancaster resulted in production by Victory Aircraft Ltd. in Canada of the B. Mk. X, a derivative of the B. Mk. III powered by 1,300 h.p. Packard-built Merlin 28s, 1,480 h.p. Merlin 38s or 1,640 h.p. Merlin 224s. KB700, the first B. Mk. X, was delivered to the R.C.A.F. on 6th August, 1943, the total of this version subsequently reaching four hundred and thirty. Variants of the Lancaster B. Mk. I were the B. Mk. I (Special)—able to accommodate the massive 8,000 lb., 12,000 lb. or 22,000 lb. bombs—and the B. Mk. I (F.E.) prepared for use with Tiger Force in the Far East with the intention of bombing Japan.

The rate of loss of the Lancaster equated with the tonnage of bombs dropped was the lowest of the four-engine heavy bombers employed by the R.A.F. in the course of the 1939–45 War, and comparatively little alteration was made in its defensive armament. Experimental work was undertaken with B. Mk. III JB456 fitted with a pair of 20 mm. Hispano cannon in a

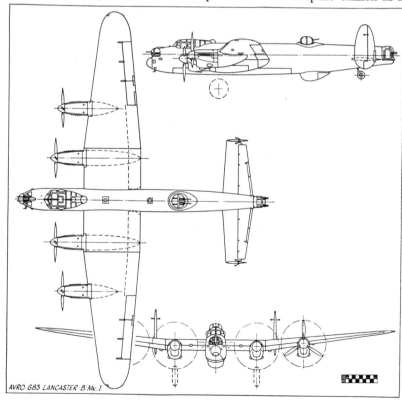

AVRO 683 LANCASTER B.Mk.1

Avro Lancaster B. Mk. I

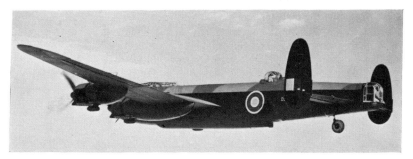

Avro Lancaster B. Mk. II, built by Armstrong Whitworth. (*Armstrong Whitworth Photo.*)

Bristol B.17 dorsal turret and with the B. Mk. I LL780 and the B. Mk. III RF268, both equipped with dorsal and ventral barbettes—housing a pair of 20 mm. cannon—operated by remote control from the tail. Two projected high-altitude versions of the Lancaster—the 684 and the 686—were still-born.

The Lancaster's first-class overall performance and bomb-carrying capacity of 14,000 lb. or one 22,000 lb. bomb, assisted by the inclusion of the radar aids Gee, Gee H, H2S, Oboe and Rebecca, were responsible for its selection to carry out many important missions—among them the attacks on the Möhne, Eder and Sorpe dams and on the battleship *Tirpitz*, the undertaking of which added even greater lustre to the celebrated name of the finest and most successful heavy bomber of the 1939–45 War and brought fame to No. 617 Squadron in particular for its courageous execution of such difficult and hazardous operations.

A. & A.E.E. Boscombe Down Report 766/Pt. 1 of 3rd March, 1941, dealt with preliminary handling trials carried out with BT308, the prototype Lancaster fitted with four Merlin XXs. A brief visit was made to Manchester by one A. & A.E.E. pilot to fly the Lancaster, and certain advance information was obtained before full official trials of the type at Boscombe Down. BT308 was fitted with a central fin and twin fins and rudders, and the test was carried out at a light weight only of 38,000 lb. The outboard throttles fell to hand satisfactorily, but the inboard levers were too short and could be manipulated by the palm of the pilot's hand only with difficulty. As in the Manchester, the control wheel boss and cross-bar made it difficult for the pilot to see the blind flying panel; consequently, it was recommended that the wheel should be lowered. The throttle levers were uncomfortably close to the dual control bar, and excessive force was needed to open the throttles with the damper applied. Avro's proposed solution, for the second pilot to apply the damper after the throttle levers had been pushed fully forwards, was not acceptable. Commented on favourably were the controls for the airscrew pitch and radiator shutters and the neat setting in line of the four switches. The instrument layout also was satisfactory. A swing to port was noted immediately the aircraft started to move on take-off, and full rudder and a touch of the brakes were ineffective in counteracting it; throttling of the starboard outer engine was the answer to this problem.

The controls were tested on the glide at over 100 m.p.h. I.A.S. to 290 m.p.h. I.A.S. in a dive. The Lancaster's elevators were lighter than those of the Manchester and superior for general handling. The ailerons were light and effective, but the rudders were found to become heavier with an increase in speed. For competitive trials it had been arranged that a set of rudders of increased size would be fitted. No difficulty was experienced in the approach and landing, the landing itself being straightforward and easy. At 4,600 ft., 2,650 r.p.m. and 4 lb./sq. in. boost, a speed run returned 242 m.p.h. T.A.S. The noise level appeared excessively high; no attempt had been made to soundproof the cabin, and this was recommended to be done straightaway.

Early impressions of the Lancaster were that it possessed very good flying qualities and promised to have a good performance. The rudders were insufficiently powerful, and the throttles needed modification to facilitate operation by the pilot. A shorter control column was suggested to improve the view of the blind flying panel, and better pilot comfort was essential. The gearing of the rudder trimming was too low, and alteration of this was also important. At the time of issue of the report a Lancaster fitted with new rudders was under test at A. & A.E.E.

A. & A.E.E. Boscombe Down Report 766/Pt. 12 of 25th October, 1941, summarized extensive take-off tests with the second prototype Lancaster DG595 equipped with four Merlin XXs at weights increasing from 49,000 to 60,000 lb. First tests at lower weights gave relatively bad results, and they were therefore repeated at the highest weight. These showed a great improvement which was ascribed to the pilot's greater experience and the lower take-off speed used. The tanks were full at the first test and refilled after every fourth run. In addition to nose and tail turrets, the aircraft had an F.N.50 dorsal turret and an F.N.64 ventral turret. No beam guns were fitted. The tests were carried out at the end of August and during September of 1941. The best flap angle at take-off was found to be from 25° to 30° at 55,000 lb., but the flap angle did not materially affect the take-off performance over a range of 15° to 40°. With less than 15° flap the take-off was found to become rapidly worse. From the tests it was concluded that the Lancaster should take-off in 970 yd. and reach 50 ft. in 1,340 yd. at 61,500 lb. Tests made at 60,000 lb. indicated that take-off and climb-away at 61,500 lb. should be satisfactory.

A. & A.E.E. Boscombe Down Report 766/Pt. 57 of 28th June, 1944, covered trials of May, 1944, with Lancaster B. Mk. I JB127 fitted with Merlin 24s driving Hamilton constant-speed, paddle-blade propellers Type A5/148. Take-off weight was 63,000 lb. In M/S gear the climb rate was 800 ft./min. at 9,500 ft. and 610 ft./min. at 16,200 ft. in F/S gear. The service ceiling was 23,500 ft., and the time to 23,000 ft. was 44 min. Maximum all-out level speed at 2,500 ft. in M/S gear was 268 m.p.h. T.A.S. at a level 3,000 r.p.m. and 280 m.p.h. T.A.S. at 10,000 ft. in F/S gear. In M/S gear no marked change in climb was noted, but in F/S gear it was 100 ft./min. better and gave an increase of 1,500 ft. in service ceiling. The time to 22,000 ft. was reduced by about 10 min., and the paddle-blade propellers increased the level speed by 6–10 m.p.h. above about 16,000 ft. Around 1,000 ft. the speed was unchanged, and below that height it was slightly inferior.

A. & A.E.E. Boscombe Down Report 766/Pt. 68 of 25th March, 1945, on Lancaster B. Mk. I PB529/G with Merlin 24s gave details of trials made in November, 1944, to ascertain climb performance and specific air range at 15,000 ft. with a 22,000 lb. bomb carried externally. The maximum rate of climb in M/S supercharger gear was 720 ft./min. to 9,900 ft. at a take-off weight of 63,700 lb.; in F/S gear it was 470 ft./min. up to 16,700 ft. The service ceiling was 21,000 ft., and time to 20,000 ft. was 38 min. PB529/G had an F.N.5 nose turret with two guns, an F.N.50 turret in the dorsal position with two guns and a faired taboo rail and an F.N.120 turret in the tail with four guns. The ventral turret was blanked off, a deeper bomb-aimer's window was fitted and the navigation blister was on the starboard side only. To accommodate the 22,000 lb. bomb the bomb-bay doors were removed and the bay was fitted with a metal fairing. The fabric-covered elevators were strengthened and the barrage cutters and de-icing equipment were deleted. One pulsometer pump cover was fitted under each wing. The Hamilton constant-speed, fully-feathering A5/159 paddle-blade propellers were 13 ft. in diameter. At 60,000 lb. the specific air range at 15,000 ft. in F/S gear was 1·11 air miles/gal. at 165 m.p.h. I.A.S. at full throttle.

A. & A.E.E. Boscombe Down Report 766a/Pt. 23 of 1st June, 1943, recorded dive tests on Lancaster B. Mk. II DS606, fitted with Hercules VIs, from 1st until 6th May, 1943. The trials were made after 150 hr. intensive flying to test the controls and the airframe. On the first dive with elevator

RE172, a Lancaster B. Mk. III. (*Avro Photo.*)

trim 2° forward, the aircraft accelerated rapidly to 370 m.p.h. I.A.S. with strong left-wing-low tendency. Very great force was needed to recover from the dive, so the machine was brought out on the elevator trimmer on a turn. On the third dive unexpected aileron overbalance was experienced at 330–340 m.p.h. I.A.S. The starboard surface overbalanced suddenly, throwing the wheel hard over clockwise, and the pilot was unable to overcome the overbalance, especially as he was pulling hard on the column to hold the speed down. 10° to 12° aileron trimmer had to be wound off and the elevators wound back 2° to 3° to assist recovery. After juddering, the ailerons returned to normal.

A. & A.E.E. Boscombe Down Report 766b/Pt. 2 of 3rd March, 1943, was in respect of performance and handling tests of a production aircraft, in this case Lancaster B. Mk. III ED453 fitted with Merlin 28s. The trials took place from 26th January until 1st February, 1943. Air Ministry policy was to test a percentage of the output of each firm making Lancasters, and ED453 was the first Lancaster selected from the output of A. V. Roe at Woodford. The tests were carried out at Scampton, and the machine was flown by an A. & A.E.E. pilot accompanied by a technical observer and a complementary operational crew from the satellite airfield at Fiskerton. 13 ft. 1 in. diameter Nash Kelvinator-built Hamilton Hydromatic A5/138 propellers were fitted, and the take-off weight of 61,370 lb. included eleven 500 lb. bombs, fuel and oil and a crew of eight. Results showed ED453 to be about 4 m.p.h. faster in M/S and 9 m.p.h. faster in F/S gear at 3,000 r.p.m. and at 9 lb./sq. in. boost than Lancaster B. Mk. I R5546 tested earlier at A. & A.E.E. At maximum weak mixture cruising power, ED453 was 10 m.p.h. faster in F/S gear than R5546, but in M/S gear ED453 was 2 m.p.h. slower at 14,000 ft. and 6 m.p.h. faster at 6,000 ft. The climb performance of ED453 at 61,370 lb. was almost identical with R5546 at 60,000 lb., the rate of climb at sea level being about 40 ft./min. lower on ED453. The service ceiling of the two aircraft was almost identical. Performance and handling characteristics were regarded as perfectly normal for the type.

A. & A.E.E. Boscombe Down Report 766/Pt. 4 of 30th June, 1944, described trials to ascertain the climb and level speed performance of a Canadian-built Lancaster B. Mk. X KB721 equipped with Merlin 38s driving 13 ft. diameter A5/138 propellers. Take-off weight was 63,000 lb. Compared with the Lancaster B. Mk. III average production model, there was very little difference in climb performance between the B. Mk. III and the B. Mk. X after allowing for the difference in weight. Compared with Lancaster B. Mk. III JA918, under maximum cruising conditions there was very little difference in level speed performance. KB721 was slightly superior in F/S gear but slightly inferior in M/S gear. There was no significant difference overall in the speed performance of the two aircraft. KB721 returned a service ceiling of 22,200 ft., a time of 46 min. to reach 22,000 ft., an all-out level speed of 270 m.p.h. at 12,600 ft. in F/S gear and 267 m.p.h. at 6,100 ft. in M/S gear and a maximum cruising speed of 254 m.p.h. at 16,300 ft. in F/S gear and 250 m.p.h. at 10,400 ft. in M/S gear.

Avro Lancaster B. Mk. X KB943 of the R.C.A.F., constructed by Victory Aircraft Ltd.

A. & A.E.E. Boscombe Down Report 766e/Pt. 5 of 28th January, 1945, was issued following brief handling trials with Lancaster B. Mk. X KB783 fitted with Merlin 24s. The tests were made during October and November, 1944, as the result of a signal received from the British Air Commission, Washington, D.C., U.S.A., following complaints made by a pilot of the Commission in the U.S.A. regarding KB783, which was a Canadian-built machine fitted with a Martin dorsal turret, 8,000 lb. bomb-bay type of doors and deflector plates ahead of the under defence position. The test flight of the Commission's pilot showed rather more signs of buffeting at the stall than was usual in the B. Mk. X. It was thought that this might be attributable to the deflector plates. With the C.G. in the full forwards position at 46,200 lb. A.U.W. control with full aft trim was at a minimum on the glide at 95 to 100 m.p.h. I.A.S. With the C.G. in the extended aft position and at 50,440 lb. A.U.W. the aircraft was slightly unstable throughout the speed range and required full forwards trim at high powers with flaps and undercarriage down, so that under conditions of going around again after a baulked landing there was only just sufficient control to take care of tail heaviness when the engines were opened up prior to raising the flaps. With the C.G. near the centre of the range the aircraft was quite satisfactory. The ailerons, however, were found to be far too heavy, and the makers were investigating this condition. The A. & A.E.E. tests showed that handling conditions in general were similar to those of the standard Lancaster B. Mk. I. Most of the comments in the report of the Commission pilot were substantially correct, but were not considered abnormal for the type of aircraft.

A. & A.E.E. Boscombe Down Report 766b/Pt. 11 was concerned with the trials made with Lancaster B. Mk. III ED825/G fitted with Merlin 28s. During April and May, 1943, tests were conducted to assess level speed performance, fuel consumption and range. The machine was modified to carry a certain item of stores which was spherical in shape. Take-off weight with the store was 63,000 lb., including one store of 11,500 lb. and 1,774 gal. of fuel. At 3,000 r.p.m. and at +9 lb./sq. in. boost the maximum level speed at 11,100 ft. was 233 m.p.h. Maximum continuous cruising level speed at 2,650 r.p.m. and at +4 lb./sq. in. boost was 206 m.p.h. at 13,600 ft. The maximum still-air range, the outward journey being made at 2,000 ft. with

WUO1, first of the Avro Lancasters supplied to the French Aéronavale. (*Avro Photo.*)

the store and the return journey being carried out, after releasing the store, at 15,000 ft., was 1,720 air miles. The practical range under the same conditions was assessed at 1,290 miles.

A. & A.E.E. Boscombe Down Report 766d/Pt. 2 recorded handling trials on Lancaster B. Mk. VI JB675 carried out during February, 1944. The machine's exterior was the same as the standard production B. Mk. I and B. Mk. III Lancasters, but Universal circular type power plants—Merlin 85s —were fitted, driving 13 ft. diameter Hamilton A5/148 paddle-blade propellers. The aircraft had nose, tail and dorsal—including cam track—turrets, extended hemispherical bomb-aimer's cupola and H2S blister. It was tested at take-off weights of 49,500 lb. and 65,000 lb., and dives were made at up to 350 m.p.h. I.A.S. Taxying and ground handling were similar to those of the B. Mk. I and B. Mk. III, and so were the take-off and initial climb. Level flight speeds revealed that the ailerons and rudders were heavier than those of the B. Mk. I and B. Mk. III, and the heaviness increased with speed until in a dive at about 350 m.p.h. I.A.S. the rudder and ailerons became practically immovable. Approach and landing were the same as those of the B. Mk. I and B. Mk. III. The aircraft was flown at 31,000 ft. to produce vapour trails to observe the slipstream flow over the fins and the rudders. The slipstream from the engines hit the fin in the middle of its upper section—about 4 ft. higher than on the B. Mk. I and the B. Mk. III, and this may have accounted for the rudder heaviness. The alteration in the flow pattern over the tail was probably owing to the larger nacelles and their different shape, resulting in a reduction in weathercock stability. Together with the heaviness of the rudders, this made turns difficult, particularly under conditions of assymetric power.

Further development of the Blenheim was envisaged with the promulgation of Specification B.6/40 of 17th September, 1940, the design to be evolved as a bomber for the direct support of the Army. With minimum alterations the Blenheim Mk. IV airframe was to be matched to a pair of 920 h.p. Mercury XV engines. Under Bristol Type 160 and named Bisley Mk. I two prototypes—AD657 and AD661—were ordered. The main alterations were to be embodied in the nose, which was to house four Brownings, the cockpit area was to be protected by armour, and two Brownings were to be mounted in the dorsal turret. Two 950 h.p. Mercury XVIs were eventually selected as power plants. Later revision of the project resulted in further modifications to suit the design as a replacement for the Blenheim Mk. IV under the new designation Blenheim Mk. V.

24th February, 1941, witnessed the maiden flight from Filton of AD657 as the two-seat, close-support variant with the four-Brownings nose. AD661 was completed as a three-seat, high-altitude, day bomber with a sloping asymmetrical nose, half of which was glazed. No more of the Type 160CS Blenheim Mk. VBs were built, the main production model being the Type 160D Blenheim Mk. VD, derived by equipping the Type 160 Blenheim Mk. VA for tropical operations. Despite its heavy armament and protective armour, the Mk. V suffered severely when set upon by hostile fighters and could only be employed where it would be unopposed in the air or could be given fighter escort.

Since the advent of the advanced Blenheim bomber, Bristol had continued to concentrate on the evolution of the fast, twin-engine monoplane, and this attention was applied with effect throughout the 1939–45 War. A project of

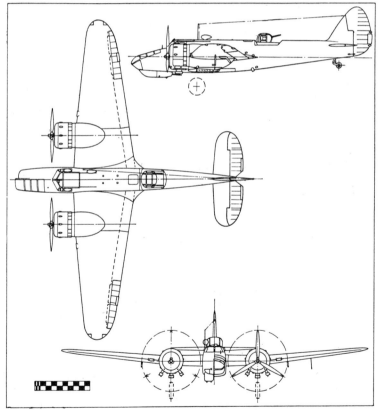

Bristol Blenheim Mk. V

337

Bristol Buckingham B. Mk. I. (*Bristol Photo.*)

1939 for the Type 157, a bomber adaptation of the Beaufighter, came to naught, but L. G. Frise prepared a further Beaufighter two-seat bomber derivative, the Type 161, to meet Specification B.7/40. Alternative engines planned were air-cooled radial Hercules for the Mk. I or liquid-cooled inline Merlins for the Mk. II.

Later in 1940, during October, Frise worked on yet another revision, the Type 162 Beaumont, which was covered by Specification B.2/41 of March, 1941. The requirement raised the complement to three and imposed demands in excess of the capabilities of the Hercules scheduled as the power plants. Consequently, in April, 1941, additional modifications resulted in the Type 163 with a pair of Centaurus engines and increased wing area. Further consultations, with attendant design alterations, took place before the issue on 11th August, 1941, of a revised B.2/41 for the Buckingham, as the new medium bomber was now known.

Capt. C. F. Uwins conducted the initial flight of DX249—the first prototype—from Filton on 4th February, 1943, the machine making its début as a massive, four-seat, mid-wing monoplane of 71 ft. 10 in. span powered by a pair of 2,400 h.p. Centaurus IVs. In company with the second prototype—DX255—DX249 was fitted with a tapered tailplane. DX259 and DX266—the third and fourth prototypes—received tailplanes of rectangular planform and larger vertical tail surfaces. The production Buckingham B. Mk. I was fitted with 2,520 h.p. Centaurus VIIs or XIs and was armed with four ·303 forwards-firing guns, four ·303s in the dorsal turret and two ·303s in the ventral bulge.

With a speed of 330 m.p.h. at 12,000 ft., in its time the Buckingham was the fastest bomber extant equipped with full conventional defensive armament. Nevertheless, by the time that production was under way the R.A.F.'s heavy bombers were succeeding handsomely in their task of subjugating the enemy by night, and the Mosquito was unapproached for speed, either by day or by night, and was able to carry the same bomb load—4,000 lb.—as the Buckingham but for a slightly shorter range. Eventually, only one hundred and nineteen production B. Mk. Is were supplied to the R.A.F.

As one of the requirements issued during the war to cover continued bomber development, Specification B.5/41 of 10th December, 1941, called for a high-altitude, heavy bomber embodying a pressure cabin for the crew and powered by four Merlins. The maximum speed was to be at least 345 m.p.h. at 31,000 ft., the service ceiling 38,500 ft. with full operational load and maximum bomb load 8,000 lb. A pilot, navigator/bomb-aimer, W/T operator, air gunner and observer were to form the crew of five. R. K. Pierson of Vickers prepared a development of the Warwick as the Mk. III Type 433 with high aspect ratio, elliptical wings. Design work continued on the Warwick Mk. III, leading eventually to an increase of 20 ft. in the wing span and of 4 ft. in the overall length with the object of improving the calculated performance. Four 1,600 h.p. Merlin 60s were selected to power the pair of B.5/41 prototypes—DW506 and DW512—which were subsequently ordered, the name Windsor being chosen for the new Vickers bomber. In the course of the genesis of the design the provisions contained in Specification B.5/41 became obsolete in the light of continued alteration in the tactical and strategic applications of aircraft in the conflict, and in September, 1942, B.5/41 was abandoned to be supplanted shortly by Specification B.3/42.

The possibility of sealing-up the basic Stirling was investigated under Specification B.8/41. The development, the Short S.36, was designed by Arthur Gouge around four Centaurus engines, the span being increased to 135 ft. 9 in., the wing area to 2,145 sq. ft. and the weight loaded to 104,000 lb. Performance envisaged included the ability to transport a bomb load of 10,000 lb. over 4,000 miles at 300 m.p.h., but the project was discontinued.

Another cancelled project—and one which appeared particularly promising —was that of the Hawker P.1005, a twin-engine, mid-wing, high-speed bomber of refined aspect which Sydney Camm designed in 1940 around two Sabre NS.8SM engines. Specification B.11/41 of 27th May, 1942, encompassed the layout, two prototypes—HV266 and HV270—having been ordered early in 1941. Cancellation ensued on 3rd July, 1942, but studies were carried out by Hawker to investigate the use in the P.1005 of a pair of the revolutionary Power Jets gas turbines under the designation P.1011.

Interest in B.11/41's requirement for an unarmed, high-altitude bomber able to carry a 4,000 lb. bomb load for 1,600 miles at a cruising speed of 350 m.p.h. at 30,000 ft. was shown by de Havilland where the D.H. 101 was evolved during October, 1941, as a projected derivative of the Mosquito based on the use of a pair of Sabres. After a few months the scheme was abandoned in April, 1942.

Although Miles Aircraft were occupied throughout the 1939–45 War with production of training aeroplanes, a great deal of design work was carried out on other types of aircraft, several of which were constructed and flown as prototypes. Among them was the M.39B Libellula U-0244, which was built as a $\frac{5}{8}$ flying scale version of a proposed twin-engine, tandem-wing, medium bomber to B.11/41, to which specification the firm was asked by the Air Ministry in 1942 to tender a layout. The Libellula was designed by G. H. Miles, who made the first flight in U-0244 on 22nd July, 1943. The basic form of the M.39B consisted of large, high-set, sweptback rear wings— carrying a pair of 130 h.p. Gipsy Majors installed as tractors—preceded by a smaller straight pair of wings mounted low on the nose. A retractable tricycle undercarriage supported the machine on the ground. Several distinct advantages were claimed for the layout, but no progress ensued towards construction of a full-size prototype, although the company carried out a series of studies involving the tandem-wing principle. Doped yellow overall in place of its camouflage of three years earlier, the M.39B—as U-4—was still being investigated in flight in the summer of 1946 by Miles after undergoing official assessment from 1944 as SR392.

One of the more unusual requirements of the war was set out in Specification X.3/41 of 25th April, 1941, in respect of a bomb-carrying adaptation of the Airspeed Horsa Mk. I glider. The military load was to be 8,250 lb., the bomb compartment replacing the Horsa's passenger cabin. The missiles were to be released by the pilot, the sole occupant of the glider, who was to be protected by 200 lb. of armour plate and provided with a parachute and a dinghy. No sight was required for aiming, and the bomb load to be accommodated was to consist alternatively of one 8,000 lb. H.C., two 4,000 lb. H.C., four 2,000 lb. H.C., four 1,900 lb. G.P. or four A Mk. I mines. Under Norway and Tiltman the A.S.52 layout was prepared by Airspeed for the modification of the Horsa, and another X.3/41 project was devised by Miles-Hooper. Neither, however, came to fruition.

Another unrealized Airspeed design of N. S. Norway and A. H. Tiltman was the A.S.47 high-speed bomber project of 1942, a twin-boom monoplane to be powered by two engines installed as a tractor and a pusher, either Merlins or Sabres being the favoured units.

A de Havilland project of the period was the D.H.102 to Specification B.4/42 for a high-performance bomber to replace the Mosquito. In company with the D.H.101 proposal, the design was a derivative of the basic D.H.98 and was, in fact, known as the Mosquito B. Mk. II. The bomb load was increased to 5,000 lb. and engines selected were either two Merlins or two Griffons. The D.H. 102 project was ultimately abandoned towards the close of 1942.

In the midst of production of its communication and training aircraft and its sub-contract work during the war, Percival Aircraft found it possible to spare some capacity to prepare several new projects, including the P.37 heavy bomber. Designed during 1943, the machine was an adaptation of the P.35 freighter proposal of 1943 and featured the all-wing concept mated to an abbreviated lifting fuselage of aerofoil section, the tail unit being mounted on twin booms. Four 2,500 h.p. Centaurus engines were proposed as the power plants, wing span being 140 ft. and the length 103 ft.

Although Bristol design capacity in 1942 was committed fully to current production and projects in the field of twin-engine medium aircraft, a request was received from the Air Ministry for proposals for a very large bomber indeed, to possess a loaded weight of 100,000 lb. and to be powered by either four Centaurus or six Hercules units. The performance asked for was on a high level, and the solution proposed to enable it to be attained was one which had been an attractive idea for many years—that of burying the engines in the wings, thereby achieving a substantial reduction of drag. Further advantages were considered to accrue if the power plants were to be coupled together, each pair to drive a single propeller. As the requirement was studied it was realized that an appreciably larger bomber than that under consideration would be capable of a far greater range, a useful attribute in a conflict which was being fought across vast areas of the earth. Accordingly, Bristol proposed the study of a new project to be capable of a range of 5,000 miles, to use six Centaurus, eight Griffon or eight Centaurus engines. The machine would have been a mid-wing monoplane of 225 ft. span and 225,000 lb. loaded weight in its final proposed version, with the Centaurus installed as four pairs coupled and buried in the wings. Before the whole project finally lapsed the ultimate design was for a very elegant high-wing monoplane with a long, slim, cylindrical fuselage, a V tail unit and four coupled pairs of engines concealed within the wings and driving pusher propellers. The proposal was known as the 100 ton bomber.

The possibility that an adaptation of the Magister two-seat trainer as a light bomber might be of some use in attacking invading German forces as they came ashore presented itself to Miles Aircraft during the summer of 1940, and a Magister was converted by fitting it with eight bomb-racks installed four at each end of a bar fitting mounted span-wise underneath the wings between the undercarriage units. In the event the Magister light bomber was not called into action, but it represented yet another example of the determination to attack the enemy in every possible way during the dangerous days of 1940. A year later, in the middle of 1941, the Magister was employed to assess a scheme whereby the range of medium bombers then in service might be increased until the larger four-engine types with greater range were available in sufficient numbers. The idea was that an auxiliary wing, loaded either with extra bombs or fuel, should be towed behind the bomber, so bestowing on the aircraft greater range or increased bomb capacity. The large auxiliary wing was mounted on a pair of booms—attached to the Magister's wings—so that it was carried just to the rear of the tail unit. Twin fins and rudders were fitted at each end of the extra wing, and an increase in the size of the Magister's rudder was found to be necessary to preserve directional stability. Trouble also arose with controlling the towed wing on the ground, but modifications introduced in the course of the trials progressively eradicated the problems. Ultimately the new heavy bombers coming into service possessed the necessary range and capacity to fulfil their rôles, and the towed wing idea was not required.

Compared with the distances flown by Bomber Command aircraft on operations over Europe, those which confronted crews involved in the war in the Far East were, on the whole, considerably greater. To meet the pressing demand for a weapon capable of prosecuting the campaign against the Japanese to the utmost effect, the basic Lancaster was appraised by Roy Chadwick and developed into the B. Mk. IV using four 1,750 h.p. Packard-built Merlin 68As. Little remained of the original Lancaster, and new designations were devised for the Avro 694, the Lancaster B. Mk. IV becoming the Lincoln B. Mk. I and the B. Mk. V the Lincoln B. Mk. II. The Lincoln retained the general lines of the Lancaster, but was somewhat larger,

Avro Lincoln B. Mk. II RF570. (*Avro Photo.*)

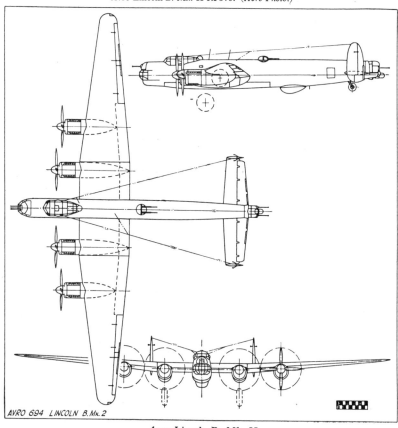

AVRO 694 LINCOLN B.Mk.2

Avro Lincoln B. Mk. II

342

the wings measuring 120 ft. in span and the fuselage 78 ft. 3·5 in. in length. The machine conformed to Specification B.14/43.

Capt. H. A. Brown was responsible for the maiden flight of PW925, the Lincoln prototype, from Ringway on 9th June, 1944. Heavier armament was applied to the Lincoln, and production B. Mk. Is carried two ·5 Browning guns in each position—nose, dorsal and tail—those at the front and rear being installed in Boulton Paul turrets, while a Bristol Type 17 Mk. II occupied the dorsal location.

The Lincoln B. Mk. II—prototype RE289—utilized four 1,750 h.p. Packard-built Merlin 68s, 68As or 300s and displayed revised defensive armament. A ventral position was added containing a ·5 Browning, and the pair in the nose were under the remote control of the bomb-aimer; the dorsal turret contained two 20 mm. Hispano cannon. The Lincoln's maximum bomb load was 14,000 lb.; the version equipped with the H2S Mk. IIIG radar bomb-sight was designated B. Mk. II (IIIG), and that with the H2S Mk. IVA sight became the B. Mk. II (IVA). The Lincoln B. Mk. IV was evolved by converting the B. Mk. II to take Merlin 85 engines.

Canadian interest resolved itself into the Lincoln B. Mk. 15—derived from the B. Mk. I—of which the first was to have been FM300, with production by Victory Aircraft Ltd. The contract was cancelled, however, before completion of any of the B. Mk. 15s. Australian plans to use the Lincoln for the R.A.A.F. bore fruit, and fifty-four Mk. 30(B)s were built. The batch of twenty-four equipped with 1,750 h.p. Merlin 102s were Mk. 30(B)s, but thirty using 1,750 h.p. Merlin 85s became Mk. 30A(B)s. Eighteen were converted during 1952 into Mk. 31(MR)s for anti-submarine patrol by extending the nose by 6 ft. to accommodate radar detection equipment.

A. & A.E.E. Boscombe Down Report 822/Pt. 16 of 10th September, 1945, recorded brief handling trials conducted with Lincoln B. Mk. I RE232 equipped with Merlin 85s during April, 1945. General handling characteristics were satisfactory to clear up to 82,000 lb. following earlier trials on the prototype B. Mk. I PW925 at weights of up to 75,000 lb. RE232 was similar to PW925 except for enlarged rudder trimmers on modified rudders and the installation of a Boulton Paul F nose turret with two ·303 Brownings. The increase in weight did not noticeably affect the stability, which was satisfactory about all axes. The aircraft was pleasant to fly, with elevator control

Avro Lincoln B. Mk. II RF575 constructed by Armstrong Whitworth. (*Armstrong Whitworth Photo.*)

Avro Lincoln Mk. 30(B) A73–8 built in Australia. (*R.A.A.F. Photo.*)

light and responsive, but the rudder and ailerons were slightly heavier and the machine was more sluggish in its movements. On RE232 the aileron trimmer was very ineffective. With flaps and undercarriage raised the stall came at 112 m.p.h. I.A.S. at about 80,000 lb.; with flaps and undercarriage down, and at the same approximate weight the stalling speed was 87 m.p.h. I.A.S. The stall was gentle without any tendency for a wing to drop, and pre-stall buffeting was noticed at about 5 m.p.h. above stalling speed. At 82,000 lb. it was concluded that the aircraft was not generally as responsive to the controls.

No. 57 Squadron became the first to operate the Lincoln, receiving three for Service Trials during August, 1945, before re-equipping with the type in the spring of 1946. By the time that the Lincoln was ready for service the war in the Far East had been over for some months, and the only distinction which eventually attached to the type was that it was the last British-designed heavy bomber with piston engines to enter the R.A.F.

The honour of being the final new light bomber of British design with two

Bristol Brigand B. Mk. 1. (*Bristol Photo.*)

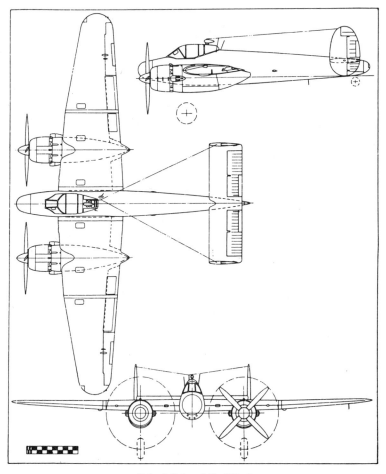

Bristol Brigand B. Mk. 1

345

piston engines to join the R.A.F. fell to the Bristol Brigand B. Mk. 1. The Brigand came into being following proposals made during July, 1942, that it might be possible to evolve a successful derivative of the Buckingham as the Mk. II to house two torpedoes. The pair of Centaurus engines, however, were deemed unable to offer the required performance with such a load at the necessary low operational altitudes, and, instead, it was suggested that a Hercules XVIII variant of the Beaufighter, to be named Buccaneer and to carry a crew of three and one torpedo only, should take its place.

Specification S.7/42 was allotted on 26th August, 1942, to cover the project, the requirement's designation being altered on 15th September, 1942, to H.7/42. For several months, discussions ensued with the object of obtaining adequate performance with the required load and proposed engines until, ultimately, four prototypes were ordered in April, 1943, of the Type 164 Brigand, which was to use the Buckingham's wings, tail unit and pair of 2,400 h.p. Centaurus VII engines matched to a slim fuselage in which three crew members were concentrated towards the nose in a single cabin.

MX988, the first prototype, was taken into the air at Filton for the first time on 4th December, 1944, by Cyril Uwins. Centaurus XVII engines were installed later in the prototypes, but production Brigands finally used two 2,500 h.p. Centaurus 57s. The first eleven Brigands emerged as T.F. Mk. 1s for delivery in 1946 to Nos. 36 and 42 Squadrons, but changes in procurement policy resulted in their modification into light bomber B. Mk. 1s carrying four nose-mounted 20 mm. guns and a 2,000 lb. external bomb load.

No. 84 Squadron, stationed at Habbaniyah in Iraq, introduced the B. Mk. 1 into the R.A.F. in 1949 as its new light bomber, a category which had by then assumed a vastly different meaning when it encompassed a twin-engine aircraft of 72 ft. 4 in. span and with a weight loading of 39,000 lb.

A. & A.E.E. Boscombe Down Report 833/Pt. 24 of 22nd May, 1950, summarized the night flying appraisal made of Brigand B. Mk. 1 VS860 on 16th March, 1950. A pair of Centaurus 57s powered the machine, which was fitted with a modified elevator spring tab and corded ailerons. VS860 needed constant attention to maintain lateral control, but general night-flying

RA356, the first prototype Fairey Spearfish. (*Fairey Photo.*)

346

characteristics were good. Take-off, at about 33,000 lb. weight, was made in starlight without a moon and with some haze on the horizon. The view over the nose for taxying was good, and the machine was easy to manoeuvre on the ground. Night landings were easy, and the lighting of the pilot's cockpit was particularly well liked.

Until it was supplanted by the first of the new generation of jet bombers, the Brigand proved itself to be a very successful design under arduous conditions abroad.

Naval interest in new equipment ultimately to replace the Barracuda became evident with the issue of Specification O.5/43 of 23rd December, 1943, for a two-seat torpedo dive bomber able to undertake also anti-submarine patrols and scouting. Any suitable British engine could be used, and maximum measurements were to be span 60 ft. extended and 20 ft. folded, length 45 ft. 6 in. and height 17 ft.

To comply with O.5/43 H. E. Chaplin devised a new Fairey monoplane, the Spearfish T.B.D. Mk. 1, RA356—the first prototype—making its maiden flight on 5th July, 1945. The Spearfish was one of the handsomest of torpedo bombers, with an imposing appearance and wings of 60 ft. 3 in. span set at mid-depth in the fuselage. The pilot—armed with two ·5 Brownings mounted one in each wing—was seated in an ideal position in line with the leading edge; the observer—responsible also for the operation of the radar equipment—was located a few feet aft under the canopy, from which point he fired the pair of ·5 Brownings housed in a low-set F.N.95 power-driven dorsal barbette immediately to his rear. Outboard of the straight centre-section, dihedral was incorporated in the tapered outer wing panels which accommodated also the retracted main undercarriage legs. Six prominent guides along the wings' trailing edge enabled the Fairey–Youngman high-lift flaps to be lowered, and dive-brakes formed part of both upper and lower wing surfaces. The wings folded to the rear to lie upright along the sides of the fuselage, and a deck arrester hook was embodied in the extreme tail. The Spearfish's capacious bomb-bay extended from the fire-wall to a point mid-way between the wings and the tail and was able to house alternative offensive loads consisting of one 18 in. or one 22·4 in. torpedo, four 500 lb. bombs, one 1,600 lb. bomb or four depth charges. When operating as a dive bomber an ejector installed in the bomb-bay was arranged to swing the bomb clear of the aircraft.

Before the power plant to be employed was settled, several alternative lay-outs were considered, among them a normal twin-engine design, the use of a piston engine in the nose together with a gas turbine at the rear, and conventionally-mounted single Centaurus, Exe or Sabre units. Eventually RA356 received the 2,585 h.p. Centaurus 57 driving a five-blade Rotol constant-speed propeller. The Spearfish's rear fuselage housed a retractable A.S.V.15 radar scanner, and sixteen Mk. VIII zero-length rocket mountings were installed beneath the wings. Further prototypes completed, with 2,800 h.p. Centaurus 58s, were RA360, RA363, RN241 and RN244—RN244 was not, in the event, flown. Forty Spearfish T.B.D.1s were ordered, to be produced by the Fairey factory at Stockport, but—despite the type's ability to fulfil a greater variety of rôles than any previous Fleet Air Arm carrier-borne design—the contract was cancelled.

In designing the Vickers Windsor R. K. Pierson was responsible for evolving the most elegant of the British four-engine heavy bombers to appear prior to the ultimate change to the new generation developed to use the gas turbine for power. Specification B.3/42 of 8th December, 1942, succeeded B.5/41—under which the original design work was conducted—and was issued to cover DW506 and DW512, the first and second Type 447 Windsors respectively, which were to use four 1,560 h.p. Merlin 61s—developed to provide a substantial output at high altitudes—and to be armed with two ·303 Brownings in the nose and two 20 mm. cannon in the tail.

During the early genesis of the first prototype, alterations took place continually in the design. Early in 1943 it was decided that DW506 should be completed with Merlin 65s using underslung radiators and that DW512—redesignated Type 457—should have annular radiators and cowling surrounding Merlin 65s or, alternatively, Griffons if the new type of engine were available in time. Concurrently, the Air Ministry specified remotely controlled armament, and, after further investigation and experiment, the decision was taken to mount the guns at the rear of the outer pair of engine nacelles. While the Windsor was being constructed its radical armament system was being developed in L9704, the second prototype Warwick, which was converted to carry two ·5 Brownings in barbettes at the back of each nacelle with sighting carried out from the position behind the tail.

The proved and reliable system of Vickers geodetic construction was applied to the Windsor which exhibited a deep fuselage of good aerodynamic form. The finely-shaped, pointed, elliptical mainplanes—with an aspect ratio of eleven—were mounted at the mid-wing position, and the elliptical outline was applied also to the tail surfaces but with well-rounded tips. The substantial weight involved in the 117 ft. 2 in. span Windsor brought a revision of undercarriage design technique, the novel expedient being adopted of four separate units—with an outer track of 50 ft.—retracting rearwards into the nacelles. This idea had been resorted to at an early stage in the B.5/41 project in September, 1941.

DW506 was assembled at Farnborough, for Capt. J. Summers to ease it from the runway there for the first time on 23rd October, 1943, but was written off some months later when it was badly damaged during a forced landing at Grove on 2nd March, 1944. DW512, the second Windsor, was equipped with 1,750 h.p. Merlin 85s in annular cowlings and made its first flight from Wisley on 15th February, 1944, piloted by Wg. Cdr. M. Summers.

NK136, the third prototype and the last Windsor to be flown, was completed with modifications, which included stiffening of the rear portion by the use of four longerons in the fuselage—as opposed to the three embodied in the first and second machines—and the use of reinforced fabric covering. When first flown on 11th July, 1944, NK136 was without its barbettes, but these, complete with two 20 mm. cannon—ammunition 600 r.p.g.—were

Vickers Windsor DW506. (*Vickers Photo.*)

installed later by the spring of 1945, to give a rectangular termination to the outer nacelles. NK136 was powered by annular-cowled Merlin 85s and was used in trials with its unusual armament until early in 1946, when the entire project was abandoned on 15th March, together with an incomplete fourth example—NN670—which had been commenced as a Type 471 but had been revised as a long-range—4,000 miles—Type 483.

The cancelled incomplete fifth, sixth and seventh Windsors were scheduled to be respectively NN673, MP829 and MP832; NN673, to use four 3,020 s.h.p. Rolls-Royce R.B.39 Clyde turboprop engines with which a maximum speed of 409 m.p.h. at 28,000 ft. was anticipated, was designated Type 601 Windsor B. Mk. 2. 1,850 h.p. Merlin 100s were the power plants intended for the Type 483 production Windsor B. Mk. 1s, three hundred of which were to be ordered to re-equip R.A.F. heavy bomber squadrons, and which would have attained a maximum speed of 360 m.p.h. at 21,000 ft. and would have carried a bomb load of 12,000 lb. Alternative engines for the production Windsors would have been the Griffon and the Clyde.

The Windsor's claim to distinction in heavy bomber evolution is that it was the ultimate expression of British concepts of piston-engine design in its class and, as such, was a worthy example with which to conclude an inspiring era of some three decades before the revolution instigated by the gas turbine.

Specification S.6/43 was drawn up to produce a new torpedo-bomber reconnaissance aircraft for the Fleet Air Arm. Projects were prepared by John Lloyd at Armstrong Whitworth for the A.W.53, by Arthur Davenport and J. F. W. Digby for Westland and by C. P. T. Lipscomb for Short Brothers.

S.6/43 was subsequently cancelled, and Lipscomb revised the Short design as the S.A.1 to meet a fresh requirement, Specification S.11/43 for a carrier-borne reconnaissance bomber with emphasis on ability to carry out long-range operations in the Far East. Two prototypes of the S.A.1—RK787 and RK791—were ordered late in 1943, but no contracts were placed for designs tendered to S.11/43 by Armstrong Whitworth for the A.W.54 and by Supermarine. As the Sturgeon P.R. Mk. I—with G. A. V. Tyson at the controls—RK787 made its maiden flight during June, 1946, as the first British twin-engine aircraft to be designed specifically from the outset for Fleet Air Arm operational duties, the first Short design for naval use since the Gurnard of 1929, the first Short service landplane since the advent of the Stirling in 1939 and the first British twin-engine aeroplane fitted with contra-rotating propellers.

The Sturgeon was a very clean, three-seat, mid-wing monoplane with power-folding wings and equipped with a pair of powerful 2,080 h.p. Merlin 140S engines, each driving a pair of three-blade, contra-rotating, Rotol co-axial propellers, with which it was capable of the excellent maximum speed of 430 m.p.h. at 19,000 ft. on combat power with +25 lb. boost. Its top cruising speed was 361 m.p.h. at 22,000 ft., and the S.A.1 possessed a climb rate of 4,120 ft./min. at sea level using +25 lb. boost. For naval strike duties the Sturgeon was able to carry a bomb load of 1,000 lb. or depth charges in the slim fuselage internally and was equipped with a pair of nose-mounted ·5 Browning guns and eight 60 lb. rocket-projectiles carried four under each wing. For long-range reconnaissance missions three vertical cameras were installed in tandem aft of the bomb-bay and a 170 gall. auxiliary fuel tank could be housed in the same location. Radar search equipment was borne in the nose.

Although it possessed excellent attributes, events conspired to nullify the requirement for a design such as the Sturgeon, and the type was eventually relegated to target-towing duties to Specification Q.1/46 as the S.A.2 T.T. Mk. 2 and the S.B.9 T.T. Mk. 3.

To some extent the Sturgeon possessed one feature in common with the projected Fairey two-seat, torpedo spotter reconnaissance monoplane—designed by H. E. Chaplin to Specification O.21/44—in the use of two Merlins to drive contra-rotating propellers. In the case of the Fairey machine, however, the concept was rather different, as the design was a revision of the single-engine Spearfish and was evolved around the use of the pair of Merlins installed in tandem in the nose, each to drive independently a three-blade propeller mounted on co-axial shafts. The principle was an extension of previous Fairey experimental work which involved the installation in Battle K9370 of the 2,240 h.p. Fairey P.24 Prince engine—consisting of two banks each of twelve cylinders—to drive independently a pair of three-blade, co-axial, contra-rotating propellers; K9370 made a successful initial flight on 30th July, 1939. Cooling of the Merlins was to be effected by the twin radiators, which were embodied one on each side in the centre-section and which incorporated wide horizontal slot intakes projecting well ahead of the leading edge.

The O.21/44 project was abandoned in the light of the great new possibilities in performance offered by the gas turbine units under development, but the basic principle of the drive to the propellers was shortly to be revived again by Fairey for successful application in a new—and original—design.

Another requirement which came to naught at the end of the piston-engine era for Service aircraft was that of Specification S.10/45, which was to cover a single-seat, strike reconnaissance bomber development for the Fleet Air Arm of the single-engine Blackburn B.48 YA.1 Firecrest.

The 1914–18 War witnessed, especially in its final stages, the realization by intelligent and unbigoted members of military and naval staffs of the eventual value of the bomber and the torpedo-bomber as weapons of incontestable force and of ever-growing value in the successful conduct of hostilities. By

RF355, an Avro Lincoln B. Mk. II. (*Avro Photo.*)

the time that the 1939–45 War had erupted in Europe the bomber had been developed in the interim as a terrifying weapon of great destructive power with numerous different applications, many of which had already been exploited in minor conflicts during the 1920s and the 1930s.

The exigencies of the 1939–45 War, and the comparatively long—and ever-lengthening—gestation period of new, advanced designs, resulted in relatively few entirely fresh British types of bomber entering squadron service between September, 1939, and August, 1945. In the main, British bomber equipment consisted of basic designs which originated shortly before the war and which, once in production, were redesigned and modified to improve their performance by many degrees. Brilliant—and outstandingly successful—exceptions to this enforced practice were the Mosquito and the Lancaster; even the Lancaster, however, came into being as an outcome of the tribulations which beset the Manchester.

The 1939–45 War saw the establishment of bombing irrefutably as the greatest single factor in modern warfare—particularly with the advent of the nuclear bomb—and witnessed at the same time the demise of the piston engine as the power plant of the bomber, a position which it had occupied un-challenged for thirty years since the bomber was born.

1717, the second of eight Avro Shackleton M.R. Mk. 3s for the S.A.A.F. (*Avro Photo.*)

CHAPTER EIGHT

METAMORPHOSIS

Despite the naïve, false and totally unrealistic assumption made during the autumn of 1945 that an extended period of peace had returned to the world, the universal impression which the performance of the bomber had made on combatants and non-combatants alike and the incontrovertible fact that it was now the primary offensive weapon in every nation's arsenal engendered its continued progressive evolution in Great Britain.

Immediately the cease-fire had been proclaimed at the conclusion of the 1939–45 War events in the United Kingdom followed the same dreary and patently dangerous path as that taken after the 1914–18 War. The ostensibly peace-seeking nations banded together to form a new organization with the same unworkable ideals as those of the earlier defunct League of Nations, with a simple change of title to that of the United Nations—soon revealed as far from 'united'. At the same time, for no apparent reason and in absolute contradiction of her fundamental social and economic structure, Great Britain allowed her immediate destiny to pass into socialist hands with, to her shame, the attendant cry of disarmament being raised without delay by a proportion of politicians supposedly responsible enough to be entrusted with the well-being of a once proud and independent nation. Thus, in the face of the knowledge of the appalling suffering undergone by the 499,242 members of the armed forces, civilian population and Merchant Navy personnel who gave their lives from 1939 until 1945 and of the many hundreds of thousands who were injured during the same period, was shown the gratitude of those who lived to enjoy the return of peace by embarking upon a policy of weakness and humility—completely foreign to the inborn nature of the vast majority of the British populace—which could only result ultimately in a repetition of the two previous holocausts of the blighted twentieth century. In common with the Army and the Royal Navy, the Royal Air Force suffered the fate of wholesale and ill-advised decimation from the end of the war.

Paradoxically, in an era of widespread disarmament, the development of British bomber aircraft entered a new, dramatic phase which was to bring about the greatest basic changes so far in each design category. Although, in the first instance, the R.A.F.'s acceptance and adoption of the gas turbine had been applied to fighter aircraft, no doubts were entertained about its concurrent application to the bomber, especially once means had been devised to reduce its initially heavy consumption of fuel. To combat the new fighters being developed with vastly increased speeds, compared with those possessed by the final piston-engine generation, the latest advances in bomber design would have to endow the new machines with a matchingly increased performance.

Bristol interest in the jet-engine bomber manifested itself during October, 1946, when the firm submitted a layout to the Air Ministry for the Type 172 long-range, high-speed, four-engine monoplane—designed by A. E. Russell— with wings of 110 ft. span and incorporating 45° sweepback. Sufficient interest was aroused for further design work to be initiated to Specification E.8/47 in 1947 on the Type 174 half-scale, single-seat, flying model of the Type 172 to be powered by one Rolls-Royce Nene centrifugal-flow jet engine. Late in 1947 the design was revised in the light of experiments carried out on the proposed Type 174 layout and was redesignated Type 176 in line with the requirement modified as Specification E.8/47 Issue 2. The 1948 Type 176 three-tenths-scale version of the Type 172 was to use a single Rolls-Royce Avon as its power plant, but, subsequently, towards the end of 1948 the entire Bristol bomber project was abandoned.

A still-born Hawker project of 1946 was the P.1051, which Sydney Camm prepared to undertake the rôle of a fleet bomber carrying a large missile.

The insular nature of Great Britain has made essential the provision of successive long-range maritime reconnaissance aircraft, and plans were discussed during 1946 to produce a new machine by adapting the Avro Lincoln to the requirement as the Mk. III. Eventually, a new design was evolved by Roy Chadwick to Specification R.5/46 of 17th March, 1947, as the 696 Shackleton M.R. Mk. 1 to use four Griffon 57 engines and to possess a service ceiling of 20,000 ft. and a range of 2,600 n.m. at 5,000 ft. with a 4,000 lb. bomb load. The Lincoln's wings and undercarriage were matched to a new fuselage of reduced length but increased cross-section, and the power plants consisted of four 2,450 h.p. Griffons—two 57s and two 57As—driving three-blade, contra-rotating propellers. The crew numbered ten and the G.R. Mk. 1—as the prototype M.R. Mk. 1 was known—was armed with two 20 mm. Hispano cannon mounted abreast one on each side at the nose, two of the same guns in the dorsal Bristol B.17 turret and with a pair of ·5 Brownings in the tail.

The first prototype M.R. Mk. 1 VW126 made its initial flight from Woodford on 9th March, 1949, piloted by J. H. Orrell, and was followed by VW131 and VW135 as the second and third prototypes. Production was to Specification R.42/46, and No. 120 Squadron became the first to operate the Shackleton in February, 1951. The fitting of four Griffon 57As in the second production batch resulted in a change in designation to M.R. Mk. 1A. The Shackleton's offensive load of bombs and depth charges was carried in a voluminous bay which extended from beneath the cockpit aft to a point mid-way along the fuselage.

Specification R.5/46 Issue 2 of 3rd July, 1950, covered the Shackleton M.R. Mk. 2, a revision of the M.R. Mk. 1 with a longer, less bluff nose and a pointed, transparent tailcone, alterations which contributed a great deal to improving the general appearance of the machine. The radar was removed from its previous position in an unsightly fixed bulge beneath the nose to a new location in a ventral housing which could be retracted almost completely and gave 360° rotation. Four Griffon 57As provided the power, and the formerly fixed tailwheel was replaced by twin wheels which retracted. VW126 was utilized to prove the various modifications evolved for the M.R. Mk. 2, and an M.R. Mk. 1A—WB833—flew initially on 17th June, 1952, as the prototype M.R. Mk. 2, the new model's maximum speed being 272 m.p.h. at 10,000 ft. In its early service form the M.R. Mk. 2 carried a pair of 20 mm. Hispano cannon in the nose, accompanied by twin ·5 Brownings in the dorsal turret. The M.R. Mk. 2 went into service towards the close of 1952, and in 1955 the dorsal gun position was deleted. The installation of improved radar and other electronic equipment in serving M.R. Mk. 2s from 1961 brought redesignation as M.R. Mk. 2Cs.

Issue 3 of Specification R.5/46 was dated 18th November, 1953, and was drawn up to deal with the Shackleton M.R. Mk. 3. In this model the Griffon 57As were retained, but the tailwheel style of undercarriage was replaced

Avro Shackleton M.R. Mk. 1 VP256. (*Avro Photo.*)

Production Avro Shackleton M.R. Mk. 2 WL791. (*Avro Photo.*)

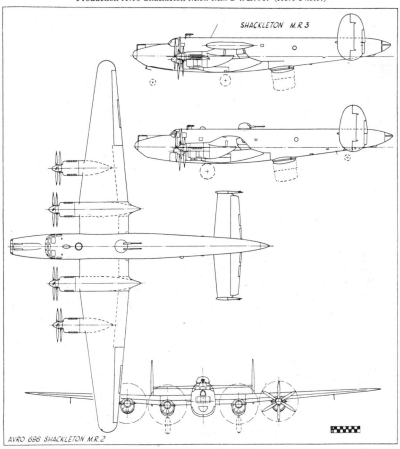

Avro Shackleton M.R. Mk. 2

355

Avro Shackleton M.R. Mk. 2 prototype VW126, an adaptation of the prototype M.R. Mk. 1.
(*Avro Photo.*)

Installation of Viper jet engine in each outer nacelle of the Avro Shackleton M.R. Mk. 3.
(*Avro Photo.*)

by a new style incorporating twin nosewheels. A pair of wheels also supplanted the single wheel previously fitted to each main undercarriage unit. Defensive armament was reduced to consist of a pair of 20 mm. Hispano cannon in the nose, vision for the two pilots was improved by removing most of the framework supporting the cockpit canopy, range was increased still further by installing an auxiliary tank at each wingtip, new outer wing panels were fitted and the comfort of the crew of ten on long patrols was catered for by the provision of a sound-proofed wardroom. WR970, the prototype 716 Shackleton M.R. Mk. 3, took-off for the first time on 2nd September, 1955, and No. 220 Squadron received the initial production M.R. Mk. 3s towards the close of 1957. The machine was able to carry a varied assortment of offensive weapons, including bombs, depth charges, torpedoes and sonobuoys, and take-off performance of the M.R. Mk. 3 was improved later by the installation in each outer Griffon's nacelle of a 2,500 lb.s.t. Bristol Siddeley Viper jet engine. At a loaded weight of 85,000 lb. the M.R. Mk. 3 was able to attain a maximum speed of 302 m.p.h. at 12,000 ft.

In addition to being employed by the R.A.F., the Shackleton M.R. Mk. 3 was used by the South African Air Force, eight being supplied.

A later development, the Shackleton M.R. Mk. 4, would have been powered

356

by four Napier Nomad E.145 compound gas turbine/diesel engines, but was abandoned before being built.

Anti-submarine patrol was also the duty to be performed by the aircraft required by Specification G.R.17/45, which was issued to produce a new carrier-borne ASW type. Both Blackburn and Fairey constructed prototypes, the Fairey machine ultimately being selected for the Fleet Air Arm.

G. E. Petty was responsible for the design of the Blackburn prototypes, three of which were built. The plan originally was to power the machine, the Y.A.5, with a coupled Napier Naiad N.Na.C.1 turboprop unit, but discontinuation of the development of this power plant compelled the adoption of an alternative, and the Armstrong Siddeley Double Mamba A.S.M.D.1, developing a total of 2,950 e.h.p., was selected. In this form the design became the Y.B.1. However, before WB797, the sole Y.B.1 prototype, was completed, two other prototypes—the Y.A.7 WB781 and the Y.A.8 WB788—were constructed and flown.

The three machines featured a very deep fuselage with low-set, dihedralled wings embodying sharp anhedral at the roots. The Y.A.7 and Y.A.8 each utilized a 2,000 h.p. Griffon 56 engine driving three-blade, contra-rotating propellers and were constructed to provide flight experience with the basic Y.B.1 airframe. The undercarriage was of the tricycle type, and the search radar—with 360° scan—contained in a retractable housing, was situated in the rear fuselage aft of the lengthy bomb-bay. The wings' leading edge of WB781 was straight, but in both WB788 and WB797 it was swept back on the outer panels. Another fundamental difference between the earlier Y.A.7 and the

Two-seat Blackburn Y.A.7 WB781. (*Blackburn Photo.*)

357

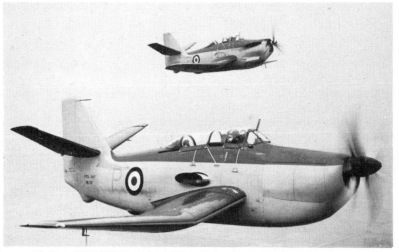

Blackburn Y.B.1 WB797 accompanied by Blackburn Y.A.8 WB788 flying to the rear.
(*Blackburn Photo.*)

Y.A.8 and Y.B.1 was that the two later versions had larger vertical tail surfaces than WB781. In each prototype the tailplane was set at a fairly acute dihedral angle. Power-folding was applied to the wings, which incorporated double folding in the system.

The two-seat Y.A.7 made its first flight from Brough during September, 1949, to be followed later by the three-seat Y.A.8 and eventually by the three-seat Y.B.1 on 19th July, 1950, when Peter Lawrence took WB797 into the air from Brough for the first time. The efflux from the Double Mambas was dispersed through jet pipes on the fuselage's flanks, the turboprop installation raising the maximum speed of the Y.B.1 to 320 m.p.h. compared with the 251 m.p.h. attained with the Griffon power of the Y.A.7 and Y.A.8. On 30th October, 1950, just over three months after its maiden flight, the Y.B.1 was landed on H.M.S. *Illustrious*. The great advantage attached to the Double Mamba power plant was that either engine could be closed down and the propeller feathered for extended economic cruising.

The same basic approach to G.R.17/45 as that displayed by Blackburn was adopted by H. E. Chaplin in designing the Fairey aspirant, known originally as the Type Q. An earlier Fairey proposal for an anti-submarine turboprop aircraft to Specification N.16/45 was not accepted, but, following the firm's tender to G.R.17/45, a prototype contract was received on 12th August, 1946.

A little over three years later—on 19th September, 1949—the two-seat Fairey 17 first prototype VR546 made its maiden flight from Aldermaston piloted by Gp. Capt. R. G. Slade. Both VR546 and the second two-seat prototype G.R.17/45 VR557 were equipped with the 2,950 e.h.p. Double Mamba 100 A.S.M.D.1, contrived, by mounting a pair of Mamba A.S.Ma.3s abreast, to drive—through a common gearbox—independent four-blade, contra-rotating, co-axial Rotol propellers. The Fairey company had thus

The prototype Fairey 17 VR546. (*Fairey Photo.*)

VR546, the prototype Fairey 17, modified with auxiliary fins and dummy third cockpit.

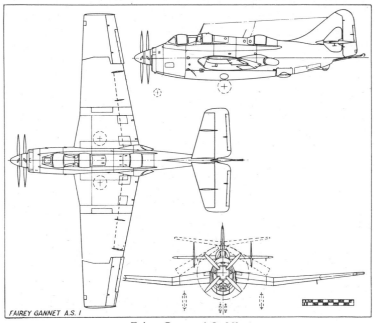

Fairey Gannet A.S. Mk. 1

WE488, the third prototype Fairey Gannet, flying on one section of its Double Mamba power plant. (*Fairey Photo.*)

again applied—and very successfully as it transpired—the experience gained some seven years before under Capt. A. G. Forsyth with the Battle P.24 engine test-bed using the same basic principles of power plant. VR557 took to the air initially on 6th July, 1950.

During the period which passed in development of the design, Admiralty policy and, consequently, requirements in anti-submarine technique underwent alterations, so that, ultimately, in June, 1949, a third prototype Fairey G.R.17/45—WE488—was ordered as a three-seater. During March, 1951, VR546 was seen to be fitted with a dummy, aerodynamic form of third cockpit installed amidships to test the layout and, concurrently, had its radar scanner moved to a new position towards the tail. Trials had indicated that an increase in fin area was advisable, so that, by June, 1951, VR546 was equipped with auxiliary fins above and below its tailplane; at the same time the previous thick deck arrester hook strut had been replaced by a far slimmer shaft. A few months later, in December, 1951, VR546's bomb-bay was extended in length. On 19th June, 1950, VR546 made its first landing at sea when it alighted on H.M.S. *Illustrious*, at the same time becoming the first turboprop aircraft to land on a carrier. WE488 was completed to make its maiden flight

XA411, the last Fairey Gannet A.S. Mk. 1, demonstrating the folding of its wings. (*Peter Lewis Photo.*)

360

on 10th May, 1951, and was fitted with the glazed version of the mock-up rear cockpit tried out on VR546. Indecision while WE488 was being built about which way the radar operator would face resulted in two seats being installed in the third prototype's rearmost cockpit.

The Fairey G.R.17/45 was ordered for the Fleet Air Arm as the Gannet A.S. Mk. 1 on 14th March, 1951, the production machines being equipped with a smaller canopy over the rearmost cockpit, in which only the radar operator was carried finally. The use of the Double Mamba employing kerosine as its fuel suited the Admiralty, particularly as it obviated the storage of large quantities of petrol aboard the parent carrier, a position which it wished to avoid if at all possible. Despite its necessarily very portly appearance, the Gannet was quite an attractive aircraft with rather pleasanter and more harmonious lines than those of the Blackburn Y.B.1. Double folding of the mid-set, 54 ft. 4 in. span wings reduced the overall width to 13 ft. 9 in., and the pilot, seated over the pair of engines in the nose, was endowed with a splendid, commanding view for take-off and landing and for attack, a rôle which the Gannet combined with its search duties. The tapered wings incorporated gentle anhedral in the centre-section into which the main wheels retracted. The extensive weapons-bay was able to house bombs, depth charges, mines or two homing torpedoes, and other weapons could be carried under the wings, including sixteen 60 lb. rocket projectiles. The Gannet's fuselage was built on the special Fairey system of envelope jigging, and the design of the machine was based largely on the assumption that most of its time airborne would be spent on the power of only one of its pair of Mambas.

No. 826 Squadron on 17th January, 1955, became the first of several operational squadrons to be equipped with the Gannet. The A.S. Mk. 1 was succeeded by the A.S. Mk. 4, the first of which—XA412—made its first flight on 13th April, 1956. In the A.S. Mk. 4 the Double Mamba 100 was replaced by the 3,035 e.h.p. Double Mamba 101 A.S.M.D.3, and other modifications were made also. The A.S. Mk. 4 version was able to accommodate alternatively two 1,000 lb. bombs, four 500 lb. bombs, two mines or two torpedoes and twenty-four 3 in. or sixteen 5 in. rocket projectiles. The designations A.S. Mk. 6 and A.S. Mk. 7 were applied to Gannets carrying revised electronic equipment.

Later in the period during which the Blackburn and Fairey G.R.17/45 prototypes were developed, C. P. T. Lipscomb evolved the Short S.B.3 from the Sturgeon as a three-seat, anti-submarine monoplane to the M.6/49 requirement. A single prototype only—WF632—was constructed, making its first flight on 12th August, 1950. The S.B.3 retained its predecessor's general mid-wing layout, but the front portion of the fuselage underwent considerable revision, becoming far deeper by virtue of the installation of a large radar scanner beneath the nose. The radar operator was able to work close to his equipment and was also provided with windows in his cabin. Folding of the outer wing panels was carried out hydraulically. The S.B.3's bomb-bay was capable of accommodating up to four depth charges, and provision was made beneath the wings for other offensive loads. A pair of

Short S.B.3 WF632. (*Short Photo.*)

1,745 s.h.p. Mamba A.S.Ma.3s, driving four-blade propellers, were used to power WF632, an endurance of over three hours being attainable by cruising at low speeds. Attendant asymmetric problems precluded the closing down of one of the two engines of the S.B.3 to prolong cruising endurance, a practice which proved perfectly feasible with the Blackburn and Fairey G.R.17/45 designs. Ultimately, further development of the Short S.B.3 came to a halt.

On 14th May, 1948, the United Nations Organization passed a resolution proclaiming the setting up of a new State—that of Israel. Immediately, Israel's hostile neighbours attacked, but, foreseeing this almost inevitable reaction towards the birth of the new country, the Israelis were prepared to meet the threat and were able to give a good account of themselves in battle. Under the title Sherut Avir—later to become the Chel Ha'avir in March, 1948—the sensible step of forming an air force had been taken. At the start improvisation was forced upon the Israeli commanders until the force could become fully organized and its equipment rationalized. Aircraft of many different types and nationalities were bought to serve in various categories, including—among the British machines to serve as bombers—Mosquitoes as well as adaptations of the British Taylorcraft Auster A.O.P. Mk. IV, the Canadian-built D.H.82C Tiger Moth with coupé top, and the D.H.89A Dragon Rapide. The heterogeneous collection of aircraft which constituted the early Israeli Air Force appeared as an anomaly compared with the modern air arms of other nations, but, none the less, proved their worth and held the Arab forces at bay until, in 1951, the Israel Defence Force/Air Force took the place of the Chel Ha'avir and proceeded to build itself up into the best trained and most effective and efficient of the air arms in the Middle East.

During 1944, after nine years as technical director of Westland, W. E. W. Petter relinquished his position and travelled North to join English Electric at Preston as chief designer. By this time the gas turbine was accepted as the type of engine ultimately to power all high-performance military aircraft, and Petter had prepared a scheme for a fast twin-engine jet bomber in which the two power plants were to be installed superimposed inside the fuselage and to receive air through a single ventral orifice.

362

The concept underlying the design constituted a continuation of the principles embodied in the highly successful Mosquito—those of a high-speed, two-seat, medium bomber without defensive armament and relying on its superior performance to enable it to avoid hostile fighter interception. The primary difference between the proposed new design and its distinguished and spirited forebear lay in the style of power plant employed. As soon as what was to be known as the jet engine had appeared in its initial and necessarily primitive form and had established itself as a practical form of new prime mover, its vast—and seemingly unlimited—power potential engendered intensive development. The new engine's qualities were applied at first to enhancing the performance of fighter aircraft, particularly in view of its relatively heavy fuel consumption and consequent restricted range in its early life. As its evolution proceeded, however, with particular emphasis on improved fuel economy and the introduction of the axial-flow type in addition to the centrifugal-flow engine, it became possible to consider its use seriously as the power plant for the next generation of bombers. Apart from the greatly increased power available and the deletion of the propeller, the shape and size of the unit itself brought to the aircraft designer hitherto unknown opportunities for the evolution of airframes exhibiting an immeasurably greater attainment of aerodynamic perfection.

D.H.89A Rapide used as a bomber in Israel. (*I.D.F./A.F. Photo.*)

Auster A.O.P. Mk. IV adapted for light bombing by Zionist forces. (*I.D.F./A.F. Photo.*)

363

VN799, the prototype English Electric Canberra B. Mk. 1. (*English Electric Photo.*)

Although destined for the honour of conceiving and producing the first British jet bomber, English Electric's experience of aircraft production—until shortly before the 1939–45 War—had been rather sporadic, a more or less complete break with aeroplane design practice having taken place since the middle 1920s. The firm's re-entry into the production field came in 1938, with contracts being placed for constructing Hampdens, to be followed by Halifaxes and, eventually, a switch to fighters with Vampires post-War. Despite a lapse of two decades in basic aircraft design work, English Electric proceeded with the intention of evolving the jet bomber and ultimately succeeded, through Petter's technical brilliance, in creating the machine.

Before the design of the EE.A1 was finalized, several alternative layouts were considered, Petter's original ideas—conceived while he was still with Westland—being revised drastically. A new design team had, perforce, to be created and integrated at Preston, and by the summer of 1945 a mid-wing monoplane using a single engine of high power had been evolved, to be rejected in favour of twin engines of smaller size installed in the roots of the wings. The removal of the power installation from the fuselage proper offered a number of useful advantages, particularly in freeing for other purposes the area which would have been occupied by the engine.

As work progressed the design was evolved to conform to Specification B.3/45 for a high-speed, light, tactical bomber incorporating aiming by radar, and it was decided to base it on a pair of the new, powerful Rolls-Royce Avon engines. Petter reversed the general trend towards swept wings and increasingly higher wing loadings by selecting a wing planform consisting of a rectangular, broad-chord centre-section of moderate thickness/chord ratio of 12%, to which, outboard of the semi-buried engines, were attached the tapered

English Electric Canberra B. Mk. 6. (*English Electric Photo.*)

English Electric Canberra B. (I). Mk. 6. (*English Electric Photo.*)

English Electric Canberra B.(I). Mk. 12 of the R.N.Z.A.F. (*R.N.Z.A.F. Photo.*)

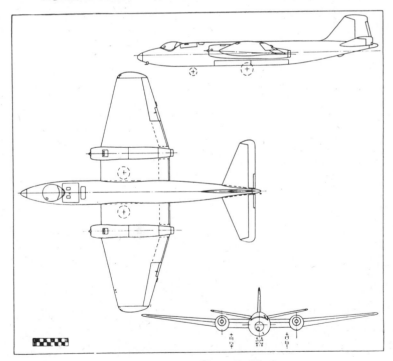

English Electric Canberra B. Mk. 2

365

outer wing panels which decreased in thickness/chord ratio to 9% at the tips. The aspect ratio of the resulting wings was 4·3, a low figure which—coupled with a wing loading of about 40–42 lb./sq. ft.—bestowed on the A1 a high operational altitude, good fuel economy, superb powers of manoeuvre—especially at great heights—and excellent low-speed characteristics. By the autumn of 1945 the design of the A1 was sufficiently advanced for it to be submitted for official consideration, with the result that four prototypes were ordered a few months later on 7th January, 1946.

Just over three years passed before VN799, the all-blue first prototype A1, was ready for Wg. Cdr. R. P. Beamont to take into the air from Warton for its maiden flight on 13th May, 1949. In its first form VN799 was fitted with a rudder with a rounded top, which was subsequently modified to an almost imperceptible gentle curve. The pilot—to port—and the navigator were seated abreast in ejector seats under a wide, clear-view canopy in the nose of the sleek fuselage. As the use of a radar bomb-sight was envisaged, the nose was entirely opaque and without any transparent aiming panel.

A pair of 6,000 lb.s.t. Avon R.A.2s powered VN799, but VN813, which Beamont flew as the second prototype initially on 9th November, 1949, was equipped with centrifugal 5,000 lb.s.t. Rolls-Royce Nene R.Ne.2s as an insurance against possible development delays with the newer axial Avon. Both VN799 and VN813 were fitted with a shallow dorsal fin extension, a surface which was removed later from VN828 and VN850, the third and fourth EE.A1 prototypes, which flew respectively on 22nd November and 20th December, 1949, both using Avons. The compact and remarkably agile EE.A1 was an unqualified success from the start, and its evolution was found to have proceeded well ahead of that of its intended radar bomb-sight.

The type was named Canberra, and the four prototypes were designated B. Mk. 1; it was decided to issue Specification B.5/47 to cover the production B. Mk. 2 using visual bombing. Two prototypes were ordered, the first B. Mk. 2—VX165—making its initial flight on 23rd April, 1950, powered by a pair of 6,500 lb.s.t. Avon 101 R.A.3 engines. A third member was added to the crew to undertake bomb-aiming from the transparent nose station. When not in the nose the bomb-aimer was seated alongside the navigator, who had been moved to the rear of the pilot. On 25th May, 1951, No. 101 Squadron received its first B. Mk. 2, becoming the initial jet bomber squadron in the Royal Air Force.

English Electric Canberra B. Mk. 20 A84–241 of the R.A.A.F. (*R.A.A.F. Photo.*)

Specification B.5/47 of 12th November, 1947, called for a tactical day bomber version of the B. Mk. 1 to B.3/45 and stipulated ability to operate in any part of the world. No armament was to be fitted, and the machine was to rely for its defence on high speed and manoeuvrability. The crew of three—pilot, navigator and bomb-aimer—were to have ejector seats. Maximum speed was to be at least 440 kt. at 20,000 ft., with minimum cruising speed 390 kt. at the same altitude. With a 7,500 lb. bomb load the range was to be 1,000 n.m. at 20,000 ft., operating height demanded was from 15,000 to 20,000 ft. and service ceiling a minimum of 40,000 ft.

Specification B.22/48 of 28th March, 1949, was drawn up to cover a visual target marker version of the B. Mk. 2, and one prototype—VX185—was built to meet it as the B. Mk. 5 using 7,500 lb.s.t. Avon 109 R.A.7 engines and embodying integral wing fuel tanks. WJ754, the first production example which flew on 26th January, 1954, served as the prototype for the B. Mk. 6, which supplanted the B. Mk. 2 as the R.A.F. bomber version of the Canberra. The B. Mk. 6 was fitted with 7,500 lb.s.t. Avon 109s and integral wing tanks; No. 101 Squadron in 1954 became the first to use the new B. Mk. 6 variant.

Further development of the basic B. Mk. 6 resulted in the B. Mk. 15 and the B. Mk. 16, both of which entered R.A.F. service. As the B. Mk. 20, the Canberra was built in Australia by the Government Aircraft Factory for the Royal Australian Air Force, and production was undertaken also in the U.S.A. by Glenn L. Martin at Baltimore, Maryland, as the B-57A, fitted with a pair of Wright J65-W-1 licence-built Armstrong Siddeley Sapphires. WD932, a Canberra B. Mk. 2, was flown nonstop across the Atlantic, without refuelling to Baltimore on 21st February, 1951, to act as a pattern aircraft for the American version. With its normal bomb load of 6,000 lb. and a maximum speed of 570 m.p.h. at 40,000 ft., the Canberra set a new standard in its particular category and accomplished many record-breaking flights. The concepts which gave birth to Petter's design philosophy were completely vindicated, and the Canberra was significant as yet another outstandingly successful product of British aeronautical design and engineering. Adaptations of the basic design followed to suit the machine for several other useful rôles, to all of which it brought its superlative qualities.

With its fine new twin-jet bomber entering service, the R.A.F. was able to look forward with anticipation to a transformation taking place shortly afterwards in its heavy bomber squadrons.

Second prototype Short Sperrin VX161. (*Short Photo.*)

CHAPTER NINE

FINAL FLING

Bomber Command had emerged from the 1939–45 War as Great Britain's primary force of offence and retaliation, and acceptance was forthcoming of the fact that, were this all-important branch of the Royal Air Force to continue to exist, its long-range means of delivery would, of necessity, sooner or later have to be brought up to date. The piston-engine Lincoln would swiftly become an anachronism, as would eventually the Boeing Washingtons, which were to enter service with Bomber Command pending the development of new advanced bombers possessing tremendous powers of destruction.

An intriguing but temporary divergence from the main course of British bomber evolution came during 1951, when Bristol submitted a proposal for a pilotless expendable bomber to Specification UB.109. Launching by catapult was intended, and the weapon—with its 5,000 lb. load of explosive—was to be directed to its target by radio control at 600 m.p.h. for a distance of 400 miles before diving earthwards. The project was prepared under Dr. A. E. Russell as the Type 182 around the power of a single Bristol BE.17 turbojet, the engine being suspended beneath the tail. The sweptback tapered wings were installed above the fuselage on a fairing in line with the tailplane mounted on top of the fin. Before proceeding with the Type 182 Red Rapier, construction was instituted of two recoverable Type 182Rs—each using an Armstrong Siddeley Viper engine—to embody variable incidence in the wings and a retractable tricycle undercarriage. After two years of work on the project and the completion of the first Type 182R, the entire scheme was abandoned.

During the same period as that of the Type 182, Bristol prepared another bomber project, the Type 186 of 1952 to Specification B.126T for a machine capable of operating specifically at low altitudes. This, too, was cancelled before construction.

The challenging requirements to be embodied in the successor to the Lincoln were expressed in Specification B.14/46 of 6th October, 1948, which stated the demand for a medium-range bomber to carry a crew of five on the power of four Avon R.A.3 engines and to be able to transport a single 10,000 lb. bomb to a target 1,500 n.m. from a base anywhere in the world. When carrying a special bomb the resulting aircraft had to be able to achieve its full range of 3,500 n.m.; the ability to bomb at all heights up to 45,000 ft. was stipulated. No orthodox armament was required, and instrumentation was to be reduced to a minimum. The crew, housed in a single pressure cabin of as small a size as possible, were to be equipped with seat-type parachutes in each case. Provision was to be made for the launching of Window, anti-radar foil strips, through chutes outside the cabin. Should the nose-wheel collapse, easy replacement of the nose section was required. The aircraft had to be able to attack for great distances inside enemy territory and, as its course would be plotted by radar and other methods over a long range, it had to be able to avoid destruction. To attain this object the machine should be able to fly at such a speed—combined with good manoeuvrability at a high cruising altitude of 40,000 ft.—that enemy fighters would be unable to manoeuvre sufficiently. Adequate warning devices were to be incorporated, together with both visual and electronic bombing facilities. Maximum performance was not to be sacrificed unduly for ease of maintenance. The design's weight was to be kept as low as possible, with an all-up weight not to exceed 140,000 lb. or, if attainable, 120,000 lb. Suitability for large-scale war production was to be borne in mind. A cruising speed of 435 kt. was demanded, together with an approach speed not exceeding 120 kt. and the ability to operate in all kinds of weather. A ceiling of 45,000 ft. was required after flying 1,500 miles from take-off, and the machine had to be capable of maintaining an altitude of 35,000 ft. with one engine out of action and 30,000 ft. on two engines only. Defence against interception was to be based mainly on speed, height and evasive action, together with radar counter-measures to deflect the beam of controlled weapons and equipment to explode prematurely weapons fitted with proximity fuses. A total bomb load of 20,000 lb. was specified to include the new range of H.E. bombs.

Under C. P. T. Lipscomb and David Keith-Lucas of Short Brothers and Harland, the Short S.A.4 was designed to comply with the provisions of B.14/46, and two prototypes—VX158 and VX161—were completed and flown; a third airframe was completed for structural testing. T. W. Brooke-Smith took VX158, the first prototype, for its initial flight on 10th August, 1951, from Aldergrove under the power of four 6,000 lb.s.t. Avon R.A.2s; VX161, with four 6,500 lb.s.t. Avon R.A.3s, made its first flight from the same venue just over a year later on 12th August, 1952. Subsequently, the name Sperrin was adopted for the S.A.4.

Basically, the S.A.4 consisted of a shoulder-wing monoplane with sharp taper on the leading edge of the wings combined with gentle taper on the trailing edge. The deep fuselage was of constant depth for most of its length. The wings were given only 1° dihedral, but the tailplane was canted upwards at a fairly sharp angle of 13°. The Sperrin was a conventional design apart from the unusual expedient adopted in the arrangement of its engines, which were mounted on the wings, with each pair of Avons superimposed in centrally-installed nacelles set at an angle of upthrust, the long jet pipes passing above and below the mainplanes. A pressurized tunnel for the bomb-aimer sloped downwards to the nose from the main crew cabin, terminating in a sphere at the front. The nosewheel retracted to the rear, and the main undercarriage units hinged inwards into the centre-section. The Sperrin's designed Mach number was 0·85. Only the first pilot was provided with a Martin–Baker ejector seat, the remaining four crew members vacating in an emergency by a ventral chute leading rearwards from the pressure cabin.

Design work on the S.A.4 started during 1947 and, in its original form, large single landing wheels were scheduled for the main units, but, finally, a pair of bogies, each containing four wheels, were devised and used. Avon R.A.2s were fitted initially in place of the R.A.3s, as the later version of the Avon was not ready; ultimately, however, the R.A.3s were installed.

Although the parent firm anticipated orders in quantity and built the three Sperrins on production jigs, the idea of the machine entering the R.A.F. for squadron service was abandoned before the first prototype flew, in view of the fact that the Vickers Valiant was in an advanced stage of preparation. Both Sperrins were therefore adapted for research, VX158 to develop radar bombing systems and VX161 for the releasing in flight of new weapons. Eventually, VX158 was modified to house the mighty 25,000 lb.s.t. de Havilland Gyron engine in its lower port nacelle in place of the Avon and made its first flight as the Gyron test-bed from Aldergrove on 7th July, 1955, with Jock Eassie as pilot, accompanied by C. D. Beaumont, chief test pilot of the de Havilland Engine Company. Later a second Gyron was fitted in the lower starboard position and flown thus in June, 1956. With four Avons installed, the Sperrin achieved a very creditable maximum speed at 15,000 ft. of 564 m.p.h.

While to the Sperrin went the distinction of becoming the first British four-jet bomber, the honour of being the first production aircraft in this category fell to a worthy candidate and competitor—the Valiant from Vickers. The advent of the high-power gas turbine put into the hands of designers the instrument whereby—in a single stage—an impressive advance could be made in bomber performance. The use of a single turbojet in a fighter had, within a short period, raised performance to vastly higher levels, and, correspondingly, the same advances could be confidently expected from multiple jet installa-tions in the large bomber class. Surprisingly, the fairly obvious advantages which could accrue from the use of sweptback flying and control surfaces were relatively unexplored and unappreciated by British designers until the results of German research began to filter through just after the war. At the higher end of the piston-engine speed scale the effects of compressibility had begun to assert themselves ominously, and the practice of sweeping wings and tail units to the rear offered a feasible solution to the new and steadily growing problem. The application of sweepback in its several forms was ultimately accepted as inevitable if British bomber performance were to keep pace with development abroad. Even so, there was for some time a dearth of reliable and adequate data upon which to base fresh projects embodying the new precepts which were, eventually, to force the greatest change in the bomber's intensive evolution. This feeling of advancing into a relatively unknown area of high-speed flight engendered a degree of caution, so that work proceeded with the relatively conventional Sperrin as an insurance against the possible initial failure of more radical designs being considered.

Design and production of the large, four-engine bomber was still entrusted to Handley Page, A. V. Roe, Short Bros. and Vickers, all firms pre-eminent in such a specialized field of aircraft engineering. The initial step towards evolving a four-jet bomber of more advanced design than that of the Sperrin was taken with the issue of Specification B.35/46, which elicited proposals from Handley Page, A. V. Roe and Vickers. The Vickers project—although advanced in concept—was less unorthodox than the designs originating in Cricklewood and Manchester, both of which were assessed as worth ordering in the first instance as prototypes. The advanced nature of the Handley Page and Avro projects, and the vast amount of attendant research to be conducted to ensure their success, made it advisable to consider the possibility of ordering the Vickers bomber also, in view of the fact that its comparatively straight-forward design would guarantee its earlier availability for service in the R.A.F.

A new requirement, Specification B.9/48, was therefore prepared to embrace the Vickers Type 660, and Issue 2 of B.9/48, dated 5th September, 1951, was drawn up to cover its production as the Valiant B. Mk. 1. Two prototypes—the Type 660 WB210 with four 6,500 lb.s.t. Avon R.A.3s and the Type 667 WB215 fitted with four Sapphires—were ordered on 2nd February, 1949. In designing the Valiant, G. R. Edwards evolved an exceedingly elegant aircraft, and one of the most graceful and refined of all British bombers. The Valiant's wings—embodying compound sweepback in two degrees on the leading edge—were mounted at shoulder level on a fuselage of cigar shape, the engines being concealed entirely within the centre-section and mounted adjacent to each other close to the fuselage. Each main undercarriage unit consisted of a pair of wheels mounted in tandem, retraction taking place out-wards into the wings. Aspiration of the Avons in WB210 was by horizontal slot intakes in the leading edge of the sharply sweptback inboard section of the wings. The Valiant's tailplane was raised well above turbulence from the wings and from the jet efflux by installing it towards mid-way on the fin.

By the late spring of 1951 WB210 was completed and ready for its maiden flight, which took place from Wisley on 18th May, 1951, with Capt. J. Summers at the controls. Successful trials were conducted with WB210 until they came to an abrupt conclusion eight months later on 12th January, 1952, when the machine—flying with 7,500 lb.s.t. Avon R.A.7s—crashed after catching fire while in flight. Only a short pause occurred in the Valiant's development

WB210, the first prototype Vickers Type 660 Valiant. (*Vickers Photo.*)

WB215, the second prototype Vickers Type 667 Valiant. (*Vickers Photo.*)

The third pre-production Vickers Type 674 Valiant B. Mk. 1 WP201. (*Vickers Photo.*)

WP214, a production Vickers Type 706 Valiant B. Mk. 1. (*Vickers Photo.*)

programme, as WB215 was ready three months afterwards to take to the air from Wisley on 11th April, 1952. Instead of using the scheduled Sapphire engines, the second prototype was equipped with 7,500 lb.s.t. Avon R.A.7s— and later Avon R.A.14s—fed through intakes with deeper, curved lips. The Valiant constituted the first of the trio of V class bombers destined for the R.A.F., WP199—the first of five pre-production, five-seat Type 674 B. Mk. 1s with 10,000 lb.s.t. Avon 201 R.A.14s—making its initial flight from Brooklands on 22nd December, 1953. No. 138 Squadron introduced the Valiant into operational service in February, 1955, the production Type 706 B. Mk. 1 differing from the prototypes in being equipped with 10,050 e.h.p. Avon R.A.28 204s or 205s exhausting through lengthened tailpipes.

Vickers Type 758 Valiant B.(K.) Mk. 1 XD829 in low-level camouflage. (*Vickers Photo.*)

Evolution of the Valiant was continued to produce the Type 710 B.(P.R.) Mk. 1, which was equipped for long-range photographic reconnaissance as well as bombing—No. 543 Squadron being the principal unit to use this version—followed by the Type 733 B.(P.R.)K. Mk. 1 developed for bombing, photographic reconnaissance and as a tanker and then the Type 758 B.(K.) Mk. 1 equipped for in-flight refuelling either as a tanker or as a recipient through a nose probe. Each of these was a variant of the basic Valiant Mk. 1, but a single prototype Type 673 Valiant B. Mk. 2 WJ954, in a glossy black finish, was flown on 4th September, 1953, from Wisley, piloted by G. R. Bryce. WJ954 was powered by four 10,000 lb.s.t. Avon 201 R.A.14s and was fitted with reinforced wings attached to a fuselage of which the nose had been lengthened ahead of the wings. The strengthening of the inner wings for low-level operations made it necessary to redesign completely the main undercarriage and, eventually, four-wheel bogie units were devised which retracted rearwards into tapered external nacelles faired into the trailing edge. Despite these excrescences, the B. Mk. 2 showed an improvement in performance, reaching a speed of 552 m.p.h. at sea level compared with 414 m.p.h.

Vickers Type 733 Valiant B.(P.R.)K. Mk. 1 WP221. *(Vickers Photo.)*

attained by the B. Mk. 1 at sea level. At 36,000 ft. the B. Mk. 1 was capable of 554 m.p.h. or Mach 0·84. With an offensive capacity of a single 10,000 lb. bomb or twenty-one 1,000 lb. bombs and the ability to deliver a nuclear bomb, the Valiant was an extremely important and successful addition to Bomber Command. Notable achievements of the Valiant were the dropping of the first British atom bomb on 11th October, 1956, and the first British hydrogen bomb on 15th May, 1957. Apart from intensive trials with flight refuelling techniques, alternative experimental work was carried out with the Valiant, including launching of the Avro Blue Steel Mk. 1 stand-off bomb —powered by a Bristol Siddeley Stentor rocket engine—by WP204 and assisted take-off by WB215 equipped with a jettisonable 4,000 lb.s.t. Super Sprite rocket unit under each wing inboard of the main undercarriage units.

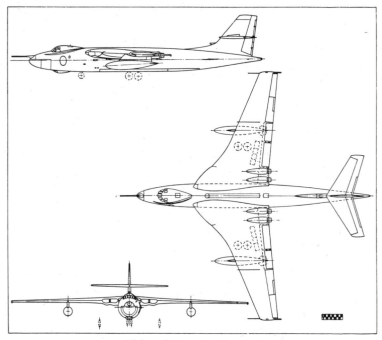

Vickers Valiant B.(K.) Mk. 1

374

The Valiant's eminent operational career of nearly ten years came to a premature close in October, 1964, when the type was grounded following the discovery of metal fatigue in the wings, a fault which could have been remedied, but, it was considered, not an economic proposition. In the course of its service the Valiant exhibited three basic styles of external finish—overall grey, overall white and, finally, a glossy grey and green camouflage scheme applied to the upper surfaces to enable the machine to operate in the low-level rôle. The Valiant went into action in the Suez campaign with four squadrons during the autumn of 1956 prior to the advent in service of the two advanced new bombers—the Vulcan and Victor—being prepared to enter Bomber Command.

The single prototype Vickers Type 673 Valiant B. Mk. 2 WJ954. (*Vickers Photo.*)

In its form dated 1st June, 1948, Specification B.35/46, to meet the requirements of which the Valiant was prepared originally, was issued to produce a medium-range bomber for the R.A.F. for use by day or night in all parts of the world, and had to be able to carry one 10,000 lb. bomb 1,500 n.m. from any base in the world. The machine was to be designed for large-scale production in wartime, with economic production of at least five hundred aircraft at a rate of not fewer than ten per month. Capabilities demanded included a high cruising speed, a high degree of manoeuvrability at high speed and altitude, a high cruising altitude, the ability to carry adequate warning devices and—although no orthodox defensive armament was required—the capacity for incorporation of defensive apparatus. 100,000 lb. was stipulated as the maximum weight, and maximum cruising speed on continuous power at progressively increasing heights from 35,000 to 50,000 ft. was to be 500 kt. The maximum approach speed was to be 120 m.p.h. and the still-air range with 10,000 lb. bomb load 3,350 n.m. The aircraft had to be able to reach 45,000 ft. in 1 hr. and 50,000 ft. in 2·5 hr. after taking-off at maximum all-up weight. 45,000 ft. was to be the cruising altitude and, although it was desirable that the machine should be able to exceed 50,000 ft. altitude, this was not essential. The crew of five—two pilots, two navigators and one signaller—were to be housed in a single pressure cabin and equipped with the new light, back-type parachutes. Offensive capacity was to include the new range of H.E. bombs, and it might ultimately be desired to instal tail armament.

Roy Chadwick was responsible for the basic design of the Avro 698, the most radical of the three types prepared to meet B.35/46, but was killed on 23rd August, 1947, just over three months before the acceptance on the following 27th November of the last—and the most unusual—of his numerous outstanding creations. The decision to adopt the distinctive delta planform for the wings of the 698 brought to the fore the paucity of adequate data, and extreme measures were adopted to remedy the deficiency. The embodiment of the delta type of wing bestowed several advantages, among them vast storage capacity in the inboard portions owing to the very deep section engendered by the great chord at the roots, the strong inflexible structure provided by the inherent low aspect ratio of a delta wing, the positive control provided throughout the speed range by the surfaces forming part of the trailing edge and the embodiment of a low thickness/chord ratio delaying the rise in drag at higher speeds.

Avro promotion of the delta wing meant an advance into an entirely new region of aerodynamics, and to assess the handling characteristics of the unusual layout an extensive programme was instituted involving the design and construction of several flying scale versions of the proposed bomber. Specification E.15/48 of 22nd October, 1948, was prepared to cover a one-third scale model of the 698 which was to reproduce and investigate low-speed control and stability characteristics of the full-size aircraft. The resulting machine was to possess a maximum speed of at least 350 kt. E.A.S. up to 10,000 ft. In all, five small Avro deltas were built, an undertaking involving the firm in a period of intense activity in addition to the enormous programme of work on the main 698 design. The first of the unorthodox and attractive miniature research aircraft to display its triangular wings was the single-seat 707 VX784 to E.15/48, powered by a 3,500 lb.s.t. Rolls-Royce Derwent—as was each of its successors—aspirated by a dorsal intake amidships behind the cockpit. The 707's control surfaces were conventional, consisting of ailerons at the wingtips, elevators inboard on the trailing edge and the rudder above the tailpipe.

A. & A.E.E. Boscombe Down served as the venue from which S. E. Esler took VX784 into the air for the first time on 4th September, 1949, but the singular machine's triumph was short-lived, as, in Esler's hands, it crashed very shortly afterwards on 30th September, killing its pilot. Work proceeded on the next Avro delta, the single-seat, mid-blue 707B VX790, but a year passed before it was ready for its first flight from Boscombe Down with Wg. Cdr. R. J. Falk on 6th September, 1950. VX790 was designed to investigate delta characteristics at low speeds to E.15/48. The upper end of the speed scale was the province of WD280, the orange 707A to Specification E.10/49 which made its maiden flight from Boscombe Down on 14th July, 1951, with Falk again in the cockpit. A basic change in the design of the 707A—which made it an even cleaner aircraft—was noticeable with the deletion of the dorsal intake for the Derwent and the substitution of a bifurcated intake fed through orifices in the wing roots. The fourth aircraft in the series, a duplicate high-speed 707A WZ736, was flown for the first time on 20th February, 1953. 1st July, 1953, witnessed the initial flight of the silver 707C WZ744, which accommodated a pair of pilots abreast under a broad, bulbous canopy.

The prototype Avro 698 Vulcan B. Mk. 1 VX770 in white finish. (*Avro Photo.*)

The brood of 707 delta research monoplanes proved to be an eminently satisfactory investment and were largely responsible for the smooth development of the ultimate object of the entire programme, the white prototype 698 VX770, which was able to fly from Woodford successfully for the first time on 30th August, 1952, in the hands—by then well versed in the peculiarities of delta flying—of Wg. Cdr. Falk. The powerful 9,750 lb.s.t. Bristol Olympus B.E.10 had been selected as the power plant for the 698, but delays in its development programme were responsible for VX770 taking to the air initially

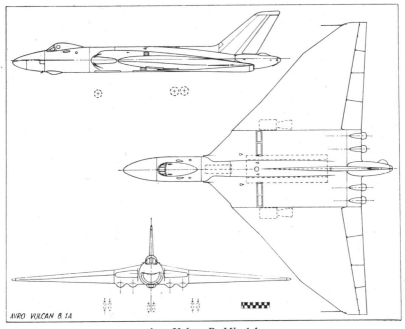

Avro Vulcan B. Mk. 1A

377

Avro Vulcan B. Mk. 2 XH535. (*Avro Photo.*)

with four 6,500 lb.s.t. Avon R.A.3s. In its prototype form the 698 retained the basic features proved in flight by the 707A, but, as first considered by Roy Chadwick—prior to modifications which resulted in the contract concluded in

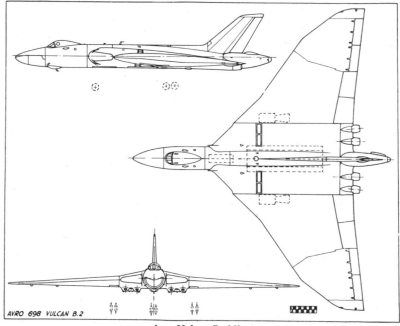

AVRO 698 VULCAN B.2

Avro Vulcan B. Mk. 2

378

January, 1948—the design was for an airframe consisting of a pair of delta wings only with the pilots housed entirely in the leading edge. The four Bristol B.E.10 engines were to be installed as superimposed pairs adjacent to each other and concealed within the deep centre portion of the triangular flying surface. A vertical fin and rudder were to be mounted at each wingtip.

Subsequent second thoughts resulted in the revised design layout in which VX770 eventually emerged, with a normal fuselage embodying the pilots' cockpit ahead of the leading edge, sweptback fin and rudder, a tricycle undercarriage in which each of the pairs of main units—consisting of an eight-wheel bogie—retracted forwards and the twin nosewheels swung upwards to the rear, and its four engines disposed in a horizontal pair in each inner wing. Some twelve months after its début, VX770 was equipped with four 8,000 lb.s.t. Sapphire A.S.Sa.6s; ultimately these were replaced, another engine change being made when 15,000 lb.s.t. Rolls-Royce Conway R.Co.7 by-pass engines were fitted for testing, in which form VX770 flew for the first time on 9th August, 1957. Subsequently, VX770 crashed on 14th September, 1958, at Syerston. VX777, the second prototype 698, made its first flight on 3rd September, 1953, equipped with four 9,500 lb.s.t. Olympus 100 B.01.1/2Bs and with a lengthened nose to accommodate the new, longer nosewheel leg when retracted. The 707A WD280 had flown with wings incorporating increased chord on the outer panels, and this feature was embodied in VX777, in which form it flew on 5th October, 1955.

The Avro 698 was adopted for the R.A.F. as the Vulcan, No. 83 Squadron taking delivery of its first B. Mk. 1s on 11th July, 1957, having previously used Vulcans lent to it by No. 230 O.C.U. since No. 83 reformed during May, 1957. Early production Vulcans completed with the straight leading edge were retrospectively modified with the new leading edge embodying compound taper, which had been adopted eventually for all Vulcans. Engines installed in the B. Mk. 1 were the 11,000 lb.s.t. Olympus 101, the 12,000 lb.s.t. Olympus 102 and the 13,000 lb.s.t. Olympus 104. The silver of the early production Vulcans was soon superseded by an overall white anti-radiation finish. As an alternative to its nuclear weapon, the striking delta bomber was able to accommodate a load of twenty-one 1,000 lb. bombs. Revisions to the electronic equipment of the B. Mk. 1 carried out during 1961 resulted in re-designation as B. Mk. 1A when an electronic counter-measures radome was incorporated in the rear of the fuselage.

The Vulcan's development potential continued to be exploited, and the availability of the 16,000 lb.s.t. Olympus brought extensive alteration to the wings, the outer chord being increased in conjunction with extension of the span from 99 ft. to 111 ft. VX777 was adapted to embody and prove the features of the B. Mk. 2, flying in this form initially on 31st August, 1957. XH533, the first production B. Mk. 2, took-off initially on 19th August, 1958, flying with 17,000 lb.s.t. Olympus 201s. On 1st July, 1960, No. 83 Squadron took delivery of the B. Mk. 2, becoming the first to receive the improved model of the Vulcan. The Vulcan B. Mk. 2 was developed to carry the Stentor-driven Avro Blue Steel Mk. 1 supersonic stand-off bomb beneath

WB771, the first prototype Handley Page Victor. (*Handley Page Photo.*)

The second prototype Handley Page Victor WB775. (*Handley Page Photo.*)

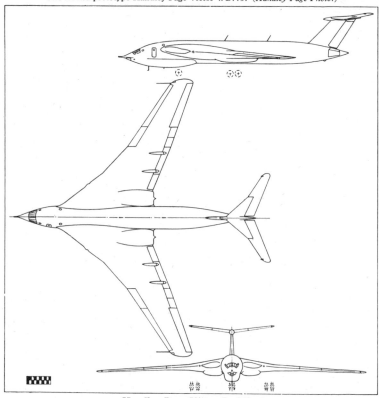

Handley Page Victor B. Mk. 1

its fuselage and was also evolved to use two Douglas Skybolt missiles, but the American weapon was subsequently abandoned. Still greater performance was extracted from the B. Mk. 2, with the installation ultimately of four 20,000 lb.s.t. Olympus 301s. Eventually, by 1964, the Vulcan was subject to further adaptation to enable it to perform at the other extreme of altitude as a low-level bomber. For this rôle the revived practice of camouflage was applied to the upper surfaces.

The appearance in British skies of the extraordinary and truly Wellsian shape of the stalwart Vulcan was followed shortly by the rather less radical shape of the third of the trio of V bombers—the Handley Page H.P.80 Victor designed to B.35/46 by R. S. Stafford. Sqn. Ldr. H. G. Hazelden was the pilot of WB771, the prototype, when its first flight took place from Boscombe Down on 24th December, 1952. Handley Page adopted also the procedure of testing the principal feature of the Victor—the unusual plan-form of its wings—on a small flying scale model. To Specification E.6/48 was constructed the H.P.88 VX330, a single-seat research aircraft which Blackburn built—as the Y.B.2—during 1948 by adapting the fuselage of the Supermarine Type 510, under the designation Type 521, and equipping it with the 5,100 lb.s.t. Nene 102 engine, together with a one-quarter-scale version of the proposed shape of the wings and the tail unit of the Victor. The H.P.88 made its first flight on 21st June, 1951, but, before much know-ledge could be gleaned from it, the machine crashed later in the same year at Stansted, killing its pilot, D. J. P. Broomfield.

In creating the H.P.80 Reginald Stafford chose to break new ground by attempting—in evolving the design's unusual feature of wings incorporating three successive decreasing degrees of sweepback from roots to tips—to embody the best features of each of the alternatives available in the light of current research and knowledge. In adopting what was to become known popularly as the crescent wing, Stafford anticipated being rewarded by the advantages offered individually by sweepback, low thickness/chord ratio and the delta shape. The resulting reduction of drag was expected to enable a high critical Mach number to be attained at a constant value across the span; at the same time the crescent wing of high aspect ratio was considered to be

Handley Page Victor B. Mk. 1 XA930. (*Handley Page Photo.*)

A load of thirty-five 1,000 lb. bombs being released by a Handley Page Victor B. Mk. 1A XH648. (*Handley Page Photo.*)

able to offer excellent range and extreme operational altitude. The deep section and broad chord of the inboard portions of the wings offered adequate stowage for engines and undercarriage, and, ultimately, together with the liberal application of high-lift devices, the wing form created for the Victor paid very handsome dividends in every way. The Victor shared the same general style of undercarriage as that of the Vulcan—each main unit consisting of an eight-wheel bogie combined with twin nosewheels. The mainplanes—of 110 ft. span—were mounted at the mid-wing position and the horizontal tail surfaces—following the same basic shape as that of the wings but with two stages of sweepback—were installed at the tip of the sweptback fin. WB771 was flown on the power of four 8,000 lb.s.t. Sapphire A.S.Sa.6 100s. With their attendant electronic equipment, the closely-grouped crew of five were housed in the pressure cabin in the distinctive deep, pointed nose. The weapons-bay was of such capacity that the Victor was able to carry a considerably greater offensive load than either the Valiant or the Vulcan, the stowage of a total of thirty-five 1,000 lb. bombs being possible. WB771 was used for just over eighteen months before it crashed on 14th July, 1954. The second of the two H.P.80 prototypes ordered during 1949, WB775, was ready shortly afterwards to make its first take-off on 11th September, 1954.

The Victor was ordered for Bomber Command in 1952 and came from the production lines powered by 11,000 lb.s.t. Sapphire 202s and with a nose lengthened by 3 ft. 4 in. and the tail unit reduced in height by 1 ft. 3 in. No. 10 Squadron was selected to introduce the Victor B. Mk. 1 into operational service during April, 1958. Evolution of the basic B. Mk. 1 produced the B.(P.R.) Mk. 1 for reconnaissance duties and the B. Mk. 1A conversion of serving B. Mk. 1s, which incorporated electronic counter-measures equip-

Handley Page Victor B.(K.) Mk. 1 XA918 with refuelling drogues extended. (*Handley Page Photo.*)

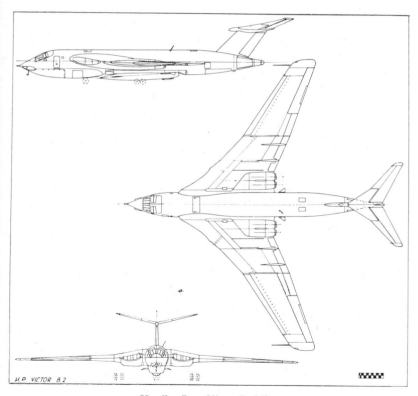

Handley Page Victor B. Mk. 2

383

Handley Page Victor B. Mk. 2 XL192 with external fairings on the upper surfaces of the wings. (*Handley Page Photo.*)

ment in the rear fuselage among other revisions. The B. Mk. 1 proved to be very fast, and XA917 demonstrated this facet of the type's many capabilities when, in a shallow dive on 1st June, 1957, at 40,000 ft. it exceeded Mach 1·0.

Bomber Command's striking power was increased still further with the production of the Victor B. Mk. 2, in which the wing span was extended to 120 ft. and which was powered in its initial production form by four 17,250 lb.s.t. Conway R.Co.11s. Another increase in power was accomplished by installing 20,000 lb.s.t. Conway R.Co.17s in later B. Mk. 2s. On 20th February, 1959, Flt. Lt. J. W. Allam took the prototype B. Mk. 2—XH668—into the air for the first time from Radlett, and February, 1962, saw No. 139 Squadron become the initial operational unit to receive the Victor B. Mk. 2. Apart from the ability to deliver conventional nuclear and high-explosive bombs, the B. Mk. 2 was designed to transport the Blue Steel Mk. 1 missile. With the arrival in service of the extremely businesslike Victor, the planned re-equipment of the Royal Air Force with its three advanced four-jet bombers had been accomplished during a hazardous period of unremitting international tension and unrest.

In common with all other categories of aeronautical design the cost of providing carrier-borne anti-submarine aircraft continued to rise very steeply after the 1939–45 War and, with the express object of reducing the outlay on what had become an essential class of Fleet Air Arm aeroplane, David Keith-Lucas of Short Brothers and Harland undertook the design of the S.B.6

Short Seamew A.S. Mk. 1. (*Short Photo.*)

Seamew to Specification M.123D, Sqn. Ldr. W. J. Runciman piloting the machine on its maiden flight from Sydenham, Belfast, on 23rd August, 1953. The first prototype, XA209, was completed in the remarkably short time of seventeen months and two weeks from the commencement of design and plainly displayed the firm's concentration on endeavouring to simplify the Seamew in every way.

A light—but at the same time strong—airframe was contrived, consisting of a slim fuselage with a nose portion of pronounced depth occasioned by the location of the pilot and observer in tandem cockpits in the nose above the low-set 1,320 e.s.h.p. Mamba A.S.Ma.3, mainplanes mounted at the mid-wing position, a prominent fin and rudder with the tailplane set half-way towards the top of the fin, and a fixed undercarriage with single-strut main units and a tailwheel. The prototype Seamew's wings were turned manually to fold to the rear, lying vertically, parallel with the sides of the fuselage; power-folding was scheduled for the production F.A.A. version. From his location high in the nose just behind the four-blade propeller, the pilot was endowed with an outstandingly good view for deck landing, for which purpose an arrester hook was provided in the rear of the fuselage in a cut-out beneath the tail unit. The 14 ft. long weapons-bay housed the load of bombs or depth-charges, and additional stores could be stowed beneath the wings. The Seamew's detection equipment with 360° scan was carried in a radome underneath the fore-fuselage and its light loaded weight of about 14,000 lb., coupled with low wing loading, excellent low-speed handling and its ability to undertake long patrols at an economic speed, made it eminently suitable for its specified rôle. Particularly useful on landing were the long-stroke main undercarriage legs and the ability to extend the tailwheel vertically to reduce the ground angle. XA213, the second prototype, was equipped with the 1,590 s.h.p. Mamba A.S.Ma.6, which was selected as the power plant of the seventy Seamew A.S. Mk. 1s ordered for the Fleet Air Arm and for the Royal Air Force. The Seamew's distinctive and pert appearance belied the fact that its wing span was 55 ft.

In spite of its inherent overall qualities and the great—and successful—effort made to limit its initial and maintenance costs, the entire Seamew programme was subsequently cancelled.

The first decade following the 1939–45 War witnessed the realization of the greatest basic changes taking place in the British bomber since its birth at the start of the 1914–18 War. The nuclear bomb, the gas turbine power plant and the great advances made in the ever-expanding field of electronics exerted a massive influence on tactical and strategic employment of the bomber, culminating in the acquisition by the Royal Air Force of the three V bombers which endowed the Service with a greater striking power than ever before.

Blackburn Buccaneer S. Mk. 50 for the S.A.A.F. (*Blackburn Photo.*)

CHAPTER TEN

SWAN SONG

In the science of aeronautics the first decade to follow the 1939–45 War was notable for the great—and indeed startling—achievements in design technique, airframe engineering and engine and electronic development and the evolution of numerous associated components, from all of which the bomber benefited.

Within a brief period a new generation of bombers of totally new concept had emerged to carry missiles capable of fantastic powers of destruction. The very sharp rise in speed and operational height had engendered a continuation of the basic operational philosophy, so brilliantly and successfully demonstrated by the Mosquito, and armament was discarded, resulting concurrently in a reduction in the number of crew members required. Weight was saved by abolishing machine-guns and cannon and their associated turrets and barbettes, but the installation of increased electronic equipment served to reduce this particular advantage. The realization that a smaller force of bombers could wreak immeasurably greater havoc than that which would previously have been achieved only by large mass formations was instrumental in smaller numbers being ordered. Another factor militating against quantity production was the very heavy increase in the cost of each aircraft. Once the Valiant, Vulcan and Victor programme was under way, a noticeable change took place in procurement policy—especially in the field of bombing aircraft—with the emergence of the fallacious conviction that the manned bomber would no longer be required, following the advent of the intercontinental ballistic missile. The rise of this assumption and the active promotion of such an incongruous and outlandish notion—in the face of completely contradictory evidence in contemporary international incidents and policies—constituted a prime example of the dangerously muddled thinking and of the ineptitude of the trustees of the United Kingdom's defences.

Despite the fact that there appeared relatively little likelihood that much use would be made in the immediate future of the company's undoubted expertise in the design and construction of advanced bomber aircraft, A. V. Roe proceeded to conduct several studies which included the Avro 721 low-level bomber project prepared in October, 1952, the 730 designed during 1955 by J. R. Ewans as a supersonic bomber using stainless-steel sandwich construction and powered by eight Armstrong Siddeley P.176 turbojets and the 732 project by Ewans of July, 1956, for a four-jet supersonic bomber. In the case of the Avro 730 it was proposed in October, 1955, that Avro 731 flying models, to three-eighths scale and powered by a pair of de Havilland Gyron Junior engines, should be constructed, but March, 1957, brought the end of the entire scheme.

The emergence of Bomber Command from the 1939–45 War as the main unit vested with the striking power of the Royal Air Force had been accompanied by a parallel increase in the importance of the Fleet Air Arm in relation to the Royal Navy. The ability of the Navy to transport its aircraft by carrier to any area where their services were required, and the fact that they could be housed and serviced in the parent ship as well as operated from it, raised the status of naval aviation to a new and very important level. Three significant and extremely valuable innovations in carrier-borne flying were provided by British designing and engineering genius—the angled deck, the steam catapult and the mirror landing device.

The Navy's investment in its very expensive carriers brought an automatic need for modern aircraft to equip the ships' squadrons, and Specification M.148T/N.A.39 was issued to produce a new two-seat, tactical strike bomber with the primary quality of being able to operate at very low altitudes. Various firms submitted tenders, and competition was keen during a period which brought a thinning out of requirements for operational aircraft. Designed by B. P. Laight, the Blackburn B.103 was eventually selected during May, 1955, as meeting the stringent demands of N.A.39, the machine's first flight being scheduled for three years ahead. In the event, a burst tyre in the course of high-speed taxying trials at R.A.E. Bedford on 21st April, 1958, prevented an improvement on this date, but, at the same aerodrome a few days later, on 30th April, Lt. Cdr. D. Whitehead took the prototype XK486—finished in an effective scheme of blue and white—into the air for a successful maiden flight of 39 min.

The new Blackburn naval all-weather bomber displayed very pronounced evidence of the application of area rule about the middle portion of its fuselage,

Blackburn Buccaneer S. Mk. 1. (*Dunlop Photo.*)

387

Blackburn Buccaneer S. Mk. 2. (*Blackburn Photo.*)

resulting in a grotesque bulge between the wings and the tail at a point where, in most cases, the body would be tapering evenly towards the rear. The mid-set, sweptback wings were square-cut and embodied compound taper on the leading edge; the pair of 7,000 lb.s.t. de Havilland Gyron Junior DGJ.1 engines were installed in elongated nacelles in the wing roots adjacent to the fuselage. A tricycle undercarriage was fitted, and the fuselage terminated in a tailcone which split vertically to allow the two halves to hinge sideways as airbrakes. The sweptback vertical tail was surmounted by the horizontal tail surfaces, and the pilot and observer—equipped with Martin–Baker ejector seats—were situated well towards the nose under a low-set canopy. Homing torpedoes were stipulated as part of the B.103's internally-borne offensive

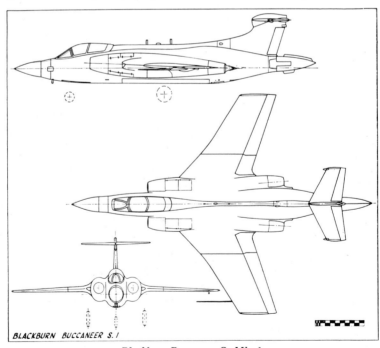

Blackburn Buccaneer S. Mk. 1

load, the machine's bombs being housed in a rotating door fitment in the weapons-bay.

The design's performance was increased by the incorporation of a boundary layer control system devised by bleeding air from the engines' compressors for the wings and the tail surfaces. Carrier stowage was facilitated by opening of the airbrakes and the folding upwards of the wings and folding of the nose sideways to port. To enable the B.103 to fulfil its strenuous rôle of flying at Mach ·9 at a low enough altitude to avoid detection by radar, a particularly strong structure was necessary, and this was achieved by liberal use of integrally-machined skins for the wings and the tailplane.

XK486 was the first aircraft of the pre-production batch of twenty machines, ordered during July, 1955, to expedite development. The remaining examples were completed to various standards of equipment to enable each aspect of the type's numerous duties to be assessed thoroughly. In October, 1959, the B.103 was ordered for the Fleet Air Arm as the Buccaneer S. Mk. 1, XN924—the first production example—being flown on 23rd January, 1962. No. 801 Squadron became the initial operational unit to take delivery of the powerful new strike aircraft, the S. Mk. 1 entering service equipped with a pair of 7,100 lb.s.t. Gyron Junior DGJ.2 101s, with which it was intended to approach its target in any weather at sea level at a very high subsonic speed beneath the radar screen to deliver its weapon by normal release or by using the technique of toss-bombing.

The belligerent-looking Buccaneer was the subject of continued development, resulting in the evolution of the S. Mk. 2 using two 11,200 lb.s.t. Rolls-Royce R.B.168-1 Spey turbofans, a type of engine offering a substantial increase in power and a useful extension of range by reduction of fuel consumption. XK526 was modified to serve as the prototype S. Mk. 2, making its first take-off on 17th May, 1963. The main external differences visible from the earlier Buccaneer lay in the provision of larger intakes for the Speys and in

Hawker Siddeley 801 Nimrod. (*Hawker Siddeley Photo.*)

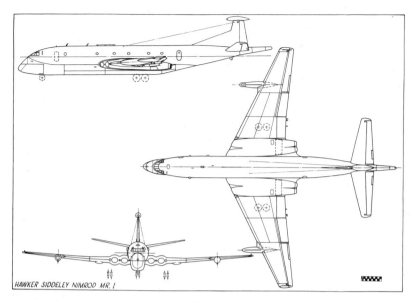

new outswept wingtips. The Fleet Air Arm's order for the S. Mk. 2 was placed during January, 1962, XN974—the first production example—flying on 5th June, 1964. As the S. Mk. 50 the Buccaneer S. Mk. 2 was ordered for the South African Air Force. The introduction of the Buccaneer provided the Fleet Air Arm with the finest strike aircraft so far procured for it, and a design which was the latest in the long line of machines in the same category which Blackburn had produced so successfully for the Service over such an extended period.

Another aircraft designed to operate over water—the Shackleton—had proved a worthwhile investment, but, eventually, the question of its replacement had to be considered. In the same way as the Shackleton had been a development of the Lincoln, so was its successor—the Hawker Siddeley 801—evolved from an earlier airframe. In the 801's case the de Havilland D.H.106 Comet was stated in the announcement of the order—made early in 1966—to form the basis of the new design, which was to be powered by four 11,500 lb. s.t. Rolls-Royce RB 168 Spey 250 turbofan engines. Subsequently it was named Nimrod, and the prototypes were evolved by converting a pair of Comet airframes. The first production M.R.1, XV226, made its initial flight on 28 June, 1968, and the order for R.A.F. units totalled thirty-eight. The Nimrod gained the distinction of becoming the first four-jet, land-based, long-range maritime reconnaissance aircraft to enter service in any air force.

In retrospect the history of the development of the bomber in Great Britain during peacetime has been bedevilled by the promotion of dangerous political dogma, procrastination, vacillation and by the continual practice of unrealistic parsimony by the Treasury. Against this daunting and frustrating background the designers of British military and naval aircraft have pursued

British Aircraft Corporation TSR-2. (*B.A.C. Photo.*)

their indispensable art for half a century and have succeeded on every occasion in creating the finest aeroplanes extant in each particular category. In the field of the bomber their greatest technical triumph came in the autumn of 1964 with the unveiling of their culminating masterpiece—the British Aircraft Corporation TSR-2—intended as a supersonic replacement for the Canberra.

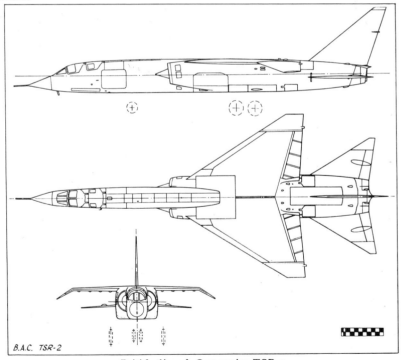

B.A.C. TSR-2

British Aircraft Corporation TSR-2

The extremely involved and gigantic task of producing such an advanced aircraft was shared by two Divisions of the British Aircraft Corporation—Vickers-Armstrongs at Weybridge and English Electric at Preston, H. H. Gardner and F. W. Page being responsible for co-ordination of the overall design of the machine. The basic precept governing the project—to Operational Requirements GOR.339 and OR.343—was that of a full weapons system completely integrated in one airframe, enabling the resulting aircraft to operate in any weather at very high speed at high or low level on tactical strike and reconnaissance duties, but the resulting design's excellent payload and range capabilities enabled its qualities to be applied also to the strategic rôle. To achieve this object successfully a vast programme of research was instituted to ensure the ultimate employment of the best possible design techniques and advanced materials and components. The crew required to man the complex aircraft was reduced to two—pilot and observer—and the entire operation of the TSR-2 devolved upon the provision of extremely comprehensive electronic equipment.

By 1955 the need to consider formulating the requirement for a Canberra replacement could no longer be deferred, and 1956 brought discussions and investigation by the Air Staff into the nature of its expected duties. GOR.339 was issued towards the end of 1957, and on 1st January, 1959, came the announcement of the decision to proceed with the TSR-2; during the spring of 1959 OR.343 was drawn up to cover the combined project by Vickers-Armstrongs and English Electric. Design work proceeded throughout 1959, and was rewarded on 7th October, 1960, with the announcement of the placing of a full development contract for nine aircraft, later increased to cover a total pre-production batch of twenty. Two 30,000 lb.s.t. Olympus B.O1.22R 320 engines with reheat were selected to power the TSR-2, being housed in the rear fuselage and receiving their air through side intakes incorporating half-cone shock bodies to vary the intake area. The 37 ft. span, 60° thin delta wings were mounted at shoulder level on the 89 ft. long fuselage.

The control system was unusual, as ailerons were deleted, pitch and roll being controlled by an all-flying tailplane in which each half operated in opposition to the other. The sweptback fin was a single surface pivoted to act as a rudder also. The tips of the wings incorporated anhedral to counter roll, and the high wing loading occasioned by the small wing area was mitigated by the provision of flap blowing and the high thrust/weight ratio. The TSR-2 was designed to operate from relatively poor surfaces, and short field performance was assisted by the provision of the flap blowing system. Twin wheels in tandem were installed on the main undercarriage legs, and the two nosewheels were mounted on an extending strut to give two ground angles. The crew, in Martin–Baker ejector seats, were located in tandem in the lengthy nose.

XR219, the all-white first TSR-2, took-off at A. & A.E.E. Boscombe Down on 27th September, 1964, to make a successful initial flight of 15 min. piloted by Wg. Cdr. R. P. Beamont. The pre-production batch was augmented by an initial production order for thirty TSR-2s, but, despite the great promise shown by XR219—the only one to fly of four constructed—6th April, 1965, brought bitter disappointment and a terrible blow to national pride and prestige with the deplorable announcement that the entire TSR-2 programme was cancelled.

In creating the machine the British Aircraft Corporation and the numerous firms associated with the project had met a tremendous challenge of the greatest possible technical magnitude and had proved equal to the task by producing in the TSR-2 an aeroplane of outstanding merit and of everlasting credit to the country's mischievously treated aircraft industry. Their endeavours were, however, in vain, for the ignoble fate suffered by the TSR-2 was to form just one more miserable link in the costly chain constituting the obnoxious and destructive criminal folly foisted upon an ashamed and uneasy British public by fanatics and opportunists concerned more with the promotion of their unsavoury and gimcrack political tenets than with the preservation of the dignity and the safety of the British Nation. The combination of

XR219, the single B.A.C. TSR-2 to be flown. (*B.A.C. Photo.*)

vicious political interference and ineptitude has contrived to decimate steadily the once virile and independent British aircraft industry, to squander untold millions of pounds of the British taxpayers' money on one cancelled project after another over two whole disastrous decades, to fail time and time again to allow and encourage the industry to maintain the strong initial lead over the rest of the world which British brains and initiative have established with numerous outstanding aeronautical inventions and techniques, and to reduce the companies constituting the British aircraft industry—which, under their original names which stood for unsurpassed quality and integrity in a highly competitive field had supplied many air arms abroad as well as the Royal Air Force and the Fleet Air Arm with their fighters, bombers and other classes of aircraft—to a state of bewilderment and well-nigh impotence in the military and naval field, with nothing to show for years of endeavour but one discarded expensive project and prototype after another. Great Britain's bombers—no less than her fighters—were instrumental to a high degree for the nation's ultimate survival in the Second World War. The fatal policy of cringing weakness—abetted by pernicious disarmament—which was responsible for the encouragement and ultimate outbreak of the 1939–45 conflict, can only have the effect of inspiring and emboldening future would-be aggressors

An impression of the Panavia 200 MRCA. (*B.A.C. Photo.*)

and has been doing so since the end of the Second World War. In the light of an intelligent interpretation of history and understanding of human behaviour and impulse, there is, therefore, no reason to subscribe to the view that Great Britain has fought her last great war; as, by design, she becomes progressively

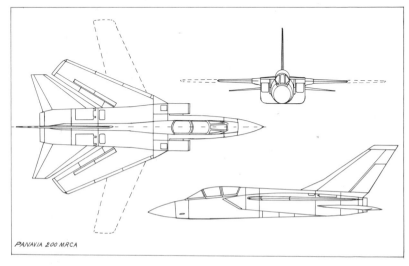

PANAVIA 200 MRCA

394

weaker, so will the danger increase. With Britain's long-established capacity for producing the fighters to defend her shores and the bombers to beat her enemies, systematically destroyed by acts of folly, what will the outcome be? With Britain's indigenous sources of design and manufacture of combatant aircraft taken from her and her professed reliance on imported aircraft from sources which could be cut off overnight at one stroke by disagreement, by shortage or by the annihilation by bombing of the factories concerned abroad, the answer is obvious.

The history of British bomber and torpedo-bomber aircraft is a glorious one of high endeavour rewarded by outstanding success—half a century of triumph terminating in the tragedy of TSR-2 and of the lack of any subsequent national advanced bomber projects.

Following the cancellation of the TSR-2, the British Aircraft Corporation has been involved in its commitment in the Multi-Role Combat Aircraft with Messerschmitt–Bölkow–Blohm in Germany and Fiat in Italy. The consortium is known as Panavia and was formed on 26 March, 1969. To enable the Panavia 200 MRCA to undertake a range of operational duties with each of its three sponsoring countries, the two-seat, twin-engine supersonic shoulder-wing design incorporates variable-geometry wings. The MRCA's intended engine is the Rolls-Royce RB-199-34R three-spool reheated turbofan. For Royal Air Force purposes, the ultimate intention is that the MRCA should replace the Buccaneer and the Vulcan for overland strike and reconnaissance missions and, eventually, that it should take over the maritime strike tasks at present undertaken by the Buccaneer.

Manufacturer/ Designer	Type No.	Name	Engine(s), h.p./lb.s.t.
A.D.	1000		3 × 310 Sunbeam
,,		Navyplane	1 × 150 Smith Static
Armstrong Whitworth	F.K.3		1 × 90 R.A.F.1a
,, ,,	F.K.8		1 × 120 Beardmore
,, ,,		Atlas Mk. I	1 × 450 Jaguar IVC
,, ,,		Ajax	1 × 550 Panther
,, ,,	A.W.17	Aries	1 × 460 Jaguar
,, ,,	A.W.19		1 × 810 Tiger VI
,, ,,	A.W.23		2 × 840 Tiger VIII
,, ,,	A.W.29		1 × 880 Tiger VIII
,, ,,	A.W.38	Whitley Mk. I	2 × 920 Tiger IX
,, ,,	A.W.41	Albemarle Mk. I	2 × 1,590 Hercules XI
Avro	504		1 × 80 Gnome
,,	510		1 × 150 Sunbeam
,,	519		1 × 150 Nubian
,,	523	Pike	2 × 160 Sunbeam
,,	529		2 × 190 Falcon
,,	533	Manchester Mk. I	2 × 320 Dragonfly I
,,	549	Aldershot Mk. I	1 × 650 Condor III
,,	557	Ava Mk. I	2 × 650 Condor III
,,	571	Buffalo Mk. I	1 × 450 Lion VA
,,	604	Antelope	1 × 480 R.-R. F.XIB
,,	652A	Anson Mk. I	2 × 350 Cheetah IX
,,	679	Manchester B. Mk. I	2 × 1,760 Vulture I
,,	683	Lancaster B. Mk. I	4 × 1,460 Merlin 20
,,		Lancaster B. Mk. II	4 × 1,650 Hercules VI
,,	694	Lincoln B. Mk. I	4 × 1,750 Merlin 85
,,	696	Shackleton M.R. Mk. 1	4 × 2,450 Griffon 57/57A
,,		Shackleton M.R. Mk. 2	4 × 2,450 Griffon 57A
,,	716	Shackleton M.R. Mk. 3	4 × 2,450 Griffon 57A
,,	698	Vulcan B. Mk. 1	4 × 11,000 Olympus 101
,,	698	Vulcan B. Mk. 2	4 × 17,000 Olympus 201
Beardmore	W.B.I		1 × 230 Adriatic
,,		Inflexible	3 × 650 Condor II
Blackburn		T.B.	2 × 100 Mono. Gnome
,,		G.P.	2 × 225 Sunbeam
,,		S.P.	2 × 250 Falcon
,,		Kangaroo	2 × 250 Falcon
,,		Blackburd	1 × 350 Eagle VIII
,,		Swift	1 × 450 Lion
,,		Dart Mk. II	1 × 450 Lion IIB
,,		Cubaroo	1 × 1,000 Cub
,,		Velos	1 × 450 Lion
,,		Ripon Mk. IIA	1 × 570 Lion XIA
,,		Baffin	1 × 565 Pegasus IM3
,,		Beagle	1 × 460 Jupiter VIIIF
,,		3.M.R.4	1 × 625 Hispano-Suiza 51
,,		M.1/30	1 × 825 Buzzard
,,		M.1/30A	1 × 825 Buzzard
,,		B-6	1 × 700 Tiger IV
,,		Shark Mk. II	1 × 700 Tiger VI
,,		B-7	1 × 700 Tiger VI
,,		Skua Mk. II	1 × 905 Perseus XII
,,		Botha G.R. Mk. I	2 × 880 Perseus X
,,	B.54	Y.A.7	1 × 2,000 Griffon 56

TABLES

Max. speed, m.p.h.	Wt. (E), lb.	Wt. (L), lb.	Span ft. in.	Length ft. in.	Prototype
			115		1358
75	2,100	3,102	36	27 9	9095
87	1,386	2,056	40 0⅜	29	5328
83·5	1,682	2,447	43 6	30 11	A2683
142·5	2,550	4,020	39 6·5	28 6·5	J8675
		4,000	36 4		J8802
		4,350	32 7		J9037
172	4,298	7,250	49 8	42 2	A-3
		24,100	88	80 9	K3585
232		9,000	49	44	K4299
192	14,275	21,660	84	69 3	K4586
265		22,600	77	59 11	P1360
82	924	1,574	36	29 5	179
70	2,080	2,800	63	38	130
					8440
97	4,000	6,064	60	39 1	
94	4,376	6,309	63	39 8	3694
114·5	4,887	7,390	60	37	F3493
	6,027	10,764	68	45	J6852
	12,760	19,920	96 10	61 9	N171
			46	36 6	G-EBNW
173	2,859	4,538	36	31 2	J9183
188	5,375	8,000	56 6	42 3	K4771
265		50,000	90 1	70	L7246
287	36,900	68,000	102	69 6	BT308
270			102	69 6	DT810
319	43,400	75,000	120	78 3·5	PW925
			120	77 6	VW126
272	56,500	98,000	120	87 3	VW126
302	57,800	100,000	119 10	92 6	WR970
			99	97 1	VW770
M. 0·95		200,000	111	99 11	VX777
91	3,410	5,600	61 6	32 10	N525
109		37,000	157 6	82	J7557
86	2,310	3,500	60 6	36 6	1510
103		8,100	74 10·25	46	1415
97	5,840	8,600	74 10·25	46	1416
100	5,284	8,017	74 10·25	46	B8837
95	3,228	3,920	52 6	36 3	N113
113		6,300	48 6	35 6	N139
110	3,843	6,400	45 6	35 6	N140
115	9,632	20,160	88	54	N166
100		9,605	48	36	
126	4,255	7,405	44 10	36 9	N203
136	4,180	7,610	45 6·5	38 3·75	B-5
140		6,120	45 6	33 1	N236
132		7,966	49 3	33 3	
160		10,400	49 4	39	S1640
160		10,400	49 6	39 10	B-3/K3591
152	4,333	8,050	46	35 2·25	B-6
152	4,333	8,050	46	35 2·25	K4295
					B-7
225	5,490	8,228	46 2	35 7	K5178
249	11,830	18,450	59	51 1·5	L6104
251		13,729	44 2	42 5	WB781

Manufacturer/ Designer	Type No.	Name	Engine(s), h.p./lb.s.t.
Blackburn	B.54	Y.A.8	1 × 2,000 Griffon 56
,,	B.54	Y.B.1	1 × 2,950 Double Mamba
,,	B.103	Buccaneer S. Mk. 1	2 × 7,100 Gyron Jr. 101
,,		Buccaneer S. Mk. 2	2 × 11,200 Spey Sp. 2
,,		Buccaneer S. Mk. 50	2 × 11,200 Spey Sp. 2/605
Boulton and Paul	P.7	Bourges Mk. IA	2 × 320 Dragonfly I
,, ,, ,,	P.15	Bolton	2 × 450 Lion
,, ,, ,,	P.25	Bugle Mk. I	2 × 400 Jupiter II
,, ,, ,,	P.29	Sidestrand Mk. III	2 × 460 Jupiter VIIIF
,, ,, ,,	P.32		3 × 575 Jupiter XFBM
Boulton Paul	P.75	Overstrand Mk. I	2 × 580 Pegasus IIM3
Bristol		T.B.8	1 × 80 Gnome
,,	24	Braemar Mk. I	4 × 230 Puma
,,	90	Berkeley	1 × 650 Condor III
,,	93	Boarhound Mk. I	1 × 425 Jupiter IV
,,	93A	Beaver	1 × 450 Jupiter VI
,,	118		1 × 590 Jupiter XFA
,,	120		1 × 650 Pegasus IM3
,,	130A	Bombay Mk. I	2 × 1,010 Pegasus XXII
,,	142M	Blenheim Mk. I	2 × 840 Mercury VIII
,,	148		1 × 840 Mercury IX
,,	149	Blenheim Mk. IV	2 × 920 Mercury XV
,,	149	Bolingbroke Mk. IVW	2 × 750 Wasp Jr. SB4G
,,	152	Beaufort G.R. Mk. I	2 × 1,130 Taurus VI
,,	160	Bisley Mk. I	2 × 950 Mercury XVI
,,	163	Buckingham B. Mk. I	2 × 2,400 Centaurus IV
,,	164	Brigand B. Mk. 1	2 × 2,500 Centaurus 57
British Aircraft Corporation		TSR-2	2 × 30,000 Olympus 22R
de Havilland	D.H.3		2 × 120 Beardmore
,, ,,	D.H.4		1 × 230 B.H.P.
,, ,,	D.H.9		1 × 230 B.H.P.
,, ,,	D.H.10	Amiens Mk. I	2 × 230 B.H.P.
,, ,,	D.H.11	Oxford Mk. I	2 × 320 Dragonfly I
:, ,,	D.H.14	Okapi	1 × 600 Condor I
,, ,,	D.H.15	Gazelle	1 × 500 B.H.P.
,, ,,	D.H.27	Derby	1 × 650 Condor III
,, ,,	D.H.42A	Dingo Mk. I	1 × 410 Jupiter III
,, ,,	D.H.56	Hyena	1 × 385 Jaguar III
,, ,,	D.H.65A	Hound	1 × 540 Lion XA
,, ,,	D.H.72		3 × 595 Jupiter XFS
,, ,,	D.H.98	Mosquito B. Mk. IV	2 × 1,460 Merlin 21
,, ,,	D.H.98	Mosquito B. Mk. XVI	2 × 1,680 Merlin 72/73
,, ,,	D.H.98	Mosquito B. Mk. 35	2 × 1,690 Merlin 113/114
Dyott		Bomber	2 × 120 Beardmore
English Electric		Canberra B. Mk. 1	2 × 6,000 Avon R.A.2
,, ,,		Canberra B. Mk. 2	2 × 6,500 Avon 101
,, ,,		Canberra B. Mk. 6	2 × 7,500 Avon 109
Fairey	F.16	Campania	1 × 250 R.-R. Mk. IV
,,	F.17	Campania	1 × 275 R.-R. Mk. I
,,	F.22	Campania	1 × 250 Maori II
,,	F.127		1 × 190 Falcon I
,,	F.128	III	1 × 260 Maori II
,,		IIIA	1 × 260 Maori II
,,		IIIB	1 × 260 Maori II
,,		IIIC	1 × 375 Eagle VIII
,,		IIID	1 × 375 Eagle VIII

Max. speed, m.p.h.	Wt. (E), lb.	Wt. (L), lb.	Span ft.	in.	Length ft.	in.	Prototype
251		13,729	44	2	42	5	WB788
320		13,091	44	2	42	5	WB797
720		46,000	42	4	63	5	XK486
		46,000	42	4	63	5	XK526
		46,000	42	4	63	5	
123·5	3,820	6,326	57	4	37		F2903
		9,500	62	6			J6584
120	5,079	8,110	65	0·5			J6984
140	6,010	10,200	71	11	46		J7938
		22,700	100		69		J9950
153	7,936	12,000	72		46		J9186
65	970	1,665	37	8	29	3	198
103·5	9,578	14,578	81	8	51	6	C4296
120	5,200	8,128	57	11	47	6	J7403
135	2,900	4,460	44	9	31	6	G-EBLG
142	2,906	4,480	44	9	31	6	G-EBQF
165	3,632	5,200	40	8	34		G-ABEZ/R-3/K2873
175	3,632	5,200	40	8	34		R-6/K3587
192	13,800	20,000	95	9	69	3	K3583
285	8,100	12,250	56	4	39	9	K7033
255	4,450	5,250	40		31		K6551
266	9,800	12,500	56	4	42	9	K7072
275	9,800	12,500	56	4	42	9	9005
260	13,100	21,230	57	10	44	3	L4441
262	11,000	17,000	56	1	43	4	AD657
335	24,040	36,900	71	10	46	10	DX249
360	25,600	39,000	72	4	46	5	MX988
			37		89		XR219
95·1	3,980	5,810	60	10	36	10	
117	2,010	2,945	42	$4\frac{5}{8}$	30	8	3696
116	2,193	3,283	42	$4\frac{5}{8}$	30	6	A7559
109	5,004	6,950	62	9	38	$10\frac{1}{8}$	C8658
117	3,795	7,000	60	2	45	2·75	H5891
122	4,484	7,074	50	5	33	11·5	J1938
139	2,312	4,773	45	$11\frac{3}{8}$	29	11	J1937
105	6,737	11,545	64	6	47	4	J6894
127	2,346	3,700	41	6	28	3	J7006
130	2,247	3,962	43		29	11	J7780
153	3,285	4,934	45		31		J9127
		21,462	95				J9184
380	13,400	21,462	54	2	40	9·5	W4072
408	14,635	23,000	54	2	41	6	MP469
422	14,635	23,000	54	2	41	6	RS699
							3687
			63	11·5	65	6	VN799
570	26,000	46,000	63	11·5	65	6	VX165
			63	11·5	66	8	WJ754
82	3,725	4,166	61	7·5	43	$3\frac{5}{8}$	N1000
90	3,713	5,506	61	7·5	43	$0\frac{5}{8}$	N1001
85	3,672	5,329	61	7·5	43	$0\frac{5}{8}$	N1006
90	2,699	3,812	50		35	6	N9
104	2,970	4,159	46	2	36		N10
109·5	2,532	3,694	46	2	31		N10
95	3,258	4,892	62	9	37	1	N2230
110·5	3,392	4,272	46	1·25	36		N2246
106	3,248	4,918	46	1·25	37		N9450

Manufacturer/ Designer	Type No.	Name	Engine(s), h.p./lb.s.t.
Fairey		Fawn Mk. III	1 × 470 Lion II
,,		Ferret Mk. I	1 × 400 Jaguar IV
,,		Fox Mk. I	1 × 480 Curtiss D-12
,,		IIIF Mk. IV	1 × 570 Lion XIA
,,		Gordon Mk. I	1 × 525 Panther IIA
,,		Seal Mk. I	1 × 525 Panther IIA
,,		Hendon Mk. II	2 × 600 Kestrel VI
,,		S.9/30	1 × 525 Kestrel IIMS
,,		T.S.R.I	1 × 635 Pegasus IIM
,,		T.S.R.II	1 × 690 Pegasus IIIM3
,,		Swordfish Mk. I	1 × 690 Pegasus IIIM3
,,		G.4/31 Mk. I	1 × 635 Pegasus IIM3
,,		G.4/31 Mk. II	1 × 750 Tiger IV
,,		Seafox	1 × 395 Rapier VI
,,		Battle Mk. I	1 × 1,030 Merlin I
,,		P.4/34	1 × 1,030 Merlin II
,,		Albacore	1 × 1,065 Taurus II
,,	100	Barracuda T.B. Mk. I	1 × 1,260 Merlin 30
,,		Spearfish T.B.D. Mk. 1	1 × 2,585 Centaurus 57
,,		Gannet A.S. Mk. 1	1 × 2,950 Double Mamba
Gloster	G.22	Goral	1 × 425 Jupiter VIA
,,	G.25	Goring	1 × 425 Jupiter VIII
,,	T.C.33		4 × 600 Kestrel IIS/IIIS
,,	F.S.36		1 × 600 Kestrel IIMS
,,	T.S.R.38		1 × 600 Kestrel IIMS
Grahame-White	18		1 × 285 Maori
,, ,,	E.IV	Ganymede	3 × 270 Maori
Handley Page	H.P.11	O/100	2 × 250 R.-R. Mk. II
,, ,,	H.P:12	O/400	2 × 360 Eagle VIII
,, ,,	H.P.15	V/1500	4 × 375 Eagle VIII
,, ,,	H.P.19	Hanley Mk. I	1 × 450 Lion
,, ,,	H.P.24	W.8d Hyderabad Mk. I	2 × 454 Lion
,, ,,	H.P.25	Hendon Type Ta	1 × 450 Lion
,, ,,	H.P.28	Handcross Type C/7	1 × 650 Condor III
,, ,,	H.P.31	Harrow Mk. I	1 × 470 Lion V
,, ,,	H.P.33	Hinaidi Mk. I	2 × 440 Jupiter
,, ,,	H.P.34	Hare	1 × 440 Jupiter VI
,, ,,	H.P.35	Clive Mk. I	2 × 440 Jupiter VIIIF
,, ,,	H.P.36	Hinaidi Mk. II	2 × 440 Jupiter VIII
,, ,,	H.P.38	Heyford	2 × 550 Kestrel II
,, ,,	H.P.43		3 × 520 Pegasus I
,, ,,	H.P.44	Hinaidi Mk. III	2 × 480 Jaguar
,, ,,	H.P.46		1 × 825 Buzzard III
,, ,,	H.P.47		1 × 690 Pegasus IIIMS
,, ,,	H.P.50	Heyford Mk. IA	2 × 525 Kestrel IIIS
,, ,,	H.P.51		2 × 700 Tiger IV
,, ,,	H.P.52	Hampden B.Mk. I	2 × 1,000 Pegasus XVIII
,, ,,	H.P.53	Hereford B. Mk. I	2 × 1,000 Dagger VIII
,, ,,	H.P.54	Harrow Mk. II	2 × 925 Pegasus XX
,, ,,	H.P.57	Halifax B. Mk. I Ser. I	4 × 1,280 Merlin X
,, ,,	H.P.59	Halifax B.Mk.II Ser.1A	4 × 1,390 Merlin XXII
,, ,,	H.P.62	Hampden B. Mk. II	2 × 1,100 Cyclone GR-1820
,, ,,	H.P.80	Victor B. Mk. 1	4 × 1,100 Sapphire 202
,, ,,	H.P.80	Victor B. Mk. 2	4 × 17,250 Conway R. Co. 11
Hawker		Horsley Mk. II	1 × 665 Condor IIIA

Max. speed, m.p.h.	Wt. (E), lb.	Wt. (L), lb.	Span ft. in.		Length ft. in.		Prototype
114		5,834	49	11	32	1	J6907
121		4,425	39	9·5	29	5·75	N190
150·5		4,117	38		31	2	J7941
120		6,041	45	9	36	$8\frac{5}{8}$	N198
145	3,500	5,906	45	9	36	$8\frac{5}{8}$	J9154
138		6,000	45	9	33	8	S1325
155	12,773	20,000	101	9	60	9	K1695
136	4,548	6,500	46		39	4·5	S1706
144		7,625	45	6			K4190
139	5,200	9,250	45	6	36	4	K4190
			53		40	10·5	F-1
157	6,987	8,790	53		40	10·5	F-1/K3905
124	3,805	5,420	40		35	5·5	K4304
241	6,647	10,792	54		52	1·75	K4303
284	6,405	8,747	47	4·5	40		K5099
161	7,200	10,600	50		39	9·5	L7074
235	8,700	11,900	49	2	39	9	P1767
292		21,010	60	3	44	7	RA356
310·5	15,069	19,600	54	4	44	6	VR546
141	2,885	4,618	46	7			J8673
136		4,916	42				J8674
146	21,900	28,500	95				J9832
157		5,816					S1705
150·5		7,650	46				S1705
105	11,500	16,000	89	3	49	9	C3481
76	8,000	14,000	100		70		1455
97·5	8,502	13,360	100		70		3138
97	16,210	24,700	126		62		B9463
114·5	3,640	6,465	46		33	6	N143
109	8,910	13,590	75		59	2	J6994
108	4,350	6,845	45	7	34	5	N9724
117	5,212	7,480	60		40		J7498
115	4,403	7,140	44		34		N205
114	7,240	14,500	75		59	2	J7745
145	3,050	5,720	50		32	2	J8622
111		14,500	75		62	10	J9126
122·5	8,040	14,500	75		59	2	J9478
138	8,750	15,500	75		58		J9130
118	13,551	22,500	114		75	9	J9833
	8,040	14,486	75		59	2	
	6,250	10,600	50		39	5	S1642
161	5,362	7,708	58		37	7·5	K2773
142	9,200	16,900	75		58		K3489
188		18,000	90		78	4	J9833
254	11,780	18,756	69	2	53	7	K4240
265	11,700	16,000	69	2	53	7	L7271
200	13,600	23,000	88	5	82	2	K6933
265	33,860	58,000	98	10	70	1	L7244
272	35,270	60,000	98	10	71	7	R9534
			69	2	53	7	X3115
			110		114	11	WB771
		200,000	120		114	11	XH668
126	4,760	7,800	56	6	38	10	J7511

Manufacturer/ Designer	Type No.	Name	Engine(s), h.p./lb.s.t.
Hawker		Harrier Mk. I	1 × 583 Jupiter VIII
,,		Hart Mk. I	1 × 525 Kestrel IB
,,		Dantorp	1 × 800 Leopard II
,,		Hardy Mk. I	1 × 530 Kestrel IB
,,		Hartbees Mk. I	1 × 608 Kestrel VFP
,,		Hind Mk. I	1 × 640 Kestrel V
,,		P.V.4	1 × 820 Pegasus X
,,		Hector Mk. I	1 × 805 Dagger IIIMS
,,		Henley	1 × 1,030 Merlin I
Hawker Siddeley	H.S.801	Nimrod	4 × 11,500 Spey 250
Kennedy		Giant	4 × 200 Salmson
Mann, Egerton	B		1 × 225 Sunbeam
Martinsyde	G.100		1 × 120 Beardmore
,,	G.102	Elephant	1 × 160 Beardmore
Nieuport		London Mk. I	2 × 320 Dragonfly I
Parnall		G.4/31	1 × 690 Pegasus IM3
Royal Aircraft Factory	B.E.2		1 × 70 Renault
,, ,, ,,	B.E.2a		1 × 70 Renault
,, ,, ,,	B.E.2c		1 × 70 Renault
,, ,, ,,	B.E.8		1 × 80 Gnome
,, ,, ,,	F.E.2b		1 × 120 Beardmore
,, ,, ,,	R.E.5		1 × 120 Beardmore
,, ,, ,,	R.E.7		1 × 160 Beardmore
Short		Folder Seaplane	1 × 160 Gnome
,,		Admiralty Type 74	1 × 100 Gnome
,,		Admiralty Type 135	1 × 135 Salmson
,,		Admiralty Type 166	1 × 200 Salmson
,,		Admiralty Type 827	1 × 135 Salmson
,,		Admiralty Type 830	1 × 135 Salmson
,,	184		1 × 225 Sunbeam
,,		Bomber	1 × 225 Sunbeam
,,	320		1 × 310 Cossack
,,	N.2B		1 × 275 Maori
,,	S.364		1 × 200 Afridi
,,		Shirl	1 × 345 Eagle VIII
,,	S.3b	Chamois	1 × 450 Jupiter VI
,,	S.29	Stirling B. Mk. I Ser. I	4 × 1,595 Hercules XI
,,	S.39	Stirling B. Mk. II	4 × 1,600 Cyclone 14
,,	S.A.1	Sturgeon P.R. Mk. I	2 × 2,080 Merlin 140S
,,	S.A.4	Sperrin	4 × 6,000 Avon R.A.2
,,	S.B.3		2 × 1,475 Mamba A.S.Ma.3
,,	S.B.6	Seamew A.S. Mk. 1	1 × 1,320 Mamba A.S.Ma.3
Siddeley	103	Sinaia Mk. I	2 × 486 Tiger
Sopwith	C		1 × 200 Salmson
,,		Admiralty Type 860	1 × 225 Sunbeam
,,		1½-Strutter	1 × 110 Clerget 9Z
,,	2.B.2	Rhino	1 × 230 B.H.P.
,,	B.1		1 × 200 Hispano-Suiza
,,	T.1	Cuckoo	1 × 200 Hispano-Suiza
,,		Cobham Mk. I	2 × 360 Dragonfly IA
Sunbeam		Bomber	1 × 200 Arab
Supermarine		Patrol Seaplane	·
,,	322		1 × 1,645 Merlin 32
Tarrant		Tabor	6 × 450 Lion
Vickers	F.B.27	Vimy	2 × 200 Hispano-Suiza

Max. speed, m.p.h.	Wt. (E), lb.	Wt. (L), lb.	Span ft.	Span in.	Length ft.	Length in.	Prototype
135·5	3,278	5,656	46	3	29	7	J8325
184	2,530	4,554	37	3	29	4	J9052
126·2	5,360	8,230	56	7·5	38	4·5	201
161	3,195	5,005	37	3	29	7	K3013
176	3,150	4,787	37	3	29	7	801
186	3,251	5,298	37	3	29	7	K2915
183	3,728	6,650	40		29	10	IPV4/K6926
187	3,389	4,910	36	11⅜	29	9·75	K2434
			47	10·5	36	5	K5115
500		178,000	114	10	126	9	XV147
	19,000		142		80		2337
							9085
95	1,759	2,424	38		26	6	4735
104	1,793	2,458	38		27		A1561
100			59	6	37	6	H1740
		6,800	57		35	9	K2772
		1,650	38	7·5	29	7·5	
70	1,274	1,600	38	7·5	29	7·5	46
75			37		27	3	
70			39	6	27	3	365
80·5	1,993	2,967	47	9	32	3	
78			44	6	26	2	26
91·3	2,285	3,290	57		31	10·5	2185
78	2,000	3,040	67		39		81
							74
60		3,700	54	6	39		135
65		4,580	57	3	40	7	161
70	2,622	3,324	53	11	35	3	822
70	2,622	3,324	53	11	35	3	819
75		5,100	63	6·25	40	7·5	184
77·5		6,800	85		45		3706
77	4,873	7,013	75		45	9	8317
88	3,119	4,741	55	2	40	2	N66
98	2,949	3,732	52		35		N110
					26	11	J7295
260	44,000	59,400	99	1	87	3	L7600
			99	1	87	3	N3657
430		23,300	60		44	7	RK787
564		115,000	109		102	2·5	VX158
			59	9	45		WF632
		14,000	55		41		XA209
		16,000	86	10			J6858
							127
							851
106	1,259	2,149	33	6	25	3	3686
103	2,185	3,590	33		27	8	X8
112	1,700	2,117	38	6	27		B1496
103·5	1,928	3,572	46	9	28	6	N74
		6,300	54		38		H671
112·5	1,915	2,952	42		31	6	N515
70	3,088	4,612	60		37	6	
279	9,175	12,000	50		40		R1810
110	24,750	44,672	131	3	73	2	F1765
90	5,420	9,120	67	2	43	6·5	B9952

403

Manufacturer/ Designer	Type No.	Name	Engine(s), h.p./lb.s.t.
Vickers	71	Vixen Mk. I	1 × 450 Lion
,,	139	Virginia Mk. X	2 × 570 Lion V
,,		Victoria Mk. V	2 × 570 Lion XI
,,	94	Venture	1 × 486 Lion
,,		Valparaiso	1 × 486 Lion
,,	113	Vespa Mk. I	1 × 515 Jupiter VI
,,	146	Vivid	1 × 590 Lion XIA
,,	131	Valiant	1 × 515 Jupiter VI
,,	150	B.19/27 Mk. I	2 × 526 Kestrel F.XIVS
,,	163		4 × 480 Kestrel III
,,	207		1 × 825 Buzzard
,,		Vildebeest Mk. IV	1 × 825 Perseus VIII
,,		Vincent	1 × 660 Pegasus IIM
,,	264	Valentia	2 × 650 Pegasus IIL
,,	253		1 × 690 Pegasus IIIM3
,,	290	Wellesley Mk. I	1 × 925 Pegasus XX
,,	415	Wellington B. Mk. IC	2 × 1,000 Pegasus XVI
,,	431	Wellington B. Mk. VI	2 × 1,600 Merlin 60
,,		Warwick B. Mk. I	2 × 1,850 Double Wasp
,,	447	Windsor	4 × 1,400 Merlin 65
,,	706	Valiant B. Mk. 1	4 × 10,000 Avon 201
,,	673	Valiant B. Mk. 2	4 × 10,000 Avon 201
Westland		Yeovil Mk. II	1 × 650 Condor III
,,		Witch	1 × 480 Jupiter VIIIF
,,		Wapiti Mk. I	1 × 420 Jupiter VI
,,		P.V.3	1 × 575 Jupiter XFA
,,		P.V.6	1 × 655 Pegasus IV
,,		Wallace Mk. I	1 × 570 Pegasus IIM3
,,		P.V.7	1 × 722 Pegasus IIM3
,,		Lysander Mk. I	1 × 890 Mercury XII
Wight		Bomber	1 × 275 R.-R.
,,		Admiralty Type 840	1 × 225 Sunbeam
,,		Twin	2 × 200 Salmson
,,		Converted Seaplane	1 × 275 R.-R. Mk. II

404

Max. speed, m.p.h.	Wt. (E), lb.	Wt. (L), lb.	Span ft.	Span in.	Length ft.	Length in.	Prototype
	3,098	4,720	40		29		G-EBEC
108	9,650	17,600	87	8	62	2·75	J6856
110	10,030	17,760	87	4	59	6	J6860
							J7277
	3,128	4,720	40		29		
126	2,468	4,370	50		33		G-EBLD
130	3,560	5,550	45	1	34	5	G-EBPY
125	2,973	5,550	45	7	34		G-EBVM
			76	6	60	4	J9131
			90		66	9	O-2
							S1641
156	4,724	8,500	49		37	8	K4164
142	4,229	8,100	49		36	8	S1714
130	10,944	19,500	87	4	59	6	K3599
161	5,628	8,350	52	7	37		K2771
228	6,369	11,100	74	7	29	3	K7556/O-9
235	18,556	28,500	86	2	64	7	K4049
							W5795
224	45,000	50,000	96	8·5	72	3	K8178
302		54,000	117	2	76	10	DW506
414		140,000	114	4	108	3	WB210
552			114	4	108	3	WJ954
120	4,660	7,550	59	6	36	10	J7508
140	3,380	6,050	61		37	8	J8596
133	3,280	4,900	46	5	31	8	J8495
163	3,580	5,600	46	6	34	2	P3/G-ACAZ/K4048
160		5,750	46	5	34	2	P6/G-AAWA/
							G-ACBR/K3488
162	3,840	5,750	46	5	34	2	K3488
173	4,515	7,172	60	3	38	8	P7
229	4,065	5,920	50		30	6	K6127
89	3,162	5,166	65	6			N501
81	3,408	4,453	61		41		831
			117				187
84·5	3,758	5,556	65	6	44	8·5	9841

INDEX

410

411

415

420